W9-ADM-980

DISCARDED

501
D23p

83362

DATE DUE			
~~Nov 1 73~~			
Dec 5 7 8			
SEP 1 9 1985			

DISCARDED

PHILOSOPHY OF SCIENCE

Readings selected, edited, and introduced
by ARTHUR DANTO
and SIDNEY MORGENBESSER

A MERIDIAN BOOK
WORLD PUBLISHING
TIMES MIRROR
NEW YORK

CARL A. RUDISILL LIBRARY
LENOIR RHYNE COLLEGE

501
D23p
83362
May 1973

AN ORIGINAL MERIDIAN BOOK

Published by The World Publishing Company
110 East 59th Street, New York, New York 10022
First printing—March 1960
Tenth printing—October 1971
Copyright © 1960 by The World Publishing Company
All rights reserved. No part of this book may be reproduced
in any form without written permission from the publisher,
except for brief passages included in a review
appearing in a newspaper or magazine.
Library of Congress catalog card number: 60-6773
Printed in the United States of America

WORLD PUBLISHING
TIMES MIRROR

CARL A. RUDISILL LIBRARY
LENOIR RHYNE COLLEGE

Contents

ACKNOWLEDGMENTS

The editors are deeply indebted to their teacher and colleague, Professor Ernest Nagel. His influence in this book will be apparent to anyone familiar with the field of philosophy of science. He has given freely of his time and knowledge in discussing these selections, and for this we are grateful, but the debt is also a spiritual one.

We are in no way oblivious to the subtle redirection in our thinking induced by conversation and argument with Professor John C. Cooley, and would like to acknowledge here our respect for his philosophical acuity. A number of philosophers have made suggestions and criticisms which affected the shape of this work: Professors Adolf Grünbaum, N. R. Hanson, Israel Scheffler, Noam Chomsky, and Harold Weisberg; Dr. Frederic Schick and Mr. Arnold Koslow. Professors Grünbaum and Hanson in addition provided us with specially revised versions of their articles. Some of the writings appear here for the first time in English. We are obliged to Dr. Frederic Schick of Columbia University and Professor Rudolph Weingartner of San Francisco State College for their lucid translations of Mach and Boltzmann; and to Mr. William Ryding and Mr. Arnold Miller, of the French Department at Columbia, for similarly clear and excellent translations of Poincaré. Finally, we wish to express our gratitude to Mr. Arthur A. Cohen, the publisher of Meridian Books, both for his enthusiasm for this project and his unremitting cooperation in realizing it. It goes without saying that we alone are responsible for the inclusions, exclusions, errors, and oversights which may mar this work.

ARTHUR DANTO and SIDNEY MORGENBESSER

1960

PREFACE

Historical research into the development of the human species from its early beginnings does not disclose any race of men without at least some competent knowledge of certain aspects of their world. Unlike most other living organisms, human beings are not equipped with built-in mechanisms for maintaining their existence automatically; and men would quickly perish were they to respond to their environments exclusively in terms of unlearned, biologically inherited forms of behavior. In order to survive at all, the human animal must discover how various things around him operate; and the place he occupies in the present scheme of organic creation is in large measure the consequence of his having learned how to exploit his intellectual capacities for such discoveries.

However, the knowledge men acquired during the greater part of human history had only a narrowly limited range of reliable application, and it was not the product of any deliberately instituted policy for obtaining competent information about the environment. Science as a process consciously directed toward achieving knowledge that is explicitly formulated, general in scope, systematically ordered, and dependable, is less than three thousand years old; and science as a continuing institutionalized inquiry, integrally woven into the social fabric, is of still more recent origin. It is by cultivating science that men have gradually achieved their remarkable intellectual and practical mastery over various sectors of animate and inanimate nature. Indeed, the pursuit of science has been the major source of transforming innovations in modern society; and there is every reason to suppose that its influence upon belief and conduct will not diminish during the foreseeable future.

It is therefore hardly surprising that ever since the beginnings of science in classical antiquity, the nature of scientific inquiry as well as of its intellectual fruits have been subjects of intimate concern to reflective men. Discussions of the aims, the methods, the grounds of validity, the limitations, and the moral significance of science occupy a central place already in the philosophical writings of the ancient Greeks; and there is scarcely a figure of note in the subsequent history of philosophy who has failed to comment at greater or lesser length on these questions.

Accordingly, although the label "philosophy of science" is of fairly recent vintage, the subject it designates is by no means novel. The currently widespread adoption of the label is in part only a recognition of the increasingly important role science is playing in modern life. But its adoption is also an expression of the need for specialized training to deal adequately with many problems subsumed under it because of their growing complexity. However, the designation as commonly employed actually covers a miscellany of problems that are only faintly related to one another, and that frequently represent incompatible conceptions of the nature and task of philosophy. For example, the catalogue of themes often classified under that heading includes: traditional issues in the epistemology of sense perception; problems concerning the genesis, the development, and the social effects of scientific ideas; projected philosophical syntheses of specialized scientific findings, not uncommonly to support some system of religious convictions; moral evaluations of the accomplishments and the likely future fruits of the scientific enterprise; axiomatizations of various branches of theoretical inquiry; proposed justifications of inductive procedures; criteria for meaningful discourse and types of definitional techniques; the structure of scientific laws; and the status and function of theoretical ideas. This list is by no means exhaustive. But the items mentioned suffice to indicate that despite the supposition that the designation "philosophy of science" marks off a specialized area of philosophical analysis, the term does not at present denote a reasonably well-defined domain of inquiry.

It would certainly be profitless to dispute whether, and if so which, items in the above list "really belong to the philosophy of science. Nevertheless, although a certain breadth of conception is essential for fixing its scope if the philosophy of science is to contribute to illuminating the character of the scientific enterprise, it is doubtful whether any coherent conception underlies an indiscriminate lumping together under a common name of themes whose only bond is a reference in some way or other to science. But in any event, much is gained in the way of clarifying the aims of philosophical analysis by limiting the philosophy of science to a group of related questions that arise in attempting to understand the intellectual products of scientific inquiry as embodied in explicitly formulated statements. On such a delimitation of the province of the philosophy of science, its problems can be handled by a unitary mode of analysis; and they fall, moreover, into a number of distinct but cognate sub-divisions: those addressed to the ways in which the conclusions of scientific inquiry are linked to the empirical evidence on which they may be based (e.g., problems relating to procedures of definition and measurement); those concerned with the logical principles involved in the assessment of the evidence and in the acceptance of the conclusions (e.g., problems relating to canons of probable inference); and those concentrating on the structure of the ideas imbedded in scientific conclusions as well as of the systems of statements to which the conclusions belong (e.g., problems relating to the character of scientific explanations or to the role of theories).

It would be gratuitous to assume that the conception of the philosophy of science just sketched controlled the selection of materials included in the present volume, although each of the selections does deal with some phase of science that requires examination when the perspective defined by this conception is accepted. But in any event, the essays here reprinted deal with central issues that any adequate philosophical analysis of science must face and attempt to resolve. Many of the articles are indeed turning points in the clarification of scientific ideas, and illustrate the capital role which the philosophical critique of science can have in advancing substantive scientific knowledge. The special questions to which the articles are addressed are sometimes undoubtedly technical. But the helpful introductions supplied by the editors facilitate immeasurably the reader's appreciation of the fundamental philosophical issues that underlie these technical formulations.

Ernest Nagel

Columbia University

GENERAL INTRODUCTION

Philosophy of science must be distinguished from the sociology and the psychology of science. We have not, therefore, included readings which concern the interrelationships between science and industry, technology, religion, or other cultural institutions, important as these interrelationships may be. Nor again do any of the selections enter upon those fascinating problems having to do with the psychology of the invention and discovery of theories and hypotheses in science. Mere familiarity with the biographies of scientists is sufficient to falsify some theories regarding the psychology of the scientific mind, e.g., the Baconian theory that scientists first gather data and then frame hypotheses, or the cruder versions of Pragmatism in accordance with which scentists are always stimulated by the urgency of some practical problem. But no such simple manner for exhaustively confirming a theory is available: this requires careful formulation of the theory to begin with, and then refined techniques for testing it. And these are matters best left to the trained psychologist. Similar considerations pertain to the sociology of science. In the end sociology and psychology are *parts* of science itself; and it is not the task of philosophy to engage in casual speculations regarding questions which science alone can answer.

It is, however, one recognized task of philosophy to analyze the nature and structure of knowledge; and it is science, considered as as body of knowledge, which, it is hoped, these readings will clarify in various ways and from various points of view. But a few general remarks concerning the concept of knowledge must be made, if only to indicate the main orientation of this book.

One familiar sense of the word "know" is that in which we speak of a person *knowing that* something is the case. As a general rule, the expression "X knows that . . ." is completed when some full sentence is put into the blank space, e.g., "X knows that oxygen has the atomic number 8," where "oxygen has the atomic number 8" is a complete sentence in English. Obviously, however, the analysis of knowledge is not simply an analysis of the sentences which can fill in the blank space in "X knows that . . ." For to say one knows that S is, is among other things, to claim that one has good evidence for the truth of S and that one believes S to be true. So a complete treatment of the nature of knowledge must include an analysis of evidence and of the criteria of belief. We abstract from these considerations here, however, and attend primarily to those sentences which the scientific community claims to be highly confirmed and in which scientific knowledge is accordingly expressed. For one way in which science (or scientific knowledge) may be philosophically studied is through the examination of the *kinds* of sentences and the *kinds* of terms figuring in these sentences, which may be said to constitute the language of science. A collateral inquiry, and one which is but weakly represented in this collection, will concern the criteria of knowledge, the conditions for the confirmation and verification of sentences that are to be accepted into the language of science insofar as the latter is supposed to furnish true descriptions of the world's structure.

Few philosophers, however preoccupied they may be with the linguistic embodiment of knowledge, are so purely involved with this as to be indifferent to those features of the world which knowledge reveals and language expresses. Some of these features are touched upon in Part Three of this book. To be interested in science at all is to be interested in what science tells us about the world. This is by no means a mere supernumerary interest on the part of philosophers. For sometimes what science tells will, if true, involve a conceptual revolution, and force philosophical reflection upon the preconceptions which deeply underlie our conceptual schemes—the most general concepts we employ for the ordering of experience. We have thus tried in Part

Three to at least *exhibit* one such conceptual revolution, brought about through changes in the concepts of space, time, and causality in mechanical theories.

Aside from Part Three we have—for reasons chiefly of space—been unable to concentrate upon conceptual issues arising in connection with specific branches of science. Ideally, we would have wished to include readings in the philosophy of the biological, psychological, and social sciences, but given the spatial limitations that dog the anthologist, it was decided to devote the bulk of this work to problems which concern the whole of science: the structure of laws and theories, and the complications, logical and epistemological, which come up in connection with relating laws and theories to observation and interpretation. These matters are taken up in Parts One and Two. Even so, not every problem of scientific knowledge is represented here, nor all the chief positions with regard to those problems we do touch upon. We particularly regret having been unable to include more on the logic of confirmation. But it is not to the point to review here the complexities of editorial decision; perhaps a later compilation will remedy the faults of omission.

Each of the three sections is prefaced with a brief introduction, the purpose of which is to furnish the minimal philosophic background for the set of readings in the section. These introductions, taken together, will reveal the structure of this book; for we have endeavored not merely to assemble a representative sampling of illuminating writings in the philosophy of science, but to construct a book by many hands, so far as this was possible. Yet the individual selections stand on their own, and the book may be read in any order. Some pieces have been included which can be read most profitably by those with a certain acquaintance with specific parts of science and philosophy of science. Yet it is hoped that every piece is sufficiently clear in its argument that, despite the occasional use made of mathematical and logical terminology, it will be accessible for the most part to the intelligent reader.

All footnotes enclosed in brackets have been supplied by the editors. The selections have been edited to make them consistent in orthography and minor matters of technical style. Notice of omissions is given in the source note on the first page of each selection not reprinted in its entirety.

PART ONE

SCIENCE, LANGUAGE, AND EXPERIENCE

INTRODUCTION

Scientific language is sometimes contrasted with ordinary language and poetic discourse, and frequently the contrast is invidiously intended. The terms of scientific language are alleged to be precise, quantitative, and operationally definable; its sentences to satisfy the Verifiability Criterion of Meaning; and its rules of inference to be clear. But ordinary and poetic language are respectively vague and metaphorical. Ordinary language, moreover, is subject to the generation of paradoxes; and sentences uttering any sort of nonsense may be constructed in conformity with its minimal and accommodating grammatical requirements. Poetic language is perhaps literally false when it is clear enough to be understood, but may nonetheless be accorded a kind of *emotive* meaning so far as it expresses or arouses feelings. Scientific language, on such an account, is the appropriate vehicle for the expression of truth. Ordinary language is too shopworn for poetic purposes; it contains too many vague terms and it lacks too many technical ones to serve the purposes of self-conscious inquiry. Philosophical language, when it is responsible, is scientific language *about* scientific language: the task of philosophy is to elucidate the logic of scientific language itself.

The above paragraph is perhaps a fair statement of what many people believe that Logical Positivists or Logical Empiricists believe. But few empiricists today would subscribe to any of these statements without considerable qualifications. First, the distinction between kinds of languages presupposes some clarity on what in general constitutes a language and what criterion in particular distinguishes scientific language. No such clarity exists in fact, however, and no satisfactory criterion for scientific language has withstood criticism. Indeed, intense philosophical investigation of the matter has served only to reveal the remarkable complexity of the problem. Furthermore, independent inquiries into the "logic of ordinary language" have convinced a whole school of philosophers that ordinary language is not the shapeless excrescence which reforming semanticists once felt it to be, but satisfies rules quite as exacting as any thought to govern scientific discourse—rules which even preclude paradoxes and, when adhered to, prevent the utterance of nonsense. The Emotive Theory of poetic meaning has been challenged; and the cognitive claims of art can no longer be dismissed by a ready appeal to the Verifiability Criterion of Meaning. For there is no single Verifiability Criterion, but rather a family of different criteria, each of which has so far resisted formulation in a way which does not eliminate, together with the nonsense it was meant to exclude, a great deal of what by common consent is significant scientific discourse. Few philosophers, again, really believe that all the terms of science are operationally definable or that the concept of operational definition is clear. The appeal to verifiability, precision, metricization, confirmation, and the like at best highlights some of the *aims* of science. But these criteria afford no simple way of once and for all distinguishing scientific language from other languages, or the scientific use of language from other uses.

The trichotomous distinction between scientific, poetic, and ordinary language might be said to reproduce in linguistic guise some ancient philosophical mistrusts. For philosophers have often in the past compared Emotion and Common Sense unfavorably with Reason, and the purported three kinds of languages are in a sense the linguistic counterparts of these. A brief review of some of these issues will, apart from any intrinsic interest it may have, afford some appreciation of some closely analogous issues currently under philosophical debate.

Philosophers from Plato to Russell have impugned common sense as an aggregate of mere opinions, embodying inadvertent metaphysical assumptions and riddled with error. Plato indeed went so far as to contend that the objects which Common Sense pretends to know about, the things of ordinary experience, are different in kind from the objects of knowledge and occupy a lower range of reality, so that in the nature of the case Common Sense is of negligible cognitive import. In a later age a related distinction was made in terms of Primary and Secondary Qualities: only the former are *real* properties of things, so that a complete accounting of the real world could be given just by specification of the Primary Qualities and their interrelations. In yet more recent times it has been argued (by Eddington, according to some) that physics reveals the structure of the world to be so radically dissimilar to what it appears to be to the senses that no belief based upon sense perception can possibly represent correctly the world's real constitution. Each of these accounts depends upon implicit criteria of knowledge and closely related but nonetheless distinguishable criteria of reality. Let us first make explicit some typical criteria of reality.

1. No property P of an object a is a real property of a if evidence used to ascribe P to a is matched by evidence to ascribe Q to a when 'P' and 'Q' are contraries.

2. No property P is a real property of an object a if the presence of some other object b is a necessary condition for the presence of P.

From (1) it follows that pennies are not really either circular nor elliptical, since the evidence on the basis of which we would say either that they are elliptical or circular is perceptual evidence. Plato generalized this to include all perceptual qualities, none of which are accordingly real; and since knowledge is of what is real, perception is not knowledge. Galileo argued on the basis of (2) that since the presence of perceptual properties requires the presence of sensate beings, perceptual properties are not real. It is apparent that the result of applying these criteria is offensive both to Common Sense and to poetic sensibility. And inasmuch as scientific information is sometimes appealed to in support of such criteria and certainly in application of them, it is understandable that Keats should have drunk a toast to the confounding of Newton, since "Newton destroyed the rainbow."

Some philosophers of science, notably N. R. Campbell, have suggested that the distinction between Primary and Secondary Qualities may be reinterpreted as a distinction between measurable and nonmeasurable properties. But most empiricists since Berkeley regard the distinction between "real" and "unreal" properties as untenable—except where "real" means "under standard conditions." But this is then irrelevant to the issue. Their argument is that all or no properties can be shown to satisfy criteria of reality once these are clearly indicated; and at any rate science can hardly be credited with "proving" the unreality of certain properties. Newton's optics doesn't destroy the rainbow: science is not black magic.

The problem of criteria of knowledge is more difficult to deal with. It is easy enough to discern ambiguities and difficulties in proposed criteria which identify instances of knowledge in terms of certain characteristics of the *objects* of knowledge, e.g., Plato's contention that an object is knowable just in case it is permanent. It is less easy to come to grips with criteria of knowledge in philosophical vogue since at least the time of Descartes, in accordance with which knowledge is analyzed as a complicated relationship between persons and sentences. Rationalists (including Descartes) often maintain that genuine knowledge is a matter of intuiting the truth of certain sentences. Part of this claim will even be allowed by some empiricists; we may indeed intuit certain sentences, and we may indeed term this knowledge of a sort; but the sentences in question are trivial and devoid of factual content. For a sentence to have factual content some criterion must be specified which has reference to sense experience. But the empiricist criterion of cognition is itself hard to make clear.

Many empiricists appear to have been committed to the view that there are certain *units* of experience (simple ideas, simple impressions) all our concepts being constructed out of these (complex ideas). *Basic* sentences will be known when they describe some unit of experience actually had by some person; other sentences—"nonbasic" sentences—are indirectly confirmed to the extent that they are reducible to basic sentences. The sophisticated empiricist of today will hardly speak any longer of units of experience. But often he will seem committed to some linguistic counterpart of these—e.g., basic Observation Sentences, which are capable of direct verification. Meaningful but non-Observation Sentences will then be reducible to the Basic Observation Sentences. But even this linguistic version of empiricism is under challenge today. Empiricists are roughly united by the conviction that having some experience is a sufficient (and possibly a necessary) condition for a fact-expressing sentence to be confirmed. Of course it is not enough just to *have* experience. The data of experience must be interpreted. But for the most part we may take for granted the scheme of interpretation and so restrict ourselves to speaking of the having of experiences and, linguistically, to the observation terms which apply to the experiences we have. The empiricist program, then, is to show that science satisfies a criterion of knowledge in terms of the having of experiences, and that the whole of scientific language is related to the observational terms which describe these experiences. Just *which* are to be observational terms—whether we are to regard "is a table" as an observational term or restrict ourselves to such terms as "appears brown"—is a family quarrel amongst philosophers. More pertinent to science is the problem of relating the *other* terms of science to the language of observation, however these are to be characterized.

For whether or not a term like "is a table" goes beyond what we actually experience, there is no doubt that "is an electron" will not be part of our observational vocabulary. Yet science is replete with such terms, theoretical terms so called, such as "field," "Psi-function," etc. Another class of terms, which are not in any obvious sense either observational terms or explicitly definable by means of these, are *dispositional* terms, e.g., "is soluble" or "is magnetic." Moreover, scientific language is, especially in the highly developed parts of science, frequently mathematical and makes use of terms the meaning of which cannot be given without reference to such inherently mathematical entities as infinite series, limits, derivatives, etc. Finally, there occur in science such terms as "perfectly frictionless plane" which function in theories somewhat in the manner in which theoretical terms do, but which do not raise all the same problems. For although few are inclined to suppose that the world contains perfectly frictionless planes, many are tempted to believe that theoretical terms denote genuine entities, that there are, in the world, such things as electrons. Some philosophers, again, will argue that the problem of the existence of theoretical entities is a matter only of whether the theories in which the theoretical terms figure are highly confirmed. Still other philosophers maintain that theoretical terms are merely scientific instruments, on a footing with test tubes and tuning forks. And since tuning forks are of the wrong logical type for the question of what they denote to arise, correspondingly we ought not to raise this question with regard to "electron."

In concluding we would like to call attention to the increasing role of formal analyses in this sort of problem. For example, it has recently been suggested that the entire problem of theoretical entities can be bypassed as a consequence of a theorem of William Craig's which shows, in effect, that a language in which both theoretical and observational terms occur can be replaced *in toto* by a language devoid of the dubious terms, providing the original language satisfies certain minimal formal requirements. The significance of Craig's theorem is not yet clear, but discussion of the issue must henceforth be in essentially formal terms. As much might be said of the problem of relating observational to nonobservational terms in science, which has been shown to require some complicated logical machinery. Finally, re-examination of the axioms of measurement has convinced many that the importance of distinction between fundamental and derived measurement has been grossly oversimplified. But expositions of these formal matters are beyond the scope of this work.

1

TWO KINDS OF PROPERTIES:

Galileo Galilei •

In accordance with the promise which I made to Your
Excellency, I shall certainly state my ideas concerning the
proposition "Motion is the cause of heat," explaining in
what way it appears to me to be true. But first it will be
necessary for me to say a few words concerning that which
we call "heat," for I strongly suspect that the commonly
held conception of the matter is very far from the truth,
inasmuch as heat is generally believed to be a true accident,
affection, or quality which actually resides in the material
which we feel to be heated.

Now, whenever I conceive of any material or corporeal
substance, I am necessarily constrained to conceive of that
substance as bounded and as possessing this or that shape,
as large or small in relationship to some other body, as in
this or that place during this or that time, as in motion or
at rest, as in contact or not in contact with some other
body, as being one, many, or few—and by no stretch
of imagination can I conceive of any corporeal body apart
from these conditions. But I do not at all feel myself compelled to conceive of bodies as necessarily conjoined with
such further conditions as being red or white, bitter or

• [This selection is from Galileo's *Il Saggitore* (*The Assayer*), which
appeared originally in 1623. The translation, by A. C. Danto, is
from *Introduction to Contemporary Civilization in the West* (2nd
ed.; New York: Columbia University Press, 1954), vol. I, pp.
719–24. Reprinted by permission of Columbia University Press.]

sweet, having sound or being mute, or possessing a pleasant or unpleasant fragrance. On the contrary, were they
not escorted by our physical senses, perhaps neither reason
nor understanding would ever, by themselves, arrive at
such notions. I think, therefore, that these tastes, odors,
colors, etc., so far as their objective existence is concerned,
are nothing but mere names for something which resides
exclusively in our sensitive body (*corpo sensitivo*), so that if
the perceiving creatures were removed, all of these qualities
would be annihilated and abolished from existence. But
just because we have given special names to these qualities,
different from the names we have given to the primary
and real properties, we are tempted into believing that the
former really and truly exist as well as the latter.

An example, I believe, will clearly explain my concept.
Suppose I pass my hand, first over a marble statue, then
over a living man. So far as the hand, considered in itself,
is concerned, it will act in an identical way upon each
of these objects; that is, the primary qualities of motion
and contact will similarly affect the two objects, and we
would use identical language to describe this in each case.
But the living body, which I subject to this experiment,
will feel itself affected in various ways, depending upon
the part of the body I happen to touch; for example, should
it be touched on the sole of the foot or the kneecap, or under
the armpit, it will feel, in addition to simple contact, a
further affection to which we have given a special name:
we call it "tickling." This latter affection is altogether our
own, and is not at all a property of the hand itself. And
it seems to me that he would be gravely in error who
would assert that the hand, in addition to movement and
contact, intrinsically possesses another and different faculty
which we might call the "tickling faculty," as though
tickling were a resident property of the hand *per se*. Again,
a piece of paper or a feather, when gently rubbed over
any part of our body whatsoever, will in itself act every-
where in an identical way; it will, namely, move and
contact. But we, should we be touched between the
eyes, on the tip of the nose, or under the nostrils, will
feel an almost intolerable titillation—while if touched in
other places, we will scarcely feel anything at all. Now
this titillation is completely ours and not the feather's, so
that if the living, sensing body were removed, nothing
would remain of the titillation but an empty name. And

I believe that many other qualities, such as taste, odor, color, and so on, often predicated of natural bodies, have a similar and no greater existence than this.

A solid body and, so to speak, one that is sufficiently heavy, when moved and applied against any part of my body whatsoever, will produce in me the sensation which we call "touch." Although this sense is to be found in every part of the body, it appears principally to reside in the palm of the hand, and even more so in the fingertips, with which we can feel the minutest differences of roughness, texture, and softness and hardness—differences which the other parts of the body are less capable of distinguishing. Some amongst these tactile sensations are more pleasing than others, depending upon the differences of configuration of tangible bodies; that is to say, in accordance with whether they are smooth or irregular, sharp or dull, flexible or rigid. And the sense of touch, being more material than the other senses and being produced by the mass of the material itself, seems to correspond to the element of earth.

Since certain material bodies are continually resolving themselves into tiny particles, some of the particles, because they are heavier than air, will descend; and some of them, because they are lighter than air, will ascend. From this, perhaps, two further senses are born, for certain of the particles penetrate two parts of our body which are effectively more sensitive than the skin, which is incapable of feeling the incursion of materials which are too fine, subtle, or flexible. The descending particles are received by the upper surface of the tongue, and penetrating, they blend with its substance and moisture. Thus our tastes are caused, pleasant or harsh in accordance with variations in the contact of diversely shaped particles, and depending upon whether they are few or many, and whether they have high or low velocity. Other particles ascend, and entering the nostrils they penetrate the various nodes (*mammilule*) which are the instruments of smell; and these particles, in like manner through contact and motion, produce savoriness or unsavoriness—again depending upon whether the particles have this or that shape, high or low velocity, and whether they are many or few. It is remarkable how providently the tongue and nasal passages are situated and disposed, the former stretched beneath to receive the ingression of descending particles, and the latter so arranged as to receive those which ascend. The arrangement whereby the sense of taste is excited in us is perhaps analogous to the way in which fluids descend through the air, and the stimulation of the sense of smell may be compared to the manner in which flames ascend in it.

There remains the element of air, which corresponds to the sense of sound. Sounds come to us indiscriminately, from above and below and from either side, since we are so constituted as to be equally disposed to every direction of the air's movement; and the ear is so situated as to accommodate itself in the highest possible degree to any position in space. Sounds, then, are produced in us and felt when (without any special quality of harmoniousness or dissonance) there is a rapid vibration of air, forming minutely small waves, which move certain cartilages of a certain drum which is in our ear. The various external ways in which this wave-motion of the air is produced are manifold, but can in large part be reduced to the vibrating of bodies which strike the air and form the waves which spread out with great velocity. High frequencies give rise to high tones; low frequencies give rise to low tones. But I cannot believe that there exists in external bodies anything, other than their size, shape, or motion (slow or rapid), which could excite in us our tastes, sounds, and odors. And indeed I should judge that, if ears, tongues, and noses be taken away, the number, shape, and motion of bodies would remain, but not their tastes, sounds, and odors. The latter, external to the living creature, I believe to be nothing but mere names, just as (a few lines back) I asserted tickling and titillation to be, if the armpit or the sensitive skin inside the nose were removed. As to the comparison between the four senses which we have mentioned and the four elements, I believe that the sense of sight, most excellent and noble of all the senses, is like light itself. It stands to the others in the same measure of comparative excellence as the finite stands to the infinite, the gradual to the instantaneous, the divisible to the indivisible, the darkness to the light. Of this sense, and all that pertains to it, I can pretend to understand but little; yet a great deal of time would not suffice for me to set forth even this little bit that I know, or (to put it more exactly) for me to sketch it out on paper. Therefore I shall ponder it in silence.

I return to my first proposition, having now shown how some affections, often reputed to be indwelling proper-

ties of some external body, have really no existence save
in us, and apart from us are mere names. I confess myself
to be very much inclined to believe that heat, too, is of this
sort, and that those materials which produce and make
felt in us the sense of heat and to which we give the general
name "fire" consist of a multitude of tiny particles of such
and such a shape, and having such and such a velocity.
These, when they encounter our body, penetrate it by
means of their extreme subtlety; and it is their contact,
felt by us in their passage through our substance, which is
the affection we call "heat." It will be pleasantly warm
or unpleasantly hot depending upon the number and the
velocity (greater or lesser) of these pricking, penetrating
particles—pleasant if by their penetration our necessary per-
spiring is facilitated, unpleasant if their penetrating effects
too great a division and dissolution of our substance. In
sum, the operation of fire, considered in itself, is nothing
but movement, or the penetration of bodies by its extreme
subtlety, quickly or slowly, depending upon the number
and velocity of tiny corpuscles of flame (*ignicoli*) and upon
the greater or lesser density of the bodies concerned. Many
bodies dissolve in such a manner that the major part of
them becomes transformed into further corpuscles of flame;
and this dissolution continues as further dissolvable material
is encountered. But that there exists in fire, apart from shape,
number, movement, penetration, and contact, some further quality which we call "heat," I cannot believe. And
I again judge that heat is altogether subjective, so that if
the living, sensitive body be removed, what we call
heat would be nothing but a simple word. Since it is the
case that this affection is produced in us by passage of tiny
corpuscles of flame through our substance and their contact with it, it is obvious that once this motion ceases,
their operation upon us will be null. It is thus that we
perceive that a quantity of fire, retained in the pores and
pits of a piece of calcified stone, does not heat—even if we
hold it in the palm of our hand—because the flame remains
stationary in the stone. But should we swish the stone
in water where, because of its weight, it has greater
propensity for movement and where the pits of the stone
open somewhat, the corpuscles of flame will escape and,
encountering our hand, will penetrate it, so that we will
feel heat. Since, in order for heat to be stimulated in us,
the mere presence of corpuscles of flame is not by itself

sufficient, and since movement is required in addition, it is with considerable reason that I declare motion to be the cause of heat.

This or that movement by which a scantling or other piece of wood is burned up or by which lead and other metals are melted will continue so long as the corpuscles of flame, moved either by their own velocity or (if this be insufficient) aided by a strong blast from a bellows, continue to penetrate the body in question; the former will resolve itself into further corpuscles of flame or into ash; the latter will liquify and be rendered fluid like water. From a common-sense point of view, to assert that that which moves a stone, piece of iron, or a stick, is what *heats* it, seems like an extreme vanity. But the friction produced when two hard bodies are rubbed together, which either reduces them to fine flying particles or permits the corpuscles of flame contained in them to escape, can finally be analyzed as motion. And the particles, when they encounter our body and penetrate and tear through it, are felt, in their motion and contact, by the living creature, who thus feels those pleasant or unpleasant affections which we call "heat," "burning," or "scorching."

Perhaps while this pulverizing and attrition continue, and remain confined to the particles themselves, their motion will be temporary and their operation will be merely that of heating. But once we arrive at the point of ultimate and maximum dissolution into truly indivisible atoms, light itself may be created, with an instantaneous motion or (I should rather say) an instantaneous diffusion and expansion, capable —I do not know if by the atoms' subtlety, rarity, immateriality, or by different and as yet unspecifiable conditions—capable, I say, of filling vast spaces.

But I should not like, Your Excellency, inadvertently to engulf myself in an infinite ocean without the means to find my way back to port. Nor should I like, while removing one doubt, to give birth to a hundred more, as I fear might in part be the case even in this timid venture from shore. Therefore, I shall await a more opportune moment to re-embark.

2

THE RELATION OF SENSE-DATA
TO PHYSICS:
Bertrand Russell ·

I. THE PROBLEM STATED

Physics is said to be an empirical science, based upon observation and experiment.

It is supposed to be verifiable, i.e., capable of calculating beforehand results subsequently confirmed by observation and experiment.

What can we learn by observation and experiment?

Nothing, so far as physics is concerned, except immediate data of sense: certain patches of color, sounds, tastes, smells, etc., with certain spatiotemporal relations.

The supposed contents of the physical world are *prima facie* very different from these: molecules have no color, atoms make no noise, electrons have no taste, and corpuscles do not even smell.

If such objects are to be verified, it must be solely through their relation to sense-data: they must have some kind of

· [This selection originally appeared in *Scientia*, 1910, and was later republished in *Mysticism and Logic* (London: George Allen & Unwin, Ltd., 1917). It is reprinted here with omission of Section XII, "Illusions, Hallucinations, and Dreams." Reprinted by permission of George Allen & Unwin, Ltd.]

correlation with sense-data, and must be verifiable through their correlation *alone*.

But how is the correlation itself ascertained? A correlation can only be ascertained empirically by the correlated objects being constantly *found* together. But in our case, only one term of the correlation, namely, the sensible term, is ever *found:* the other term seems essentially incapable of being found. Therefore, it would seem, the correlation with objects of sense, by which physics was to be verified, is itself utterly and forever unverifiable.

There are two ways of avoiding this result.

1. We may say that we know some principle *a priori*, without the need of empirical verification, e.g., that our sense-data have *causes* other than themselves, and that something can be known about these causes by inference from their effects. This way has been often adopted by philosophers. It may be necessary to adopt this way to some extent, but insofar as it is adopted physics ceases to be empirical or based upon experiment and observation alone. Therefore this way is to be avoided as much as possible.

2. We may succeed in actually defining the objects of physics as functions of sense-data. Just insofar as physics leads to expectations, this *must* be possible, since we can only *expect* what can be experienced. And insofar as the physical state of affairs is inferred from sense-data, it must be capable of expression as a function of sense-data. The problem of accomplishing this expression leads to much interesting logico-mathematical work.

In physics as commonly set forth, sense-data appear as functions of physical objects: when such-and-such waves impinge upon the eye, we see such-and-such colors, and so on. But the waves are in fact inferred from the colors, not vice versa. Physics cannot be regarded as validly based upon empirical data until the waves have been expressed as functions of the colors and other sense-data.

Thus if physics is to be verifiable we are faced with the following problem: Physics exhibits sense-data as functions of physical objects, but verification is only possible if physical objects can be exhibited as functions of sense-data. We have therefore to solve the equations giving sense-data in terms of physical objects, so as to make them instead give physical objects in terms of sense-data.

II. CHARACTERISTICS OF SENSE-DATA

When I speak of a "sense-datum," I do not mean the whole of what is given in sense at one time. I mean rather such a part of the whole as might be singled out by attention: particular patches of color, particular noises, and so on. There is some difficulty in deciding what is to be considered *one* sense-datum: often attention causes divisions to appear where, so far as can be discovered, there were no divisions before. An observed complex fact, such as that this patch of red is to the left of that patch of blue, is also to be regarded as a datum from our present point of view: epistemologically, it does not differ greatly from a simple sense-datum as regards its function in giving knowledge. Its *logical* structure is very different, however, from that of sense: *sense* gives acquaintance with particulars, and is thus a two-term relation in which the object can be *named* but not *asserted,* and is inherently incapable of truth or falsehood, whereas the observation of a complex fact, which may be suitably called perception, is not a two-term relation, but involves the propositional form on the object-side, and gives knowledge of a truth, not mere acquaintance with a particular. This logical difference, important as it is, is not very relevant to our present problem; and it will be convenient to regard data of perception as included among sense-data for the purposes of this paper. It is to be observed that the particulars which are constituents of a datum of perception are always sense-data in the strict sense.

Concerning sense-data, we know that they are there while they are data, and this is the epistemological basis of all our knowledge of external particulars. (The meaning of the word "external" of course raises problems which will concern us later.) We do not know, except by means of more or less precarious inferences, whether the objects which are at one time sense-data continue to exist at times when they are not data. Sense-data at the times when they are data are all that we directly and primitively know of the external world; hence in epistemology the fact that they are *data* is all-important. But the fact that they are all that we directly know gives, of course, no presumption that they are all that there is. If we could construct an impersonal metaphysic, independent of the accidents of our knowledge and ignorance, the privileged position of the actual data would probably disappear, and they would probably appear as a rather haphazard selection from a mass of objects more or less like them. In saying this, I assume only that it is probable that there are particulars with which we are not acquainted. Thus the special importance of sense-data is in relation to epistemology, not to metaphysics. In this respect, physics is to be reckoned as metaphysics: it is impersonal, and nominally pays no special attention to sense-data. It is only when we ask how physics can be *known* that the importance of sense-data re-emerges.

III. SENSIBILIA

I shall give the name *sensibilia* to those objects which have the same metaphysical and physical status as sense-data, without necessarily being data to any mind. Thus the relation of a *sensibile* to a sense-datum is like that of a man to a husband: a man becomes a husband by entering into the relation of marriage, and similarly a *sensibile* becomes a sense-datum by entering into the relation of acquaintance. It is important to have both terms; for we wish to discuss whether an object which is at one time a sense-datum can still exist at a time when it is not a sense-datum. We cannot ask "Can sense-data exist without being given?" for that is like asking "Can husbands exist without being married?" We must ask "Can *sensibilia* exist without being given?" and also "Can a particular *sensibile* be at one time a sense-datum, and at another not?" Unless we have the word *sensibile* as well as the word "sense-datum," such questions are apt to entangle us in trivial logical puzzles.

It will be seen that all sense-data are *sensibilia*. It is a metaphysical question whether all *sensibilia* are sense-data, and an epistemological question whether there exist means of inferring *sensibilia* which are not data from those that are.

A few preliminary remarks, to be amplified as we proceed, will serve to elucidate the use which I propose to make of *sensibilia*.

I regard sense-data as not mental, and as being, in fact, part of the actual subject-matter of physics. There are arguments, shortly to be examined, for their subjectivity, but these arguments seem to me only to prove *physiological* subjectivity, i.e. causal dependence on the sense-organs, nerves, and brain. The appearance which a thing presents to us is causally dependent upon these,

in exactly the same way as it is dependent upon intervening fog or smoke or colored glass. Both dependences
are contained in the statement that the appearance which
a piece of matter presents when viewed from a given
place is a function not only of the piece of matter but also
of the intervening medium. (The terms used in this statement—"matter," "view from a given place," "appearance,"
"intervening medium"—will all be defined in the course of
the present paper.) We have not the means of ascertaining
how things appear from places not surrounded by brain and
nerves and sense-organs, because we cannot leave the
body; but continuity makes it not unreasonable to suppose
that they present *some* appearance at such places. Any
such appearance would be included among *sensibilia*. If—
per impossibile—there were a complete human body with
no mind inside it, all those *sensibilia* would exist, in relation to that body, which would be sense-data if there
were a mind in the body. What the mind adds to *sensibilia*,
in fact, is *merely* awareness: everything else is physical or
physiological.

IV. SENSE-DATA ARE PHYSICAL

Before discussing this question it will be well to define
the sense in which the terms "mental" and "physical" are
to be used. The word "physical," in all preliminary discussions, is to be understood as meaning "what is dealt
with by physics." Physics, it is plain, tells us something
about some of the constituents of the actual world; what these
constituents are may be doubtful, but it is they that are to
be called physical, whatever their nature may prove to be.

The definition of the term "mental" is more difficult,
and can only be satisfactorily given after many difficult
controversies have been discussed and decided. For present
purposes therefore I must content myself with assuming
a dogmatic answer to these controversies. I shall call a
particular "mental" when it is aware of something, and
I shall call a fact "mental" when it contains a mental
particular as a constituent.

It will be seen that the mental and the physical are not
necessarily mutually exclusive, although I know of no
reason to suppose that they overlap.

The doubt as to the correctness of our definition of the
"mental" is of little importance in our present discussion.
For what I am concerned to maintain is that sense-data

are physical, and this being granted it is a matter of indifference in our present inquiry whether or not they are also mental. Although I do not hold, with Mach and James and the "new realists," that the difference between the mental and the physical is *merely* one of arrangement, yet what I have to say in the present paper is compatible with their doctrine and might have been reached from their standpoint.

In discussions on sense-data, two questions are commonly confused, namely: (1) Do sensible objects persist when we are not sensible of them? in other words, do *sensibilia* which are data at a certain time sometimes continue to exist at times when they are not data? And (2) are sense-data mental or physical?

I propose to assert that sense-data are physical, while yet maintaining that they probably never persist unchanged after ceasing to be data. The view that they do not persist is often thought, quite erroneously in my opinion, to imply that they are mental; and this has, I believe, been a potent source of confusion in regard to our present problem. If there were, as some have held, a *logical impossibility* in sense-data persisting after ceasing to be data, that certainly would tend to show that they were mental; but if, as I contend, their nonpersistence is merely a probable inference from empirically ascertained casual laws, then it carries no such implication with it, and we are quite free to treat them as part of the subject-matter of physics.

Logically a sense-datum is an object, a particular of which the subject is aware. It does not contain the subject as a part, as for example beliefs and volitions do. The existence of the sense-datum is therefore not logically dependent upon that of the subject; for the only way, so far as I know, in which the existence of A can be *logically* dependent upon the existence of B is when B is part of A. There is therefore no *a priori* reason why a particular which is a sense-datum should not persist after it has ceased to be a datum, nor why other similar particulars should not exist without ever being data. The view that sense-data are mental is derived, no doubt, in part from their physiological subjectivity, but in part also from a failure to distinguish between sense-data and "sensations." By a sensation I mean the fact consisting in the subject's awareness of the sense-datum. Thus a sensation is a complex of which the subject is a constituent and which therefore is mental. The sense-datum, on the other hand, stands over against the subject as that external object of which in sensation the subject is aware. It is true that the sense-datum is in many cases in the subject's body, but the subject's body is as distinct from the subject as tables and chairs are, and is in fact merely a part of the material world. So soon, therefore as sense-data are clearly distinguished from sensations, and as their subjectivity is recognized to be physiological not psychical, the chief obstacles in the way of regarding them as physical are removed.

v. "SENSIBILIA" AND "THINGS"

But if *sensibilia* are to be recognised as the ultimate constituents of the physical world, a long and difficult journey is to be performed before we can arrive either at the "thing" of common sense or at the "matter" of physics. The supposed impossibility of combining the different sense-data which are regarded as appearances of the same "thing" to different people has made it seem as though these *sensibilia* must be regarded as mere subjective phantasms. A given table will present to one man a rectangular appearance, while to another it appears to have two acute angles and two obtuse angles; to one man it appears brown, while to another, toward whom it reflects the light, it appears white and shiny. It is said, not wholly without plausibility, that these different shapes and different colors cannot coexist simultaneously in the same place, and cannot therefore both be constituents of the physical world. This argument I must confess appeared to me until recently to be irrefutable. The contrary opinion has, however, been ably maintained by Dr. T. P. Nunn in an article entitled: "Are Secondary Qualities Independent of Perception?"[1] The supposed impossibility derives its apparent force from the phrase *"in the same place,"* and it is precisely in this phrase that its weakness lies. The conception of space is too often treated in philosophy —even by those who on reflection would not defend such treatment—as though it were as given, simple, and unambiguous as Kant, in his psychological innocence, supposed. It is the unperceived ambiguity of the word "place" which, as we shall shortly see, has caused the difficulties to realists and given an undeserved advantage to

[1] *Proc. Arist. Soc.*, 1909–1910, pp. 191–218.

their opponents. Two "places" of different kinds are involved in every sense-datum, namely the place *at* which it appears and the place *from* which it appears. These belong to different spaces, although, as we shall see, it is possible, with certain limitations, to establish a correlation between them. What we call the different appearances of the same thing to different observers are each in a space private to the observer concerned. No place in the private world of one observer is identical with a place in the private world of another observer. There is therefore no question of combining the different appearances in the one place; and the fact that they cannot all exist in one place affords accordingly no ground whatever for questioning their physical reality. The "thing" of common sense may in fact be identified with the whole class of its appearances—where, however, we must include among appearances not only those which are actual sense-data, but also those *sensibilia*, if any, which, on grounds of continuity and resemblance, are to be regarded as belonging to the same system of appearances, although there happen to be no observers to whom they are data.

An example may make this clearer. Suppose there are a number of people in a room, all seeing, as they say, the same tables and chairs, walls and pictures. No two of these people have exactly the same sense-data, yet there is sufficient similarity among their data to enable them to group together certain of these data as appearances of one "thing" to the several spectators, and others as appearances of another "thing." Besides the appearances which a given thing in the room presents to the actual spectators, there are, we may suppose, other appearances which it would present to other possible spectators. If a man were to sit down between two others, the appearance which the room would present to him would be intermediate between the appearances which it presents to the two others: and although this appearance would not exist as it is without the sense-organs, nerves, and brain of the newly arrived spectator, still it is not unnatural to suppose that, from the position which he now occupies, *some* appearance of the room existed before his arrival. This supposition, however, need merely be noticed and not insisted upon.

Since the "thing" cannot, without indefensible partiality, be identified with any single one of its appearances, it came to be thought of as something distinct from all of them and underlying them. But by the principle of Occam's razor, if the class of appearances will fulfil the purposes for the sake of which the thing was invented by the pre-historic metaphysicians to whom common sense is due, economy demands that we should identify the thing with the class of its appearances. It is not necessary to *deny* a substance or substratum underlying these appearances; it is merely expedient to abstain from asserting this unnecessary entity. Our procedure here is precisely analogous to that which has swept away from the philosophy of mathematics the useless menagerie of metaphysical monsters with which it used to be infested.

VI. CONSTRUCTIONS VERSUS INFERENCES

Before proceeding to analyze and explain the ambiguities of the world "place," a few general remarks on method are desirable. The supreme maxim in scientific philosophizing is this:

Wherever possible, logical constructions are to be substituted for inferred entities.

Some examples of the substitution of construction for inference in the realm of mathematical philosophy may serve to elucidate the uses of this maxim. Take first the case of irrationals. In old days, irrationals were inferred as the supposed limits of series of rationals which had no rational limit; but the objection to this procedure was that it left the existence of irrationals merely optative, and for this reason the stricter methods of the present day no longer tolerate such a definition. We now define an irrational number as a certain class of ratios, thus constructing it logically by means of ratios, instead of arriving at it by a doubtful inference from them. Take again the case of cardinal numbers. Two equally numerous collections appear to have something in common: this something is supposed to be their cardinal number. But so long as the cardinal number is inferred from the collections, not constructed in terms of them, its existence must remain in doubt, unless in virtue of a metaphysical postulate *ad hoc*. By defining the cardinal number of a given collection as the class of all equally numerous collections, we avoid the necessity of this metaphysical postulate, and thereby remove a needless element of doubt from the philosophy of arithmetic. A similar method, as I have shown elsewhere, can be applied to classes themselves, which need not be supposed to have any metaphysical reality, but can be regarded as symbolically constructed fictions.

The method by which the construction proceeds is closely analogous in these and all similar cases. Given a set of propositions nominally dealing with supposed inferred entities, we observe the properties which are required of the supposed entities in order to make these propositions true. By dint of a little logical ingenuity, we then construct some logical function of less hypothetical entities which has the requisite properties. This constructed function we substitute for the supposed inferred entities, and thereby obtain a new and less doubtful interpretation of the body of propositions in question. This method, so fruitful in the philosophy of mathematics, will be found equally applicable in the philosophy of physics, where, I do not doubt, it would have been applied long ago but for the fact that all who have studied this subject hitherto have been completely ignorant of mathematical logic. I myself cannot claim originality in the application of this method to physics, since I owe the suggestion and the stimulus for its application entirely to my friend and collaborator Dr. Whitehead, who is engaged in applying it to the more mathematical portions of the region intermediate between sense-data and the points, instants, and particles of physics.

A complete application of the method which substitutes constructions for inferences would exhibit matter wholly in terms of sense-data, and even, we may add, of the sense-data of a single person, since the sense-data of others cannot be known without some element of inference. This, however, must remain for the present an ideal, to be approached as nearly as possible, but to be reached, if at all, only after a long preliminary labor of which as yet we can only see the very beginning. The inferences which are unavoidable can, however, be subjected to certain guiding principles. In the first place they should always be made perfectly explicit, and should be formulated in the most general manner possible. In the second place the inferred entities should, whenever this can be done, be similar to those whose existence is given, rather than, like the Kantian *Ding an sich*, something wholly remote from the data which nominally support the inference. The inferred entities which I shall allow myself are of two kinds: (*a*) the sense-data of other people, in favor of which there is the evidence of testimony, resting ultimately upon the analogical argument in favor of minds other than my own; (*b*) *sensibilia* which would appear from places where there happen to be no minds, and which I suppose to be real although they are no one's data. Of these two classes of inferred entities, the first will probably be allowed to pass unchallenged. It would give me the greatest satisfaction to be able to dispense with it, and thus establish physics upon a solipsistic basis; but those—and I fear they are the majority—in whom the human affections are stronger than the desire for logical economy will, no doubt, not share my desire to render solipsism scientifically satisfactory. The second class of inferred entities raises much more serious questions. It may be thought monstrous to maintain that a thing can present any appearance at all in a place where no sense-organs and nervous structure exist through which it could appear. I do not myself feel the monstrosity; nevertheless I should regard these supposed appearances only in the light of a hypothetical scaffolding, to be used while the edifice of physics is being raised, though possibly capable of being removed as soon as the edifice is completed. These *sensibilia* which are not data to anyone are therefore to be taken rather as an illustrative hypothesis and as an aid in preliminary statement than as a dogmatic part of the philosophy of physics in its final form.

VII. PRIVATE SPACE AND THE SPACE OF PERSPECTIVES

We have now to explain the ambiguity in the word "place," and how it comes that two places of different sorts are associated with every sense-datum, namely the place *at* which it is and the place *from* which it is perceived. The theory to be advocated is closely analogous to Leibniz's monadology, from which it differs chiefly in being less smooth and tidy.

The first fact to notice is that, so far as can be discovered, no *sensibile* is ever a datum to two people at once. The things seen by two different people are often closely similar, so similar that the same *words* can be used to denote them, without which communication with others concerning sensible objects would be impossible. But, in spite of this similarity, it would seem that some difference always arises from difference in the point of view. Thus each person, so far as his sense-data are concerned, lives in a private world. This private world contains its own space, or rather spaces, for it would seem that only experience teaches us to correlate the space of sight with the space of touch and with the various other spaces of other senses. This multiplicity of private spaces, however, though interesting to the psychologist, is of no great importance in regard to our present problem, since a merely solipsistic experience enables us to correlate them into the one private space which embraces all our own sense-data. The place *at* which a sense-datum is, is a place in private space. This place therefore is different from any place in the private space of another percipient. For if we assume, as logical economy demands, that all position is relative, a place is only definable by the things in or around it, and therefore the same place cannot occur in two private worlds which have no common constituent. The question, therefore, of combining what we call different appearances of the same thing in the same place does not arise, and the fact that a given object appears to different spectators to have different shapes and colors affords no argument against the physical reality of all these shapes and colors.

In addition to the private spaces belonging to the private worlds of different percipients, there is, however, another space, in which one whole private world counts as a point, or at least as a spatial unit. This might be described as the space of points of view, since each private world may be regarded as the appearance which the universe presents from a certain point of view. I prefer, however, to speak of it as the space of *perspectives,* in order to obviate the suggestion that a private world is only real when someone views it. And for the same reason, when I wish to speak of a private world without assuming a percipient, I shall call it a "perspective."

We have now to explain how the different perspectives are ordered in one space. This is effected by means of the correlated *sensibilia* which are regarded as the appearances, in different perspectives, of one and the same thing. By moving, and by testimony, we discover that two different perspectives, though they cannot both contain the same *sensibilia,* may nevertheless contain very similar ones; and the spatial order of a certain group of *sensibilia* in a private space of one perspective is found to be identical with, or very similar to, the spatial order of the correlated *sensibilia* in the private space of another perspective. In this way one *sensibile* in one perspective is correlated with one *sensibile* in another. Such correlated *sensibilia* will be called "appearances of one thing." In Leibniz's monadology, since each monad mirrored the whole universe, there was in each perspective a *sensibile* which was an appearance of each thing. In our system of perspectives, we make no such assumption of completeness. A given thing will have appearances in some perspectives, but presumably not in certain others. The "thing" being defined as the class of its appearances, if κ is the class of perspectives in which a certain thing θ appears, then θ is a member of the multiplicative class of κ, κ being a class of mutually exclusive classes of *sensibilia*. And similarly a perspective is a member of the multiplicative class of the things which appear in it.

The arrangement of perspectives in a space is effected by means of the differences between the appearances of a given thing in the various perspectives. Suppose, say, that a certain penny appears in a number of different perspectives; in some it looks larger and in some smaller, in some it looks circular, in others it presents the appearance of an ellipse of varying eccentricity. We may collect together all those perspectives in which the appearance of the penny is circular. These we will place on one straight line, ordering them in a series by the variations in the apparent size of the penny. Those perspectives in which the penny appears as a straight line of a certain thickness will similarly be placed upon a plane (though in this case there will be many different perspectives in which the penny is of the same size; when one arrangement is completed these will form a circle concentric with the penny), and ordered as before by the apparent size of the penny. By such means, all those perspectives in which the penny presents a visual appearance can be arranged in a three-dimensional spatial order. Experience shows that the same spatial order of perspectives would have resulted if, instead of the penny, we had chosen any other thing which appeared in all the perspectives in question, or any other method of utilizing the differences between the appearances of the same things in different perspectives. It is this empirical fact which has made it possible to construct the one all-embracing space of physics.

The space whose construction has just been explained, and whose elements are whole perspectives, will be called "perspective-space."

VIII. THE PLACING OF "THINGS" AND "SENSIBILIA" IN PERSPECTIVE SPACE

The world which we have so far constructed is a world of six dimensions, since it is a three-dimensional series of perspectives, each of which is itself three-dimensional. We have now to explain the correlation between the perspective space and the various private spaces contained within the various perspectives severally. It is by means of this correlation that the one three-dimensional space of physics is constructed; and it is because of the unconscious performance of this correlation that the distinction between perspective space and the percipient's private space has been blurred, with disastrous results for the philosophy of physics. Let us revert to our penny: the perspectives in which the penny appears larger are regarded as being nearer to the penny than those in which it appears smaller, but as far as experience goes the apparent size of the penny will not grow beyond a certain limit, namely, that where (as we say) the penny is so near the eye that if it were any nearer it could not be seen. By touch we may prolong the series until the penny touches the eye, but no further. If we have been traveling along a line of perspectives in the previously defined sense, we may, however, by imagining the penny removed, prolong the line of perspectives by means, say, of another penny; and the same may be done with any other line of perspectives defined by means of the penny. All these lines meet in a certain place, that is, in a certain perspective. This perspective will be defined as "the place where the penny is."

It is now evident in what sense two places in constructed physical space are associated with a given *sensibile*. There is first the place which is the perspective of which the *sensibile* is a member. This is the place *from* which the *sensibile* appears. Secondly there is the place where the thing is of which the *sensibile* is a member, in other words an appearance; this is the place *at* which the *sensibile* appears. The *sensibile* which is a member of one perspective is correlated with another perspective, namely, that which is the place where the thing is of which the *sensibile* is an appearance. To the psychologist the "place from which" is the more interesting, and the *sensibile* accordingly appears to him subjective and where the percipient is. To the physicist the "place at which" is the more interesting, and the *sensibile* accordingly appears to him physical and external. The causes, limits and partial justification of each of these two apparently incompatible views are evident from the above duplicity of places associated with a given *sensibile*.

We have seen that we can assign to a physical thing a place in the perspective space. In this way different parts of our body acquire positions in perspective space, and therefore there is a meaning (whether true or false need not much concern us) in saying that the perspective to which our sense-data belong is inside our head. Since our mind is correlated with the perspective to which our sense-data belong, we may regard this perspective as being the position of our mind in perspective space. If, therefore, this perspective is, in the above defined sense, inside our head, there is a good meaning for the statement that the mind is in the head. We can now say of the various appearances of a given thing that some of them are nearer to the thing than others; those are nearer which belong to perspectives that are nearer to "the place where the thing is." We can thus find a meaning, true or false, for the statement that more is to be learnt about a thing by examining it close to than by viewing it from a distance. We can also find a meaning for the phrase "the things which intervene between the subject and a thing of which an appearance is a datum to him." One reason often alleged for the subjectivity of sense-data is that the appearance of a thing may change when we find it hard to suppose that the thing itself has changed—for example, when the change is due to our shutting our eyes, or to our screwing them up so as to make the thing look double. If the thing is defined as the class of its appearances (which is the definition adopted above), there is of course necessarily *some* change in the thing whenever any one of its appearances changes. Nevertheless there is a very important distinction between two different ways in which the appearances may change. If after looking at a thing I shut my eyes, the appearance of my eyes changes in every perspective in which there is such an appearance, whereas most of the appearances of the thing will remain unchanged. We may say, as a matter of definition, that a thing changes when, however near to the thing an appearance of it may be, there are changes in appearances as near as, or still nearer to, the thing. On the other hand we shall say that the change is in some other thing if all appearances of the thing which are at not more than a certain distance from the thing remain unchanged, while only comparatively distant appearances of the thing are altered. From this consideration we are naturally led to the consideration of *matter*, which must be our next topic.

IX. THE DEFINITION OF MATTER

We defined the "physical thing" as the class of its appearances, but this can hardly be taken as a definition of matter. We want to be able to express the fact that the appearance of a thing in a given perspective is causally affected by the matter between the thing and the perspective. We have found a meaning for "between a thing and a perspective." But we want matter to be something other than the whole class of appearances of a thing, in order to state the influence of matter on appearances.

We commonly assume that the information we get about a thing is more accurate when the thing is nearer. Far off, we see it is a man; then we see it is Jones; then we see he is smiling. Complete accuracy would only be attainable as a limit: if the appearances of Jones as we approach him tend toward a limit, that limit may be taken to be what Jones really is. It is obvious that from the point of view of physics the appearances of a thing close to "count" more than the appearances far off. We may therefore set up the following tentative definition:

The *matter* of a given thing is the limit of its appearances as their distance from the thing diminishes.

It seems probable that there is something in this definition, but it is not quite satisfactory, because empirically there is no such limit to be obtained from sense-data. The definition will have to be eked out by constructions and definitions. But probably it suggests the right direction in which to look.

We are now in a position to understand in outline the reverse journey from matter to sense-data which is performed by physics. The appearance of a thing in a given perspective is a function of the matter composing the thing and of the intervening matter. The appearance of a thing is altered by intervening smoke or mist, by blue spectacles or by alterations in the sense-organs or nerves of the precipient (which also must be reckoned as part of the intervening medium). The nearer we approach to the thing, the less its appearance is affected by the intervening matter. As we travel further and further from the thing, its appearances diverge more and more from their initial character; and the causal laws of their divergence are to be stated in terms of the matter which lies between them and the thing. Since the appearances at very small distances are less affected by causes other than the thing itself, we come to think that the limit toward which these appearances tend as the distance diminishes is what the thing "really is," as opposed to what it merely seems to be. This, together with its necessity for the statement of causal laws, seems to be the source of the entirely erroneous feeling that matter is more "real" than sense-data.

Consider for example the infinite divisibility of matter. In looking at a given thing and approaching it, one sense-datum will become several, and each of these will again divide. Thus *one* appearance may represent *many* things, and to this process there seems no end. Hence in the limit, when we approach indefinitely near to the thing, there will be an indefinite number of units of matter corresponding to what, at a finite distance, is only one appearance. This is how infinite divisibility arises.

The whole causal efficacy of a thing resides in its matter. This is in some sense an empirical fact, but it would be hard to state it precisely, because "causal efficacy" is difficult to define.

What can be known empirically about the matter of a thing is only approximate, because we cannot get to know the appearances of the thing from very small distances, and cannot accurately infer the limit of these appearances. But it *is* inferred *approximately* by means of the appearances we can observe. It then turns out that these appearances can be exhibited by physics as a function of the matter in our immediate neighborhood; e.g., the visual appearance of a distant object is a function of the light-waves that reach the eyes. This leads to confusions of thought, but offers no real difficulty.

One appearance, of a visible object for example, is not sufficient to determine its other simultaneous appearances, although it goes a certain distance towards determining them. The determination of the hidden structure of a thing, so far as it is possible at all, can only be effected by means of elaborate dynamical inferences.

X. TIME

It seems that the one all-embracing time is a construction, like the one all-embracing space. Physics itself has become conscious of this fact through the discussions connected with relativity.

Between two perspectives which both belong to one person's experience, there will be a direct time-relation of before and after. This suggests a way of dividing history in the same sort of way as it is divided by different experiences, but without introducing experience or anything mental: we may define a "biography" as everything that is (directly) earlier or later than, or simultaneous with, a given *sensibile*. This will give a series of perspectives, which *might* all form parts of one person's experience, though it is not necessary that all or any of them should actually do so. By this means, the history of the world is divided into a number of mutually exclusive biographies.

We have now to correlate the times in the different biographies. The natural thing would be to say that the appearances of a given (momentary) thing in two different perspectives belonging to different biographies are to be taken as simultaneous; but this is not convenient. Suppose A shouts to B, and B replies as soon as he hears A's shout. Then between A's hearing of his own shout and his hearing of B's there is an interval; thus if we made A's and B's hearing of the same shout exactly simultaneous with each other, we should have events exactly simultaneous with a given event but not with each other. To obviate this, we assume a "velocity of sound." That is, we assume that the time when B hears A's shout is halfway between the time when A hears his own shout and the time when he hears B's. In this way the correlation is effected.

What has been said about sound applies of course equally to light. The general principle is that the appearances, in different perspectives, which are to be grouped together as constituting what a certain thing is at a certain moment, are not to be all regarded as being at that moment. On the contrary they spread outward from the thing with various velocities according to the nature of the appearances. Since no *direct* means exist of correlating the time in one biography with the time in another, this temporal grouping of the appearances belonging to a given thing at a

given moment is in part conventional. Its motive is partly
to secure the verification of such maxims as that events
which are exactly simultaneous with the same event are
exactly simultaneous with one another, partly to secure formulation of causal laws.

XI. THE PERSISTENCE OF THINGS AND MATTER

Apart from any of the fluctuating hypotheses of physics,
three main problems arise in connecting the world of physics
with the world of sense, namely:

1. the construction of a single space;
2. the construction of a single time;
3. the construction of permanent things or matter.

We have already considered the first and second of these
problems; it remains to consider the third.

We have seen how correlated appearances in different
perspectives are combined to form one "thing" at one
moment in the all-embracing time of physics. We have
now to consider how appearances at different times are
combined as belonging to one "thing," and how we arrive
at the persistent "matter" of physics. The assumption of
permanent substance, which technically underlies the
procedure of physics, cannot of course be regarded as
metaphysically legitimate: just as the one thing simultaneously
seen by many people is a construction, so the one thing
seen at different times by the same or different people
must be a construction, being in fact nothing but a certain
grouping of certain *sensibilia*.

We have seen that the momentary state of a "thing"
is an assemblage of *sensibilia*, in different perspectives,
not all simultaneous in the one constructed time, but
spreading out from "the place where the thing is" with
velocities depending upon the nature of the *sensibilia*. The
time *at* which the "thing" is in this state is the lower
limit of the times at which these appearances occur. We
have now to consider what leads us to speak of another
set of appearances as belonging to the same "thing" at a
different time.

For this purpose, we may, at least to begin with, confine ourselves within a single biography. If we can always
say when two *sensibilia* in a given biography are appearances of one thing, then, since we have seen how to
connect *sensibilia* in different biographies as appearances
of the same momentary state of a thing, we shall have

all that is necessary for the complete construction of the history of a thing.

It is to be observed, to begin with, that the identity of a thing for common sense is not always correlated with the identity of matter for physics. A human body is one persisting thing for common sense, but for physics its matter is constantly changing. We may say, broadly, that the common-sense conception is based upon continuity in appearances at the ordinary distances of sense-data, while the physical conception is based upon the continuity of appearances at very small distances from the thing. It is probable that the common-sense conception is not capable of complete precision. Let us therefore concentrate our attention upon the conception of the persistence of matter in physics.

The first characteristic of two appearances of the same piece of matter at different times is *continuity*. The two appearances must be connected by a series of intermediaries, which, if time and space form compact series, must themselves form a compact series. The color of the leaves is different in autumn from what it is in summer; but we believe that the change occurs gradually, and that, if the colors are different at two given times, there are intermediate times at which the colors are intermediate between those at the given times.

But there are two considerations that are important as regards continuity.

First, it is largely hypothetical. We do not observe any one thing continuously, and it is merely a hypothesis to assume that, while we are not observing it, it passes through conditions intermediate between those in which it is perceived. During uninterrupted observation, it is true, continuity is nearly verified; but even here, when motions are very rapid, as in the case of explosions, the continuity is not actually capable of direct verification. Thus we can only say that the sense-data are found to *permit* a hypothetical complement of *sensibilia* such as will preserve continuity, and that therefore there *may* be such a complement. Since, however, we have already made such use of hypothetical *sensibilia*, we will let this point pass, and admit such *sensibilia* as are required to preserve continuity.

Secondly, continuity is not a sufficient criterion of material identity. It is true that in many cases, such as rocks, mountains, tables, chairs, etc., where the appearances change slowly, continuity is sufficient, but in other cases, such as the parts of an approximately homogeneous fluid, it fails us utterly. We can travel by sensibly continuous gradations from any one drop of the sea at any one time to any other drop at any other time. We infer the motions of sea water from the effects of the current, but they cannot be inferred from direct sensible observation together with the assumption of continuity.

The characteristic required in addition to continuity is conformity with the laws of dynamics. Starting from what common sense regards as persistent things, and making only such modifications as from time to time seem reasonable, we arrive at assemblages of *sensibilia* which are found to obey certain simple laws, namely those of dynamics. By regarding *sensibilia* at different times as belonging to the same piece of matter, we are able to define *motion,* which presupposes the assumption or construction of something persisting throughout the time of the motion. The motions which are regarded as occurring, during a period in which all the *sensibilia* and the times of their appearance are given, will be different according to the manner in which we combine *sensibilia* at different times as belonging to the same piece of matter. Thus even when the whole history of the world is given in every particular, the question what motions take place is still to a certain extent arbitrary even after the assumption of continuity. Experience shows that it is possible to determine motions in such a way as to satisfy the laws of dynamics, and that this determination, roughly and on the whole, is fairly in agreement with the common-sense opinions about persistent things. This determination, therefore, is adopted, and leads to a criterion by which we can determine, sometimes practically, sometimes only theoretically, whether two appearances at different times are to be regarded as belonging to the same piece of matter. The persistence of all matter throughout all time can, I imagine, be secured by definition.

To recommend this conclusion, we must consider what it is that is proved by the empirical success of physics. What is proved is that its hypotheses, though unverifiable where they go beyond sense-data, are at no point in contradiction with sense-data, but, on the contrary, are ideally such as to render all sense-data calculable when a sufficient collection of *sensibilia* is given. Now physics has found it empirically possible to collect sense-data into series, each series being regarded as belonging to one "thing," and behaving, with regard to the laws of physics, in a way in which series not belonging to one thing would in general not behave. If it is to be unambiguous whether two appearances belong to the same thing or not, there must be only one way of grouping appearances so that the resulting things obey the laws of physics. It would be very difficult to prove that this is the case, but for our present purposes we may let this point pass, and assume that there is only one way. Thus we may lay down the following definition: *Physical things are those series of appearances whose matter obeys the laws of physics.* That such series exist is an empirical fact, which constitutes the verifiability of physics.

3

RUSSELL'S PHILOSOPHY OF SCIENCE:
Ernest Nagel ·

Russell's concern with the positive sciences is dominated almost exclusively by "the problem of the relation between the crude data of sense and the space, time, and matter of mathematical physics." [1] Like many of his contemporaries, he has been impressed by the highly abstract character of physical theory, and by the *prima facie* difference between the manifest traits of the world which are exhibited in our daily experience with it and its constitution as reported by the theoretical sciences. The theories of classical physics already provided ample materials for embroidering this difference; those theories employed such notions as that of instantaneous velocities, point-particles, mathematically

· [This selection is extracted from Nagel's contribution to *The Philosophy of Bertrand Russell* (Evanston and Chicago: Northwestern University Press, 1944, 1951, The Library of Living Philosophers, Paul Arthur Schilpp, Editor; published also by Tudor Publishing Company and Harper & Brothers, Torchbook Series). Nagel's article there also is concerned with Russell's philosophy of mathematics and with his analysis of scientific objects. A reply by Russell may be found in the same volume. The abbreviations in the footnotes are as follows: OKEW—*Our Knowledge of the External World*; AM—*The Analysis of Matter*; IMT—*An Inquiry into Meaning and Truth*; P—*Philosophy*; ABC—*The ABC of Relativity*; CBP—*Contemporary British Philosophy*. Reprinted by permission of Ernest Nagel and Paul Arthur Schilpp.]

[1] *OKEW*, p. viii.

continuous motions, and perfectly rigid and elastic bodies, although there appears to be nothing in our common experience to which these notions are applicable. But it was the advent of relativity theory and quantum mechanics, with their novel geometries and chronometries and their revolutionary conceptions of matter and causality, which supplied the chief stimulus to Russell's preoccupation with the problem.

However, the "critique of abstractions" for which the problem apparently calls may take several different forms. Russell's conception of the task of such a critique is controlled entirely by his view that the familiar concrete objects of daily life, no less than the abstract and remote entities of theoretical physics, are logical constructions. His approach to the problem must be clearly differentiated from so-called "operational" or "functional" analyses of scientific concepts —analyses which take "common-sense" knowledge and "common-sense" objects for granted. Something must therefore be said at the outset about the general pattern of Russell's views.

Like most philosophers, Russell believes that any discussion of the relation between theoretical physics and experience starts with admitting the familiar facts of common knowledge. But he maintains that on the one hand this knowledge is vague, complex, and inexact, and that on the other hand some types of its "data" are more certain and more "indubitable" than others. In order to obtain a secure foundation for knowledge we must therefore separate out those beliefs which are "inferred" from or "caused" by other beliefs, from the beliefs which are both logically and psychologically prior to all others. The "hardest" or "most certain" of all data (that is, data which "resist the solvent influence of critical reflection") are the truths of logic and the particular facts of sense.[2] The logical starting point of a philosophical inquiry into physics must therefore be with our immediate, direct perceptions. The problem of the relation of theoretical physics to the facts of experience can therefore be amplified as follows:

The laws of physics are believed to be at least approximately true, though they are not logically necessary; the evidence for them is empirical. All empirical evidence consists, in the last analysis, of perceptions; thus the world of physics must be,

[2] OKEW, p. 75.

in some sense, continuous with the world of perceptions, since it is the latter which supplies the evidence for the laws of physics. . . .

The evidence for the truth of physics is that our perceptions occur as the laws of physics would lead us to expect—e.g., we see an eclipse when the astronomers say there will be an eclipse. But physics never says anything about perceptions; it does not say that we shall see an eclipse, but something about the sun and the moon. The passage from what physics asserts to the expected perception is left vague and casual; it has none of the mathematical precision belonging to physics itself. We must therefore find an interpretation of physics which gives a due place to perceptions; if not, we have no right to appeal to the empirical world.[3]

Russell's problem has therefore a twofold aspect. One phase of it consists in finding an "interpretation" for physics which will make its propositions relevant to the crude materials of sense; and, as will appear, this concern leads Russell to adopt the view that all the objects of common-sense and developed science are logical constructions out of *events* —our perceptions being a proper subclass of the class of events. The other phase of the problem consists in justifying the truth-claims of physics; and this concern leads Russell to examine what data may serve as the most indubitable foundation for our knowledge, and to a discussion of the causal theory of perception as the ground for assuming the existence of events that are not perceptions. The two aspects of the problem are not independent, since the resolution of the second depends in part on the answer to the first, whereas the first requires that the "indubitable entities" (which it is the business of the second to specify) are already available. However, in the remainder of the present section I shall briefly examine some of Russell's views on perceptive knowledge; the discussion of his analysis of scientific objects will be left for the final section.

According to Russell, the original datum of experience consists of perceptions which are held to be known "non-inferentially"; included in this original datum are such items as specific shapes and colors, and relations like something being earlier than something else or something being above something else. Common-sense objects like tables and books, on the other hand, must be regarded as in some sense "inferred." They are said to be "inferred," not be-

[3] *AM*, pp. 6–7.

cause we have actually inferred them, but because our knowledge of them rests upon correlations between perceptions. These correlations are not invariable, and since we may be led to entertain false expectations by relying on them we do not "genuinely know" common-sense objects.[4] The proper comment upon this conclusion, so it seems to me, is to insist that we sometimes *do* know physical objects like tables and chairs, in a perfectly good and familiar sense of "know," in spite of the fact that we may sometimes be deceived about them. But this is not the issue I now wish to raise, important though it is. The question I want to put is whether, in distinguishing between perceptions as primitive and physical objects as derivative from perceptions, Russell is doing logic or psychology. Russell's *problem* certainly requires the distinction to be one of logic, for his aim is to *define* physical objects in terms of sensory qualities. From this point of view it is clearly *irrelevant* whether in the genesis of our knowledge the apprehension of discrete sensory qualities comes before or after the apprehension of configurations of qualities. Russell himself frequently makes it plain that it is not questions of psychology with which he is concerned.[5] Nevertheless, he also says that the primitive data of knowledge must not only be logically but also psychologically prior to the knowledge he regards as derivative. Thus, he declares that the "space" into which all the percepts of one person fit is a "constructed space, *the construction being achieved during the first months of life.*"[6] And here Russell is obviously talking psychology. However that may be, the empirical evidence drawn from modern psychology is certainly unfavorable to the notion that perceptions are psychologically primitive. On the contrary, that evidence supports the view that sensory qualities and relations are obtained only as the end-products of a deliberate process of discrimination and analysis, a process which is carried on within the framework of a "common-sense" knowledge of physical objects.

What reasons are there for regarding perceptions as the most indubitable data of knowledge? As far as one can ascertain, Russell rests his case on the simple dictum that

[4] *AM,* p. 186.

[5] See, for example, his quite explicit statement on this point in his "Professor Dewey's 'Essays in Experimental Logic,'" *The Journal of Philosophy,* Vol. XVI, 1919, pp. 8 ff.

[6] *AM,* p. 252, italics not in the text.

what is more primitive is also the more certain. Thus, he asserts that:

When we reflect upon the beliefs which are logically but not psychologically primitive, we find that, unless they can on reflection be deduced by a logical process from beliefs which are also psychologically primitive, our confidence in their truth tends to diminish the more we think about them.

And he concludes that "There is . . . more need of justifying our psychologically derivative beliefs than of justifying those that are primitive."[7] Why should this be so? Russell's answer is: because the derivative beliefs are nondemonstratively "inferred" from the primitive ones and are therefore less certain than the premises from which they are drawn, and because a belief is the more certain the "shorter" is the causal route from the cause of a belief to the belief.[8]

These views seem to me to rest on unsatisfactory evidence. Russell calls those data "hard" which resist the solvent influence of critical reflection. But in order to undertake such reflection, it is necessary to employ *some* principles in terms of which the attribution of "hardness" to specific data is to be evaluated; and such principles, if their authority is to count for anything, must be better warranted than the materials under judgment. However, such principles can themselves be warranted only by the outcome of our general experience, and their certainty—of whatever degree this may be—cannot therefore be a consequence of their being psychologically primitive. Russell's entire argument, moreover, is based on a principle of reasoning which I find most debatable—the principle that the conclusion of a nondemonstrative inference cannot be more certain than any of its premises. Quite the contrary appears to be the case in general. To take a simple illustration, if a number of witnesses testify to the occurrence of some event, the proposition that the event did occur may be more certain than any single item in the testimony, provided those items are independent. It is indeed partly in terms of the principle embodied in this example that the credibility of scientific

[7] *OKEW*, pp. 74–5.

[8] *IMT*, pp. 164, 200. He also says: ". . . A given reaction may be regarded as knowledge of various different occurrences. . . . The nearer our starting point [in the process leading to a certain event in the brain] is to the brain, the more accurate becomes the knowledge displayed in our reactions." *P*, p. 132.

theories is augmented. And if one accepts it as generally valid, little ground remains for the view that our psychologically primitive beliefs are also our most certain ones.[9]

Russell is not unaware of how difficult it is to identify primitive, "noninferred" data. Thus, he notes that the records of any observation or experiment always involve an "interpretation" of the facts by the help of a certain amount of theory. He also acknowledges that "perceptions of which we are not sufficiently conscious to express them in words are scientifically negligible; our premises must be facts which we have explicitly noted." [10] And elsewhere he insists that "a form of words is a social phenomenon," so that a person must know the language of which it is a part, as well as be exposed to certain stimuli, if he is to make true assertions.[11] The admission of the socially conditioned character of significant perception would normally be considered as a good ground for rejecting the view that perceptions are psychologically primitive. Nevertheless, Russell believes that it is possible to whittle away the element of interpretation in perceptive knowledge, and that "we can approach asymptotically to the pure datum."[12] But if pure data can be reached only asymptotically—and that means they are never *actually* reached—why is it important to try to base all our knowledge upon them? Moreover, Russell admits that some "interpretations" which accompany perceptions "can only be discovered by careful theory, and can never be made introspectively obvious"; and he thinks that such interpretations, at any rate, "ought to be included in the perception."[13] One cannot therefore help asking: If our actual data involve an element of "interpretation" and "inference," how in principle can we exclude physical objects as objects of knowledge on the ground that physical objects involve an element of "interpretation" and "inference," how in principle can we exclude physical objects as objects of knowledge on

[9] On some of the difficulties in the view that the "shortness" of the causal route between a belief and its cause can be taken as a measure of the certainty of the belief, see my "Mr. Russell on Meaning and Truth," *The Journal of Philosophy*, Vol. XXXVIII, 1941.

[10] *AM*, p. 200.

[11] *P*, p. 262.

[12] *IMT*, p. 155.

[13] *AM*, p. 189.

the ground that physical objects involve an element of "inference"? The distinction between the primitive and the "inferred" certainly shows the mark of being irrelevant to a working epistemology.

In any event, by his mixing up questions of logic with those of psychology Russell compromises at the very outset his program of exhibiting common-sense and scientific objects as logical constructions. That program presumably requires the analysis of these objects as structures of elements which are experientially accessible. If such an analysis is to be more than a formal logical exercise, those elements cannot simply be *postulated* to exist; and Russell's psychologically primitive "pure data" apparently have just this status.

Russell introduces another distracting confusion when, in order to establish the importance of regarding physical objects as constructions, he argues the case for an epistemological dualism and against "naïve realism." The truth or falsity of epistemological dualism does not seem to me germane to the question whether physical objects are analyzable into structures of specified entities. I shall therefore comment only briefly on the following views central to Russell's epistemology: that our percepts are located in our brains; that the causal theory of perception is the ground for inferring the existence of unperceived events; and that our knowledge of physical objects is "inferred" from percepts in our brain.

Russell maintains that, although it may be natural to suppose that what a physiologist sees when he is observing a living brain is in the brain he is observing, in fact, "if we are speaking of physical space, what the physiologist sees is in his own brain."[14] This seems to me incredibly wrong if the word "see" is being used in the ordinary sense in which we talk about seeing a physical object; and it is this ordinary sense of the word which Russell is employing when he supposes a physiologist to be observing a brain. There might indeed be a sense of "see" in which I see my own brain, though I have not the slightest inkling as to what that sense is. I do know, however, that I have never seen any portion of my own brain, and that I have seen many physical objects—where the statement that I have not seen one but seen the other is to be understood in the customary

[14] *P*, p. 140.

sense of "see." To deny the facts expressed by the statement seems to be absurd; and such a denial can be understood only if we suppose that the person making the denial is misusing language. Moreover, such facts seem to me basic for every sound epistemology and every sound interpretation of science; and, however difficult it may be to do so, the findings of physics and physiology must be interpreted so as to square with them.

The evidence Russell offers for the causal theory of perception derives whatever plausibility it has from the tacit assumptions of common-sense knowledge; accordingly, it is not this theory which can justify such common-sense assumptions as that our perceptions may have unperceived causes. Russell's chief argument for that theory consists in showing that if we accept the theory we can formulate the course of events in "simple causal laws." For example, he declares that if many people see and hear a gun fired, the further they are situated from it the longer is the interval between the seeing and the hearing. He thinks it is therefore "natural to suppose that the sound travels over the intervening space, in which case something must be happening even in places where there is no one with ears to hear."[15] But why does it seem "natural" to suppose this? Does not the "naturalness" receive its support from the experimental confirmations which are found for such assumptions in the context of our manipulating physical objects? Russell also thinks that, although the phenomenalist view (that there are no unperceived events) is not logically impossible, it is an implausible view, because it is incompatible with physical determinism.[16] But why is the assumption implausible that "imaginary" or "fictitious" entities are causally efficacious? If the implausibility does not rest upon the findings of disciplined experience, embodied in common-sense knowledge, upon what can it rest?

Though Russell speaks much of "inferring" things, it is not clear in what sense he believes physical objects to be "inferred" from perceptions. He uses the term "inference" in at least the following distinct ways: in the ordinary sense of logically deducing one proposition from another; in the familiar sense of asserting a proposition on evidence which

15 *AM*, p. 209.
16 *AM*, p. 214.

makes that proposition probable; in the sense in which something which is perceived with an "accompanying interpretation" is obtained from something else that is supposed to be perceived directly or without interpretation; and finally, in the sense in which something that is a logical construction is obtained from entities out of which it is constructed. It is evident that when Russell says that the sun is inferred from our percepts, he does not mean that it is inferred in either of the first two senses specified, and he repeatedly asserts that he does not mean it in these senses. On the other hand, he declares that:

So long as naïve realism remained tenable, perception was knowledge of a physical object, obtained through the senses, not by inference. But in accepting the causal theory of perception we have committed ourselves to the view that perception gives no immediate knowledge of a physical object, but at best a datum for inference.[17]

In this passage Russell is apparently using the third sense of "inference"; and when he uses the term in this way he sometimes talks of an inference as an unconscious physiological process. But elsewhere he also says that "Modern physics reduces matter to a set of events. . . . The events that take the place of matter in the old sense are inferred from their effect on eyes, photographic plates, and other instruments. . . ."[18] And in this passage what is "inferred" is a physical object, viewed as a construction out of such events as perceptions. Russell does not therefore distinguish between the last two senses of "inference" listed above, and as a consequence it is difficult to extract a coherent formulation of how physical objects are inferred from percepts. However that may be, if our knowledge of the sun is "inferred" in the third sense of the term, the inference is presumably grounded in the causal theory of perception, and therefore in the procedures involved in common-sense knowledge of things. On the other hand, if that knowledge is "inferential" in the fourth sense, the fact that the sun is a logical construction (if it is a fact) in no way prejudices the claim that we do have knowledge of it; for the exhibition

[17] *AM*, p. 218. Cf. also: "Our knowledge of the physical world is not at first inferential, but this is only because we take our percepts to *be* the physical world." *P*, p. 130.

[18] *P*, p. 157.

of the sun as a construction out of events like perceptions obviously requires knowledge of the sun.

It is a common error of Russell's critics to interpret his view that the physical world is a logical construction, as if he intended to deny that there are physical objects in the ordinary sense of this phrase. For this misunderstanding he is at least partly to blame. Thus he declares: "Common sense imagines that when it sees a table it sees a table. This is gross delusion."[19] Again, commenting on Dr. Johnson's refutation of Berkeley, he maintains that "If he had known that his foot never touched the stone, and that both were only complicated systems of wave-motions, he might have been less satisfied with his refutation."[20] And elsewhere he says that on the view he is recommending, "the 'pushiness' of matter disappears altogether. . . . 'Matter' is a convenient formula for describing what happens where it isn't."[21]

There are indeed several not always compatible tendencies struggling for mastery in Russell's use of his supreme maxim for philosophizing. One of them is that represented by the conception of experience according to which the objects of what is immediately "known" are in the brain; a second is the view that if something is a logical construction, it is *we* who have constructed it in time; another is stated by the conception that so long as some "indubitable set of objects" can be specified which will satisfy given formulae, then any object in that set may be substituted for the "inferred" object satisfying those formulae; and a fourth is the view that an object is a construction when it is *analyzable* into a structure of identifiable elements.

It has already been argued that the first of these tendencies is essentially irrelevant to (or at any rate, can be kept distinct from) the use of Russell's maxim. The second is often explicitly disavowed by Russell himself, though he often betrays his disavowal. But before examining the incidence of the remaining two tendencies upon his reconstruction of physical theory, I want to comment on the passages cited from Russell in the opening paragraph of this section. Is it a delusion when, under appropriate circumstances, we claim to see a table? A table may indeed be a logical construc-

[19] *ABC*, p. 213.
[20] *P*, p. 279.
[21] *P*, p. 159.

tion; but in the sense in which we ordinarily use the words "see" and "table," it may be quite true that we do see a table: this mode of expressing what is happening is the appropriate way of putting the matter. Again, if when Dr. Johnson kicked a stone his foot never touched the stone, what *did* his foot do? To say that his foot never touched the stone because both his foot and the stone were systems of radiation is to *misuse* language; for in the specified context the words "foot," "stone," "kicked," and "touched" are being so used that it is correct to say Dr. Johnson kicked a stone and therefore his foot touched it. To be sure, under some other circumstances, and for the sake of certain ends, it might be advisable to use a different language in describing what had happened. But it obviously cannot be wrong to employ ordinary language in accordance with ordinary usage. And finally, it seems to me grotesque to say that the "pushiness" of matter can disappear as a consequence of a new analysis or redefinition of matter. We have learned to apply the word "pushy" to certain identifiable characteristics of material objects; and such a use of the word is correct simply because that is the usage that had been established for it. Whatever may be the outcome of analyzing material objects, their identifiable properties will remain their identifiable properties, and it will be correct to apply the standardized expressions to them. It will certainly not be correct to designate a physical body as a formula.

Let us turn to Russell's reinterpretation of physics. The first question I want to ask is what marks, if any, distinguish something which is a construction from something that is not. Russell seems to suggest at least two. One is the suggestion that something is a construction when it has properties which satisfy some mathematical formula or equation. He says, for example:

The electron has very convenient properties, and is therefore probably a logical structure upon which we concentrate attention just because of these properties. A rather haphazard set of particulars may be capable of being collected into groups each of which has very agreeable smooth mathematical properties; but we have no right to suppose Nature so kind to the mathematician as to have created particulars with just such properties as he would wish to find.[22]

[22] *AM*, p. 319. At another place Russell proposes as a supplement to Occam's razor the principle "What is logically convenient is likely to be artificial." *AM*, p. 290.

One doesn't know how seriously to take such statements, especially since they imply what is questionably the case, that it is we who invariably manufacture the properties which are convenient for the purposes of mathematical physics. It is certainly not evident what right we have to suppose that we have no right to suppose that Nature created at least some of them. It is one thing to say that for the sake of developing mathematical physics we have *isolated* certain features of things and ignored others; it is quite another thing to maintain that what we have selected we have also manufactured. Moreover, it is not clear why, on this criterion, the events out of which electrons and other objects are said to be constructions should not themselves be regarded as constructions. After all, as will be seen presently, they too have remarkably smooth mathematical properties: they fall into groups having exquisitely neat internal structures.

The second suggestion is more important. According to it, something is a construction when it is complex. Accordingly, since physical bodies as well as scientific objects like electrons are analyzable—indeed, on Russell's view into relations between ultimate simples—whereas perceptions and other events are not, the former are constructions out of the latter. The "ultimate furniture of the world" thus consists of a very large, perhaps infinite, number of events which have various specific relations to each other. When described in terms of spatiotemporal characteristics, these "particulars" are assumed to have quite small spatial and temporal dimensions. Moreover, some of these particulars (though not all) are perceived, and at least some of their qualities and relations are also immediately apprehended. Events, their simple qualities and their relations, are thus the building materials, the "crude data," in terms of which physics is to be "interpreted."

Russell admits that, although he believes his particulars are simples, in the sense that they have no "parts" or internal "structure," it is impossible to prove once for all that they are such. And although he also admits that simples are not directly experienced "but known only inferentially as the limit of analysis," he maintains it is desirable to exhibit objects as constructions out of simples. His belief in the existence of simples rests on self-evidence: "It seems obvious to me . . . that what is complex must be composed of simples, though the number of constituents may be infinite."[23] Against such a view it is arguable that simplicity is a relative and systemic notion, and that the justification for taking anything to be a simple rests on the clarification, the systematization, or the control of subject-matter which follows from a given mode of analysis. The issue is, however, not of great importance for the sequel. An issue of more serious concern is raised by Russell's admission that simples can be known only as the limits of analysis. For in the first place, he must also admit that we cannot in consequence literally *begin* with simples, trace through sequentially the complex patterns of their interrelations, and so finally reach the familiar objects of daily life. And in the second place, it becomes difficult to understand, even if we did succeed in exhibiting objects as constructions out of simples, just what such an analysis contributes to bridging the gulf between the propositions of physics and the familiar world of daily experience. However, Russell's subsequent analyses are not vitally affected by these doubts: whether events are ultimate particulars or not, the important part of his claim is that at least some of them are perceptions, and that they are relevant to the analysis only because of their relations to other things, and not because of a demonstrated lack of internal structure.[24]

One point is clear: Russell does not exhibit the logical structure of the physical world *entirely* in terms of entities which he regards as "known," since his particulars include events that are not perceptions. Such events are held by him to be "inferred," largely on the strength of the causal theory of perception and in order to avoid the "implausible" consequences of a radical phenomenalism. Russell's own remark on the inclusion of unperceived (and therefore "inferred") events into the ultimate furniture of the world is one that many of his readers must have whispered to themselves: "If we have once admitted unperceived events, there is no very obvious reason for picking and choosing

[23] *CBP*, p. 375.

[24] Russell declares in this connection: "Atoms were formerly particulars; now they have ceased to be so. But that has not falsified the chemical propositions that can be enunciated without taking account of their structure." *AM*, p. 278. The first sentence in this passage is seriously misleading, since it suggests that whether something is a particular or not depends on the state of our knowledge, and that therefore a construction is something made by us.

among the events which physics leads us to infer."[25] How many needless excursions into sterile epistemological speculations could have been avoided if this remark had been taken seriously! But the remark does make it plain that the significance of exhibiting things as constructions does not consist in circumventing the need for making inferences or in denying the existence of physical objects. The remark shows that the importance of the enterprise lies in *analyzing* or *defining* the sense of such expressions as "physical object," "point," "electron," and so on.

[25] *AM*, p. 325

4

"FURNITURE OF THE EARTH":
L. Susan Stebbing ·

Imagine the following scene. You are handed a dish containing some apples—rosy-cheeked, green apples. You take the one nearest to you, and realize that you have been "had." The "apple" is too hard and not heavy enough to be really an apple; as you tap it with your fingernail it gives out a sound such as never came from tapping a "real" apple. You admire the neatness of the imitation. To sight the illusion is perfect. It is quite sensible to contrast this ingenious fake with a "real" apple, for a "real" apple just is an object that *really* is an apple, and not only *seems* to be one. This fake is an object that looks to your eyes to be an apple, but neither feels nor tastes as an apple does. As soon as you pick it up you know that it is not an apple; there is no need to taste it. We should be speaking in conformity with the rules of good English if we were to say that the dish contained real apples and imitation apples. But this mode of speaking does not lead us to suppose that there are two varieties of *apples*, namely, real and imitation apples, as there are Bramley Seedlings and Blenheim pippins. Again, a shadow may be thrown on a wall, or an image may be thrown through a lantern on to a screen. We distinguish the shadow from the object of which it is the

· [This selection is a chapter in Stebbing's *Philosophy and the Physicists* (London: Methuen & Co., Ltd., 1937; New York: Dover Publications, Inc., 1958). It is reprinted, with some repetitions and cross-references omitted, by permission of Methuen & Co., Ltd.]

shadow, the image from that of which it is the image. Shadow and image are apprehensible only by sight; they really are visual, i.e., *seeable*, entities. I can see a man, and I can see his shadow; but there is not both a *real* man and a *shadow* man; there is just the shadow of the man.

This point may seem to have been unduly labored. It is, however, of great importance. The words "real" and "really" are familiar words; they are variously used in every-day speech, and are not, as a rule, used ambiguously. The opposition between a *real* object and an *imitation* of a real object is clear. So, too, is the opposition between "really seeing a man" and having an illusion. We can speak sensibly of the distinction between "the real size" and "the apparent size" of the moon, but we know that both these expressions are extremely elliptical. The significance of the words "real" and "really" can be determined only by reference to the context in which they are used. Nothing but confusion can result if, in one and the same sentence, we mix up language used appropriately for the furniture of earth and our daily dealings with it with language used for the purpose of philosophical and scientific discussion.

A peculiarly gross example of such a linguistic mixture is provided by one of Eddington's most picturesque passages:

I am standing on a threshold about to enter a room. It is a complicated business. In the first place I must shove against an atmosphere with a force of fourteen pounds on every square inch of my body. I must make sure of landing on a plank travelling at twenty miles a second round the sun—a fraction of a second too early or too late, the plank would be miles away. I must do this whilst hanging from a round planet head outward into space, and with a wind of aether blowing at no one knows how many miles a second through every interstice of my body. The plank has no solidity of substance. To step on it is like stepping on a swarm of flies. Shall I not slip through? No, if I make the venture one of the flies hits me and gives me a boost up again; I fall again and am knocked upwards by another fly; and so on. I may hope that the net result will be that I remain steady; but if unfortunately I should slip through the floor or be boosted too violently up to the ceiling the occurrence would be, not a violation of the laws of Nature, but a rare coincidence. (*Nature of the Physical World*, p. 342.)

Whatever we may think of Eddington's chances of slipping through the floor, we must regard his usage of language in this statement as gravely misleading to the common reader. I cannot doubt that it reveals serious confusion in Eddington's own thinking about "the nature of the physical world." Stepping on a plank is not in the least like "stepping on a swarm of flies." This language is drawn from, and is appropriate to, our daily intercourse with the familiar furniture of earth. We understand well what it is like to step on to a solid plank; we can also imagine what it would be like to step on to a swarm of flies. We know that two such experiences would be quite different. The plank is solid. If it be securely fixed, it will support our weight. What, then, are we to make of the comparison of stepping on to a plank with stepping on to a swarm of flies? What can be meant by saying that "the plank has no solidity of substance"?

Again, we are familiar with the experience of shoving against an obstacle, and with the experience of struggling against a strong head wind. We know that we do not have "to shove against an atmosphere" as we cross the threshold of a room. We can imagine what it would be like to jump on to a moving plank. We may have seen in a circus an equestrian acrobat jump from the back of a swiftly moving horse on to the back of another horse moving with approximately the same speed. We know that no such acrobatic feat is required to cross the threshold of a room.[1]

I may seem too heavy-handed in my treatment of a picturesque passage, and thus to fall under the condemnation of the man who cannot see a joke and needs to be "in contact with merry-minded companions" in order that he may develop a sense of humor. But the picturesqueness is deceptive; the passage needs serious criticism since Eddington draws from it a conclusion that is important. "Verily," he says, "it is easier for a camel to pass through the eye of a needle than for a scientific man to pass through a door. And whether the door be barn door or church door it might be wiser that he should consent to be an ordinary man and

[1] Eddington's words suggest that he is standing on a stationary plank and has to land on to another plank that is moving, relatively to himself, with a speed of twenty miles a second. It would be charitable to regard this as a slip, were it not that its rectification would spoil this part of his picture. There is an equally gross absurdity in the statement that he is "hanging head outward into space."

walk in rather than wait until all the difficulties involved in a really scientific ingress are resolved." It is, then, suggested that an ordinary man has no difficulty in crossing the threshold of a room but that "a really scientific ingress" presents difficulties[2] The suggested contrast is as absurd as the use of the adjective "scientific" prefixed to "ingress," in this context, is perverse. Whatever difficulties a scientist, by reason of his scientific knowledge, may encounter in becoming a member of a spiritual church, these difficulties bear no comparison with the difficulties of the imagined acrobatic feat. Consequently, they are not solved by the consideration that Eddington, no less than the ordinary man, need not hesitate to cross the threshold of his room. . . .

If Eddington had drawn this picture for purely expository purposes, it might be unobjectionable. The scientist who sets out to give a popular exposition of a difficult and highly technical subject must use what means he can devise to convey to his readers what it is all about. At the same time, if he wishes to avoid being misunderstood, he must surely warn his readers that, in the present stage of physics, very little can be conveyed to a reader who lacks the mathematical equipment required to understand the methods by which results are obtained and the language in which these results can alone find adequate expression. Eddington's picture seems to me to be open to the objection that the image of a swarm of flies used to explain the electronic structure of matter is more appropriate to the old-fashioned classical conceptions that found expression in a model than to the conceptions he is trying to explain. Consequently, the reader may be misled unless he is warned that nothing resembling the spatial relations of flies in a swarm can be found in the collection of electrons. No concepts drawn

[2] In the article "The Domain of Physical Science" (*Science, Religion and Reality*) a similar passage begins as follows:

"The learned physicist and the man in the street were standing together on the threshold about to enter a room.

"The man in the street moved forward without trouble, planted his foot on a solid unyielding plank at rest before him, and entered.

"The physicist was faced with an intricate problem." (There follows much the same account of the difficulties as in the passage quoted.)

Eddington here goes on to suggest that the physicist may be "content to follow *the same crude conception* of his task that presented itself to the mind of his unscientific colleague" (my italics).

from the level of common-sense thinking are appropriate
to subatomic, i.e., microphysical, phenomena. Consequently,
the language of common sense is not appropriate to the
description of such phenomena. Since, however, the man in
the street tends to think in pictures and may desire to know
something about the latest developments of physics, it is
no doubt useful to provide him with some rough picture.
The danger arises when the scientist uses the picture for
the purpose of making explicit denials, and expresses these
denials in common-sense language used in such a way as
to be devoid of sense. This, unfortunately, is exactly what
Eddington has done in the passage we are considering,
and indeed, in many other passages as well.

It is worth while to examine with some care what exactly
it is that Eddington is denying when he asserts that "the
plank has no solidity of substance." What are we to understand by "solidity"? Unless we do understand it we cannot
understand what the denial of solidity to the plank amounts
to. But we can understand "solidity" only if we can truly
say that the plank is solid. For "solid" just is the word we
use to describe a certain respect in which a plank of wood
resembles a block of marble, a piece of paper, and a cricket
ball, and in which each of these differs from a sponge,
from the interior of a soap bubble, and from the holes in
a net. We use the word "solid" sometimes as the opposite
of "empty," sometimes as the opposite of "hollow," sometimes
as the opposite of "porous." We may also, in a very slightly
technical usage, contrast "solid" with "liquid" or with
"gaseous." There is, no doubt, considerable variation in the
precise significance of the word "solid" in various contexts.
Further, as is the case with all words, "solid" may be misused,
and may also be used figuratively. But there could not be
a *misuse,* or a *figurative* use, unless there were some correct
and literal usages. The point is that the common usage of
language enables us to attribute a meaning to the phrase
"a solid plank"; but there is no common usage of language
that provides a meaning for the word "solid" that would
make sense to say that the plank on which I stand is not
solid. We oppose the solidity of the walls of a house to the
emptiness of its unfurnished rooms; we oppose the solidity
of a piece of pumice stone to the porous loofah sponge. We
do not deny that the pumice stone is to some degree porous,
that the bricks of the wall have chinks and crevices. But we
do not know how to use a word that has no sensible oppo-

site. If the plank is nonsolid, then what does "solid" *mean?* In the companion passage to the one quoted above, and to which reference was made in a preceding footnote, Eddington depicts the physicist, about to enter a room, as reflecting that "the plank is not what it appears to be—a continuous support for his weight." This remark is absurd. The plank appears to be capable of supporting his weight, and, as his subsequent entry into the room showed, it *was* capable of supporting his weight. If it be objected that the plank is "a support for his weight" but not "a *continuous* support," I would reply that the word "continuous" is here used without any assigned meaning. The plank appears *solid* in that sense of the word "solid" in which the plank is, in fact, solid. It is of the utmost importance to press the question: If the plank appears to be *solid,* but is really *nonsolid,* what does "solid" mean? If "solid" has no assignable meaning, then "nonsolid" is also without sense. If the plank is nonsolid, then where can we find an example to show us what "solid" means? The pairs of words, "solid"—"empty," "solid"—"hollow," "solid"—"porous," belong to the vocabulary of common-sense language; in the case of each pair, if one of the two is without sense, so is the other.

This nonsensical denial of solidity is very common in popular expositions of the physicist's conception of material objects. The author of a recently published book says: "A table, a piece of paper, no longer possess that solid reality which they appear to possess; they are both of them porous, and consist of very small electrically charged particles, which are arranged in a peculiar way." How are we to understand the statement that the table *no longer* possesses "the solid reality" which it appears to possess? The context of the statement must be taken into account. The sentence quoted occurs in a summary of the view of the physical world according to classical physics. It immediately follows the statement: "This picture formed by the physicists has one great drawback as compared with the picture formed by the non-scientific man in the street. It is much more abstract." There are, then, two pictures. Of what, we must ask, are they pictures? Where are we to find application for the words "solid reality," which we may not use with reference to the table? Again we must ask: If the table is nonsolid, what does "solid" mean?

No doubt the author had in mind the nineteenth-century view of the ultramicroscopic world as consisting of solid, absolutely hard, indivisible billiard-ball-like atoms, which were assumed to be solid and hard in a perfectly straightforward sense of the words "solid" and "hard." If so, it would be more appropriate to say that the modern physicist no longer believes that the table *consists* of solid atomic balls than to say that "the table no longer possesses solid reality." There is, indeed, a danger in talking about *the table* at all, for the physicist is not, in fact, concerned with tables. The recent habit of talking as though he were is responsible for much confusion of thought. It leads Eddington into the preposterous nonsense of the "two tables." This view will be familiar to everyone who is interested in the philosophy of the physicists. Nevertheless, it is desirable to quote a considerable part of Eddington's statement, since it is important to examine his view in some detail.

I have settled down to the task of writing these lectures and have drawn up my chairs to my two tables. Two tables! Yes; there are duplicates of every object about me—two tables, two chairs, two pens. . . . One of them has been familiar to me from earliest years. It is a commonplace object of that environment which I call the world. How shall I describe it? It has extension; it is comparatively permanent; it is coloured; above all, it is *substantial*. . . . Table No. 2 is my scientific table. It is a more recent acquaintance and I do not feel so familiar with it. . . . My scientific table is mostly emptiness. Sparsely scattered in that emptiness are numerous electric charges rushing about with great speed; but their combined bulk amounts to less than a billionth of the bulk of the table itself. Notwithstanding its strange construction it turns out to be an entirely efficient table. It supports my writing paper as satisfactorily as table No. 1; for when I lay the paper on it the little electric particles with their headlong speed keep on hitting the underside, so that the paper is maintained in shuttlecock fashion at a nearly steady level. If I lean upon this table I shall not go through; or, to be strictly accurate, the chance of my scientific elbow going through my scientific table is so excessively small that it can be neglected in practical life. . . . There is nothing *substantial* about my second table. It is nearly all empty space—space pervaded it is true by fields of force, but these are assigned to the categories of 'influences,' not of 'things.' [3]

There is so much to criticize in this passage that it is difficult to know where to begin. . . .

[3] *N.Ph.W.*, pp. xi–xiii. I assume the reader's familiarity with the rest of the chapter in which this passage occurs.

Perhaps the first comment that should be made is that Eddington takes quite seriously the view that there are *two tables;* one belongs to "the external world of physics," the other to "a world of familiar acquaintance in human consciousness." Eddington's philosophy may be regarded as the outcome of a sustained attempt to answer the question: How are the two tables related to one another? It never seems to occur to him that the form of the question is absurd. In answering the question he is hampered from the start by his initial assumption that the tables are *duplicates* of each other, i.e., that it really isn't nonsensical to speak of two *tables.* I hazard the conjecture that Eddington is an inveterate visualizer, and that once he has committed himself to the language of "two tables" he cannot avoid thinking of one as the shadow and of the other as the substance. (In this sentence, I have used the word "substance" simply as the correlative of "shadow." . . .)

Certainly there is much in the passage about the two tables that seems to conflict with the view of the scientific table as a shadow. It is said to be "mostly emptiness," but scattered in the emptiness are numerous electric charges whose "combined bulk" is compared in amount with "the bulk of the table itself." Is "the table itself" the familiar table? I think it must be. But the comparison of the *two* bulks is surely nonsensical. Moreover, a shadow can hardly be said to have *bulk.* Yet Eddington insists that the two tables are "parallel"—an odd synonym, no doubt, for a "shadow." He contrasts the scientific *table,* which has a familiar *table* parallel to it, with the scientific electron, quantum, or potential, which have no familiars that are parallel. Of the latter he says that the physicist is scrupulously careful to guard them "from contamination by conceptions borrowed from the other (i.e., the familiar) world." But if electrons, belonging to world No. 2, are to be scrupulously guarded from contamination by world No. 1, how can it make sense to say that they "keep on hitting the underside" of a sheet of paper that, indubitably, is part of the familiar furniture of earth? It is Eddington who reintroduces contamination when he talks in this fashion, and he does so because he supposes that there is a scientific table parallel to the familiar table. I venture to suggest that it is as absurd to say that there is a scientific table as to say that there is a familiar electron or a familiar quantum, or a familiar potential. Eddington insists upon the lack of familiar parallels in the latter cases; surely he is justified in doing so. What is puzzling is his view that there are parallel *tables*. It suggests a return to the days when physicists demanded a model: "The physicist," says Eddington, "used to borrow the raw material of his world from the familiar world, but he does so no longer." But if the "scientific table" is to be regarded as the product of the "raw material of the scientific world," how can it be regarded as parallel to the familiar table? Eddington seems unable to free himself from the conviction that the physicist is concerned with things of the same nature as the things of the familiar world; hence, *tables* are to be found in both world No. 1 and world No. 2. There is a statement in his exposition of "The Downfall of Classical Physics" that shows how deep-rooted this conviction is. "The atom," he says, "is as porous as the solar system. If we eliminated all the un-filled space in a man's body and collected his protons and electrons into one mass, the man would be reduced to a speck just visible with a magnifying glass" (*N.Ph.W.*, pp. 1–2). The comparison is useful enough; the absurdity comes from speaking of the speck as a *man*. If this statement stood alone, it might well be regarded as an expository device. But the constant cropping up of the parallel tables shows that Eddington does not regard it as absurd to think of the reduction as still leaving a *man*. . . .

It seems to me that in his theory of the duplicate worlds Eddington has fallen into the error of which Berkeley accused the Newtonians. Berkeley was strongly convinced that the sensible world was pre-eminently a *seeable* world. No doubt he overstressed the sense of sight at the expense of the other senses, but in the climate of opinion in which he was living this overemphasis served a useful purpose. Consider the following passage:

How vivid and radiant is the lustre of the fixed stars! how magnificent and rich that negligent profusion, with which they appear to be scattered throughout the whole azure vault! Yet if you take the telescope, it brings into your sight a new host of stars that escape the naked eye. . . . Is not the whole system immense, beautiful, glorious beyond expression and beyond thought? What treatment then do those philosophers deserve, who would deprive these noble and delightful scenes of all reality? How should those principles be entertained, that lead us to think all the visible beauty of the creation a false imaginary glare? [4]

It seemed to Berkeley that the metaphysics of Descartes and Newton resulted in the description of a "real world" that had all the properties of the sensible world except the vital property of being seeable. "Ask a Cartesian," he said,[5] "whether he is wont to imagine his globules without colour. Pellucidness is a colour. The colour of ordinary light of the sun is white. Newton in the right in assigning colour to the rays of light. A man born blind would not imagine Space as we do. We give it always some dilute, or duskish, or dark colour—in short, we imagine it as visible, or intro-mitted by the eye, which he would not do." *Black* also is, in the sense required, a *color*; a "dark world" is no less a world apprehensible only by sight than a "bright world" is. But the pure mathematician cannot take note of color. Hence, under the influence of the *Mathematical Principles of Natural Philosophy* and of the rapidly developing science of optics, Berkeley's contemporaries looked to the principles of optics to account for the *seeability* of things. It is Berkeley's merit to have realized that the Cartesian–Newtonian philosophers, seeking to account for a *seeable* world, succeeded only in substituting a world that could in no sense be *seen*. He realized that they had substituted a theory of optics for a theory of visual perception. The outcome of this mistake is a duplication of worlds—the Image-World, sensibly perceived by men, the Real-World apprehended only by God. Newton is quite explicit on this point:

Was the Eye contrived without Skill in Opticks, and the Ear without Knowledge of Sounds? . . . Is not the sensory of Animals that place to which the sensitive Substance is present, and into which the sensible Species of Things are carried through the Nerves and Brain, that there they may be perceived by their immediate presence to that Substance? And these things being rightly dispatch'd, does it not appear from Phaenomena that there is a Being incorporeal, living, intelligent, omnipresent, who in infinite Space, as it were in his Sensory, sees the things themselves intimately, and thor-

[4] *Three Dialogues between Hylas and Philonous* (Second Dialogue).

[5] *Commonplace Book*, G. A. Johnston, Ed., p. 50.

oughly perceives them, and comprehends them wholly by their immediate presence to himself: Of which things the Images only carried through the Organs of Sense into our little Sensoriums, are there seen and beheld by that which in us perceives and thinks.[6]

Berkeley saw the absurdity of this duplication; he failed to realize that it was rendered necessary only by the confusion of the theory of optics with the theory of vision. He saw that the question—How is perception possible?—is devoid of sense; he saw that it is no less absurb to look to physics for an answer to the question. Unfortunately he accepted the account of objects of sight that was provided by the Optical Theory, and thus abolished the duplication of worlds only by locating (however indirectly) "the things by me perceived" in the Mind of the Infinite Spirit. Newton had transferred colors from *things seen* into "our little Sensoriums"; he conceived them as optical Images; accordingly, there were still required the things in themselves of *which* they were Images. These things must be found in the Sensory of God. Berkeley abolished the Images but only by carrying to a conclusion the absurdities initiated by the use of the language of Optics.

The achievement of Newton in the theory of Optics was that by his discovery of differently refrangible rays he discovered *measurable correlates of color*; he thereby made the use of quantitative methods possible in a domain which would otherwise be excluded from the scope of physics. His extremely confused metaphysics is the result of his refusal to admit that there is anything in the perceived world except the measurable correlates, which ought, accordingly, to be regarded as the correlates of nothing. Newton saved himself from this manifest contradiction by having resort to a transmissive theory of Nature, and thus to a causal theory of perception. Allowing for the difference of phraseology we may surely see in the following quotation from Newton an anticipation of Eddington's theory of the sensible world.

The homogeneal Light and Rays which appear red, or rather make Objects appear so, I call Rubrifick or Redmaking; those which make Objects appear yellow, green,

[6] *Opticks,* Query 28.

blue, and violet, I call Yellow-making, Green-making, Blue-making, Violet-making, and so of the rest. And if at any time I speak of Light and Rays as coloured or endued with Colours, I would be understood to speak not philosophically and properly, but grossly, and accordingly to such Conceptions as vulgar People in seeing all these experiments would be apt to frame. For the Rays to speak properly are not coloured. In them there is nothing else than a certain Power and Disposition to stir up a Sensation of this or that Colour. For as Sound in a Bell or musical String, or other sounding Body, is nothing but a trembling Motion, and in the Air nothing but that motion propagated from the Object, and in the Sensorium 'tis a Sense of that Motion under the Form of Sound; so Colours in the Object are nothing but a Disposition to reflect this or that sort of Rays more copiously than the Rest; in the Rays they are nothing but their Dispositions to propagate this or that Motion into the Sensorium, and in the Sensorium they are Sensations of those Motions under the Forms of Colours.[7]

This wholly fallacious argument has been strangely persuasive to physicists. Sensible qualities have no place in the world; they are *nothing but* dispositions to propagate this or that motion into the Sensorium." There they undergo a transformation, not in the mathematical sense of that word, but a strange transformation indeed—a metamorphosis of "the external world of physics" into "a world of familiar acquaintance in human consciousness." [8] The transformation remains inexplicable. Small wonder that Mr. Joad, reflecting upon the philosophical consequences of "modern physics," exclaimed in perplexity, "But, if I never know directly events in the external world, but only their alleged effects on my brain, and if I never know my brain except in terms of its alleged effects on my brain, I can only reiterate in bewilderment my original questions: 'What sort of thing is it that I know? and 'Where is it?'" [9] Such perplexity can be resolved only by reconsidering the assumptions that led to the asking of these unanswerable questions. We shall find that the problem of perception, in this form, arose only because we have allowed the physicists to speak of a "real world" that does not contain any of the qualities relevant to perception. To adopt the striking phrase of

[7] *Opticks*, Bk. I, Pt. II (1931 ed., pp. 124–5).

[8] See *N.Ph.W.*, p. xiv.

[9] *Aristotelian Society*, Supp. Vol. IX, p. 137.

Professor E. A. Burtt, we have allowed the physicists "to make a metaphysic out of a method." In so doing they have forgotten, and philosophers do not seem to remember, that their method has been designed to facilitate investigations originating from a study of "the furniture of the earth."

5

LANGUAGE AND EXPERIENCE:
R. L. Goodstein ·

Problems concerning the nature of signs and the relation of language to reality find expression in such questions as: "Is language no more than a system of signs? Has language a *content,* or does it float above reality like a bubble above the earth? Can language point to something outside itself, has it roots in some actuality, or are the truths of language independent of all experience? If language is a medium of communication (between human beings) then what is it that is communicated, and how is this communication effected?" As a preliminary to an examination of these questions, let us consider what we ordinarily say—and do— when we seek to decide whether a proposition is true or false. Suppose the proposition is "The entrance to the College is in University Road." To see whether or not this is true we might first seek the address of the College in a Street Directory, then we might ask various people the question "Where is the College?" receiving the answer "University College is in University Road," and lastly we might walk along University Road looking at each building in turn until we reach one bearing the name-plate "University College Leicester."

That the first two criteria are of the same character

· [This selection is reprinted from the author's *Constructive Formalism: Essays on the Foundations of Mathematics* (Leicester: University Press, 1951), Chapter VIII. Reprinted by permission of R. L. Goodstein and Leicester University Press.]

may be seen by supposing that the directory we consult is a machine which reproduces (from a record) the address of any institution when the name of the institution is spelt out on a dial on the machine. (For the present we ignore the sort of doubt which might be expressed by saying "The man who is asked the question does not just *answer* [like the machine] but must think first before he can answer.") When however we turn our attention to the third criterion we are inclined to think not only that it is fundamentally different from the other criteria but that it is conclusive in a way the others could not be; the reference book might contain a misprint, our informants might be mistaken or even willfully deceive us, but "we cannot doubt the evidence of our own eyes." To see what this last criterion has in common with the preceding, we shall describe yet another form a reference book might take. The book might contain photographs of streets so that to find whether the proposition "The College is in University Road" is true we look at the photograph of University Road to see if it contains a picture of the College. Thus we might contrast the criteria by saying that in the one we look at the object itself and in the other at a photograph of the object. Since we can use the reference book which contains the sentence "University College is in University Road" and the reference book which contains the picture of the College in University Road in exactly the same way, the sentence "University College is in University Road" and the picture of the College in University Road, must stand to one another in the relation of syntactically equivalent sentences, like a French and English sentence with the same meaning. To translate from one word-language to another we place side by side the words which may be writen one for the other; to translate from a word- to a picture-language (like the directory containing photographs) we place side by side words and pictures. Thus the correspondence between a word- and a picture-language is established in the same sort of way as the correspondence between two word-languages is established. But if we can find a correspondence between the sentence "University College is in University Road" and a picture of the College in University Road, how can we doubt the existence of a correspondence between the sentence and that of which the photograph is a *photograph*, namely, the College building standing in University Road? Can we not translate from a picture-language to a "real-object" language? If we want a man to build us a house can we give him only a picture of what we want (like the word "house" or a photograph of a house) and can we not just point to a house? When a pure formalist maintains that there is no such process as deriving the truth of a proposition from some nonverbal occurrence, in what sense is he using the term "verbal"? He accepts as a criterion of the truth of a sentence that the sentence form one of a certain list of sentences. He affirms the possibility of deciding whether or not two rows of signs form the same *sentence*; for when he speaks of the consistency of two sentences, it is the shape of the signs which compose the sentences to which he refers, and he speaks of the possibility of changing from one notation to another, translating from one language to another. But if one admits the possibility of translating from one word-language to another then one must admit the possibility of translating from a word- to a picture-language, and must therefore accept the *nonverbal* criterion of the truth of a sentence that a sentence is true if it is a translation of a picture ("sentence") that forms one of a certain collection of pictures. And if one accepts this criterion why should one not accept also the criterion of translation from an "object-language"?

Of course, the formalist may say that he meant no less than this himself, that by "verbal" he meant anything that could be "used as a word," but if this is so his statement loses its entire point; for if "verbal" no longer serves to distinguish words from other signs, then "nonverbal" has no meaning left to it, and if "word" is being used in this new sense then to say that the world is the world of sentences is only to say that the world is the "familiar" world of facts. We cannot deny the formalist the right to call University College standing in University Road a *sentence;* for some purposes this is a valuable form of expression, and harmless so long as we do not forget that it is a metaphor and not, as the formalists seem to imply, the expression of a new discovery about the world, the discovery that the world is a world of (what we used to call) sentences.

Talking to someone, sending someone a letter, communicating with someone, have the character of drawing someone's attention to something, holding something in front of someone, *pointing to something*. Pointing to a nut on a table and then pointing to the table may be called *saying* the sentence "A nut is on the table" in the "real-object" language, a sentence of which "A nut is on the table" is the translation in the English word-language. Saying what one sees, hears, feels, describing an experiment, recording an observation, are all translation processes. *Perceiving* a relation, *observing* a difference, *recognizing* a likeness, are akin to *naming* a relation, a difference, a likeness. Pointing to a pencil and saying "pencil" is one of the ways in which we translate from an object- to a word-language. Were it necessary, as the formalist maintains, not just to point but to say some such sentence as "That which you see is called a pencil," learning a word-language would be impossible; when a child is taught to say "sugar" each time it is shown a lump of sugar, it does not first have to understand the phrase "That which you see is called. . . ." We just attract the child's attention to the lump of sugar and say "sugar," perhaps once, perhaps many times, and eventually the child says "sugar" when we show it a lump of sugar. We teach the child to use the word "sugar" as a token; if it wants a lump of sugar it must first give us the word "sugar" in payment. What we teach is an exchange of *things*. Failure to understand this is one of the sources of the formalist's confusion; he feels that a definition must be a definition in words and accordingly he interprets the ostensive definition as defining the equivalence of the object-word and the ostensive definition sentence "That which you see is called. . . ."

Bound up with the problem of the ostensive definition we meet one of the oldest of the problems of philosophy, the problem concerning the universal word. How is it possible, one might ask, for a child to learn that the word "sugar" means, is a token for, any lump of sugar and not just some one particular lump? Must the child first perceive what various lumps of sugar have in common (whatever that may be) before it can learn to give the word "sugar" as a token for any lump of sugar? Certainly, we could make a slot machine that would take only one particular coin, and reject all others, but we can also make slot machines that will take any penny piece, rejecting only coins of other values or coins that differ in some other way from penny pieces. A child does not perceive what various lumps of sugar have in common, but fails to perceive such *differences* as there may be. Overlooking some differences in objects, but not overlooking others, is the fundamental operation in language. We regard a child's ability to learn languages quickly as a mark of intelligence, yet a too subtle and discerning child might never learn to speak his mother-tongue.

Let us examine more closely the three criteria we described above to decide the truth or falsehood of the sentence "University College is in University Road." We have already observed that the third criterion seems to be necessarily decisive, whereas the first and second are liable to error. Yet could we not conceive of the possibility of error also in the third criterion? If I walk along University Road and perceive a building bearing the name-plate "University College Leicester," may it not be that I am deluded and suffering from a hallucination? Is there in fact any criterion which is quite conclusive? Can we not doubt the validity of any criterion whatever? But if there is *no* criterion or combination of criteria that we are prepared to accept and call decisive, then the sentence "University College is in University Road" is isolated from the language system and deprived of its function, like a currency that has lost its purchasing power. One might say that in choosing the criterion, the conventions according to which the sentence is true or false, one is choosing the language in which the given complex of signs operates as a sentence. Accordingly, if we say that the reference book criterion for the truth of the sentence "University College is in University Road" may be doubted, and, furthermore, that any criterion we conceive of may be doubted, then it is only in relation to some other criterion or group of criteria that a particular criterion may be said to be doubtful. If there were but a single criterion for the truth of a sentence then it would make no sense to say that *this* criterion is doubtful; though in fact we do not ordinarily accept one criterion, we might do so. Language itself provides for the possibility of doubt as is shown by such words as "mistake," "falsehood," and "hallucination," and the corresponding truth criterion of the assent of the majority. *They are said to be deluded who do not see what the majority see, whose world is not the world of the majority of men.*

It may seem to us, for we have grown accustomed to believing so, that only a madman could place any criterion above the criterion of experience, yet a few hundred years ago the criterion of the reference book (particularly the works of Aristotle and the Bible) was accepted in preference to the criterion of experience. That is not to say that men were then blind, ignorant, or foolish (except according to our present criteria of knowledge). If what Aristotle said is *the* criterion of truth and if Aristotle said that a large object falls more swiftly than a small one, then Galileo was deluded, and however many times we drop objects of different weights, in a vacuum, and observe that they fall with the same speed, we are "tricked by our senses" (and we might account for this trick in many different ways just as subtle as the theory of relativity). It is not a fact which is in dispute but the choice of a mode of expression. We do not dispute the fact that different objects are seen to fall with the same speed; the question is whether we shall use a language which says that the sentence "Different objects fall with the same speed" is *true* because we perceive that different objects fall with the same speed, or whether we shall say that it is *false* and the perception a delusion.

The criterion which we called the criterion of experience, the criterion according to which the sentence "University College is in University Road" is true if we see a building bearing the name-plate "University College Leicester" as we walk along University Road, might be formulated as a rule of logic permitting the derivation of the sentence "*p*" from the sentence "I see *p*." This formulation, however, raises the problem of the nature of such expressions as "I see a red patch," "I hear a ringing noise," "I imagine a red patch," etc. We feel that these expressions have the certainty of necessary truths, yet they are neither linguistic conventions nor demonstrable sentences. The expression "I see a red patch" has the conventional sentence form but does not play a sentence role in language; it makes no sense to ask "How do I know I see a red patch?" for there is nothing which we should call the process of finding out that I see a red patch. Saying "I see a red patch" is analogous, not to saying "I have a red shirt," but to *painting a red patch;* in other words, saying "I see a red patch" is like saying "red patch." The distinction which we express by "I see a red patch," "I imagine a red patch" is not a distinction between two activities but is rather the difference between painting a vivid red patch and painting a faint one.

Seeing a red patch and saying "red," as opposed to "defining" the word "red" by pointing to a red patch, is a cause and effect phenomenon. Imagine what mechanism we may (association, the action of light on the eye, etc.), we cannot bridge the gulf between seeing the red patch and saying "red." It may help to make this clearer if we replace "red" by painting a red patch. If a man looks at a red patch and then paints a red patch, is there a *logical* connection between what he saw and what he painted? Does it make sense to ask how he knows that the patch he is looking at and the patch he painted have the same color? It is not whether he *may* be in doubt that puzzles us, but rather how he can fail to be in doubt. Suppose that on a shelf stand a number of bottles, each bottle bearing a label of a particular color. I draw from a box a colored token, place the token against each label in turn, reject bottle after bottle and then take down from the shelf the bottle which bears a label of the same color as the token. How do I know that just this label has the same color as the token? It cannot be necessary that I know what the colors are (called) since I may be unable to speak a word-language, and if we say that I must *perceive* that the two colors are the same, then in what does this perception consist but in taking down the bottle which I did take down? It might be objected that I must have seen *something*, else why did I choose just that bottle and no other, but what criterion have we for deciding this? I may say that I acted mechanically, that when I placed my token against that particular label I just reached for the bottle, and this may well be what happened; but that is not to say that I acted mechanically as opposed to consciously, for it is what we ordinarily call a conscious action that I am now tempted to call mechanical. We could in fact easily construct a machine which selected a bottle bearing a label of the same color as a token placed in the machine; what puzzles us about the analogy with the machine is that we feel that when *we* choose a bottle *we* are guided by the *sensation of seeing the colors match,* whereas a *machine* cannot have sensations. Yet to say we are guided by our sensations is only to offer a hypothetical mechanism to account for our actions; for whatever sensation we experienced, how could this sensation bridge the gulf between *seeing* the label and the token and *reaching* for the bottle?

Just as saying "I see x," where "x" is an object word, is akin to saying "x," so saying "I see p," "I imagine p," "I believe p," etc., where "p" is a sentence, is akin to saying "p." Accordingly, the experience criterion for the truth of a sentence may be expressed by saying that a sentence "p" is derivable from the sentence "A says p." Of course, the sentence "A says p" may itself be derived from other sentences of the form "B says that A says p" and so on, and the choice of the initial sentence in the derivation process is quite arbitrary. Remember the legal convention that "p" is derivable from "A says p and B says p and C says p," but not from "A says p." Propositions for which the (accepted) criterion of truth is derivability from sentences of the form "A says p" may be called experimental propositions.

The reference book criterion for the truth of a proposition may be used in two essentially different ways. We might, for example, say that a sentence "d" is true if it is one of the sentences in Euclid's geometry, or that "d" is true if it is one of the sentences in the first book on a certain shelf. Suppose that a, b, c, d, are the sentences in Euclid's geometry so that the expression "the sentences in Euclid's geometry" is synonymous with the class of sentences "a, b, c, d"; then "d is one of the sentences in Euclid's geometry" is derivable from "d is a member of the class a, b, c, d" which is derivable from the linguistic convention "a, b, c, d is the class whose members are a and b and c and d," so that "d" is true. In this case "d" does *not* express an experiential proposition; for the sentence "a, b, c, d are the sentences in Euclid's geometry" says "the sentences a, b, c, d are *called* Euclid's geometry" and accordingly the sentence expresses a linguistic convention about the use of the expression "Euclid's geometry" and is not a derivative of such a sentence as "X says that a, b, c, d are the sentences of Euclid's geometry." But if we say that a, b, c, d are the sentences in the first book on a certain shelf, this is an experiential proposition and the sentence "*d*" which is derived from it expresses an experiential proposition.

The primary difficulty connected with the use of the criterion of experience may perhaps best be expressed by asking "How do I know that you see what I see? Might not two signs seem to you to have the same form and different forms to me?" Is this a question about experience or about reality or about language? If we maintain that it is *impossible* to know whether you see the same thing that I see and if we refuse to accept any criterion according to which we should say that we see the same things, then the impossibility of which we speak is a *logical*, not a *physical*, impossibility. We say that no man can lift ten tons, and accept the test of men trying to lift the weight and failing, and admit that of course a man may sometime in the future lift the weight. We do not say that any creature which lifts the weight shall not be called a man. Inability to lift the weight is not a defining characteristic of "men." But when we say that under no circumstances is it possible for *me* to know what *you* see, then it is with the use of the words *me* and *you* that we are concerned, and not with the nature of experience. As Wittgenstein has observed, it is not *what* is seen that is in doubt but the choice of a language—whether we shall use the same word for what *you* see as for what I see, i.e., whether we shall admit both the sentences "I see an *X*" and "You see an *X*," or whether we shall allow the use of the object word *X* only in the sentence "I see an *X*" and use some other word, *Y* say, in the sentence "You see a *Y*" to express what is now expressed by "You see an *X*." But once we make this change we perceive that it is redundant; for the difference between the sentences "I see an *X*," "You see an *X*," is already clearly shown by the opposition of "I" to "you."

Another form which the difficulties associated with this problem take may be expressed by asking "How could I ever have learned the meaning of the sentence 'I see a chair,' for how could anyone else know *what* my sensations are when I say 'I see a chair,' and, not knowing these sensations, how could they have taught me to call just *these* sensations 'I see a chair'" (or, "How could I

ever learn the meaning of 'toothache,' for how could anyone else know when I have the experience *they* call 'toothache'?"). Don't *I* mean something different when I say "I
see a chair" from what you mean when you say this
sentence? I know what private experience I call seeing a
chair, but I don't know what experience you call seeing a
chair, nor even that you have any experience at all. Yet
are the sensations I experience when I say "I see a chair"
the *meaning* of this sentence? If I behaved exactly as I
now behave, brought you a chair when you asked for it,
walked across the room without stumbling into the furniture, sat on a chair when I was tired, took my place in a
row when you pointed to it, *and yet had none of the sensations which at present accompany my saying "I see a chair,"*
would you not still say that I understood the sentence?
You might think that I could not behave as I do unless I
have the sensations and experiences which I now have,
but this is only a hypothesis. Imagine, for example, that the
sensations I experience when I look at a red object and the
sensations I experience when I look at a green object are
interchanged, but I retain my present use of the words
"red" and "green"; that is to say, I continue to use "red"
and "green" in the way other people use these words: I
stop my car when I see a red light, a red light still brings
the word danger to my mind, and so on, even though the
color sensation I experience now is that which I experienced before on seeing a green light. I might notice the
change myself in the sense in which I might notice that
yesterday drinking cold water gave me a toothache,
whereas today it does not, but the change would not be
perceived in any other way. It could not have been my
special *incommunicable* experience that I was taught to call
red or I should now be obliged to change my language
with the change in that experience.

Can a man show *all* the "outward" signs of unhappiness
and yet be happy? If he weeps and moans and presses
his hand against his heart, rejects his food and speaks in a
piteous voice of his grief—can this man, nevertheless, really
be happy? Is it not possible, I might ask, that only my
unhappiness is genuine and that others only simulate unhappiness; how can I know that another really feels as I
feel when I say I am unhappy? But if I choose to say this
and decide that the words "I am genuinely unhappy" only

make sense in my mouth, and if I know say "he simulates unhappiness" where before I said "he is genuinely unhappy," then to what is "he is simulating" opposed? Consider the antithesis I formerly expressed by "he is genuinely unhappy," "he is simulating unhappiness." My friend A, on receiving a letter telling him that his father has died, shows all the familiar signs of grief and mourning, and another friend B, on receipt of the same news, gives similar evidence of great grief; I know, however, that A has always spoken affectionately of his father, imitated him in many ways, showed contentment in his company, and expressed great concern over his illness, whereas B lost no opportunity to avoid his father's society, spoke disparagingly of him, and impatiently awaited the inheritance his father's death would bring him. I should say that B only simulated unhappiness, but I should say this from what I know of the "context" of his grief, not because I know of some private sensation which A experienced but B did not.

If we admit the possibility of doubting any truth criterion, that is to say, if we maintain that logic leaves us free to choose any language we please, we seem to lose the connection between language and reality which we thought the concept of truth established, or rather, if we maintain that connection, then reality loses its uniqueness and is set free to revolve alongside the turning wheel of language. The correspondence of language and reality takes on again the character of an illusion, for the correspondence subsists only so long as we build the world in the image of our language. "Was that," runs a Chinese aphorism, "Lao-tse dreaming he was a butterfly or this a butterfly dreaming he is Lao-tse?" I see a piece of wood before me. I put out my hand and touch it, feel the contact in my finger tips, see my fingers touching the wood. I take a saw and saw through the piece of wood, watch the dust falling, smell the fragrance of pine, observe the grain, indent the surface with my thumbnail, place the sawn-off piece in a basin of water and watch it float. Do these things prove that wood is a *real* substance? Might I not just be watching a private cinema show, or dreaming? And if others talk to me and tell me they too see the wood and smell the pine and hear the rasp of the saw, might not all this too be part of my dream? Can I ever be sure that I have found *reality*? Yet why do I use the word *real*? I know perfectly well how I distinguish between a real piece of wood and an artificial piece of wood, how I distinguish between sawing a piece of wood and dreaming that I am sawing a piece of wood. I use the familiar words, but I want to give them a new and special sense, and it is essential that this new sense be private to me alone, that I cannot communicate this sense, for if I could communicate it I should have to draw a distinction between *real* and something else, and this I don't want to do.

A real object, one might say, has a length. What is the length of this bar of iron? I place my standard (millimeter) measuring rod alongside the bar of iron and find that I can set it off on the bar between 120 and 121 times. Accordingly, I say that the length of the bar is between 120 and 121 millimeters. You object and say that I omitted to take into account the temperature. I repeat the operations (obtaining the same result) and write alongside my result the temperature 30° Centigrade recorded by my thermometer. Next day, when the thermometer records 35° Centigrade, I find I can set off my measuring rod between 121 and 122 times along the bar. What is the *real* length of the bar of iron? We should answer, without hesitation, that there is no sense to the question; for the length of the rod depends upon the temperature, unless we choose some particular temperature as a standard and call the real length of the iron bar the length associated with this standard temperature. If we observed, however, that whatever the variation in temperature (between some assigned limits perhaps) the length of the bar was always between 120 and 122 millimeters, we might call "between 120 and 122" the *real* length of the bar and this would be in effect a change of unit, for, if our standard measuring rod was 2 millimeters long, we should now record the length as between 60 and 61 units.

Suppose, however, we said, "Keeping the temperature constant, surely the rod must have an *exact* length to which the measurement 'between 120 and 121 millimeters' is only an approximation." If by this we mean only that, with no matter what unit we carried out the measurement, we could imagine it carried out with a smaller unit, then it is true; but if we mean that we shall call "the length of the bar" not the result obtained by any measurement but only the "limit" toward which the successive measurements converge, then we have deprived the word "length" of its use; for however many measurements we carried out there would remain the unlimited possibility of carrying out further measurements and the length of the bar is now *unattainable by definition*.

If we accept some other criterion than measurement for the determination of the length of the bar, for instance some calculation based upon the velocities of the end points of the bar, then we are giving the word "length" a new use and must be prepared for the possibility of a different answer to the question "What is the length of the bar of iron?" Thus when the relativist says "That which you thought to be a bar of fixed length is really shorter when it lies in some positions than others, only it is impossible for you to detect this difference as your measuring rod also changes its length and your physical organs change in such a way that you are not aware either of this change or of the changes in the lengths of objects," he is using the words "length" and "change of length" in two different ways. Has the relativist shown that the ordinary man's use of "length" is wrong? Is the relativist's answer to the question "What is the length of the iron bar?" the *true* answer and the answer which the measuring rod gives *false?* Was it just a foolish prejudice, a habit of thought, to think that we can measure lengths with a measuring rod, a prejudice from which the relativist sets us free? The relativist mistakenly expresses a new convention about the use of the word "length" in the form of a discovery about the nature of the world. It is not a new fact that the relativist records, but a change of language. If we mean by "length," as we ordinarily mean, that which is determined by a measuring rod, then it makes no sense to talk of a change in the length of the measuring rod, for the measuring rod (the standard of length) has no length. By changing the meaning of the word "length" we appear to make the strange discovery that that which we thought to be the instrument of measurement in some way has now been shown to measure itself.

The effect of radium on living tissues is a new fact, the Copernican astronomy a new language. In the history of the human race the discovery of a new language may be of greater importance than any discovery of the experimental sciences, but for the philosopher a new language is *only* a new language, valuable for purposes of comparison, but having no greater claim on his attention than any other language. The Copernican or the relativist use of the word "motion" is just *one* of the uses of the word. There is a common belief that the Copernican use of the term "motion" was forced upon us by the overwhelming evidence of facts, that in some sense we were driven to "admit" the motion of the earth which ignorance had hidden from us; whereas what Copernicus discovered was no new fact of the Universe but that the paths of the heavenly bodies were *more simply described* if by motion we meant motion round the sun and not motion round the earth.

Parallel to the question "What is the nature of reality?" we might ask "What is the nature of experimental science?" or "What validity has the scientific method?" We photograph the motion of a planet across the sky during some interval of time; the photograph presents the motion of the planet as a strip of light across a darkened background. We wish to prolong this strip of light, but, of the unlimited possibilities of prolongation, there is no one particular prolongation that is logically necessary. If two photographs are taken, one for six months and the other for this and a further six months, can we, without looking at the second photograph, fill in on the first "unfinished" photograph the path that the second photograph is recording? That is the problem of the experimental sciences. Theoretical physics singles out some particular one of the unlimited possibilities of prolongation as *the* correct prolongation, the "reasons" given for this choice constituting the so-called theory of the science, and this prolongation is compared with the second photograph. If the prolongation is a good fit, other experiments of a similar character (choosing a prolongation according to the theory) are carried out, and if no marked discrepancy between the "theoretic" prolongation and the second photograph is observed, the theory is said to be well founded and provisionally adopted.

If we look more closely at the "reasons" given for a particular guess (theoretic prolongation) we find a mixture of observational and linguistic sentences. Some reasons, like "The velocity of light is independent of the velocity of the source of light," are linguistic statements, expressed in the form of observational statements. "The velocity of light is independent of the velocity of the source of light" tells us how the expression "the velocity of light" is going to be used. Such a statement lays down the way we have decided to talk about our experiments, serves to choose between conflicting evidence—just as a principle of law like "a man is innocent until he is proved guilty" tells us, not something about the character of human beings (that a man cannot have done wrong unless he is proved to have done so), but something of the way we are going to use the words "innocent" and "guilty" and serves to guide our *treatment* of untried prisoners. Moreover, even as we are prepared to change a principle of law—i.e., to adopt a new legal language—we are prepared to change the reasons we give for our guesses (apart from changing the guesses themselves).

One might say that theoretical physics is a link between language and experience, the so-called theory forming a dictionary for translating observational sentences into mathematical equations and vice versa. Consider the statement "Forces are added by the parallelogram law." Is this an observational statement? Certainly we can use this rule to build bridges and certainly bridges built according to it have "stood the test of time"; but might not a bridge built tomorrow according to the rule fall down when tested? Contrast the statement with "Vectors are added by the parallelogram law" which is the mathematical *definition of addition* for vectors. We can imagine a time when men perceived how forces are added, and stated that forces add by the parallelogram law just as one might observe that twenty people pass one's window every day. At such a time the parallelogram law is a statement of fact, not a generalization from particular instances, not an induction, but a statement of fact. At some subsequent time the statement of the parallelogram law ceased to be used as a statement of fact and became a linguistic convention. Though certain experiences in the future may lead us to abandon the use of the word "force" given by this convention, we might retain the convention in spite of any experience whatever. In the same way the propositions of arithmetic "evolved" from observational truths to linguistic conventions. It might happen in the future that when we placed books on a shelf or apples in a bag or men in a room and counted them one by one we never found

a total beyond five; that is to say, after counting the books
and finding there are five on the shelf, and then placing
further books on the shelf and counting again, we still obtain the answer five, and similarly after counting and re-
counting apples and men and so on. In such a world we
might lose our interest in our common arithmetic (which
of course is not invalidated by such experiences any more
than it is validated by our present experiences) and adopt
instead an arithmetic in which the sum of five and one
is five. On the other hand, we might still retain our common arithmetic and say that there are really six or seven,
etc., books on the shelf but some have coalesced so that
we seem to have only five. Compare this with the position
in which present day physics finds itself. Shall we say there
are material particles which behave like waves, or waves
which behave like material particles?

The microscope shows a drop of water as a universe of
active and brightly colored creatures, of forms unfamiliar
to the naked eye. Which is the real drop of water, that
which the unaided eye shows us or this myriad of tiny
creatures? Does the microscope enlarge our knowledge of
reality or does it destroy the possibility of belief in any
world of the senses? If we answer that there are two
worlds, the world of our (ordinary) vision and the microscope world, which of these is the real world? And perhaps the creatures of the microscope would likewise under
some more powerful microscope reveal themselves just as
organizations of other (smaller) creatures. Related to these
questions is the metaphysical problem "Are not human beings just parts of some greater organism of which we can
have no conception?" and the allied problems such as "Have
human beings an independent existence or do they just
serve some higher organisms, call them nations or civiliza-
tions, even as we perceive that the creatures which dwell
in our blood live but to serve us?" Another form in which
we can express these questions is "Are microbes real?" or
"Is there really a microbe in this drop of water?" It is
important to remember that if we say microbes can only
be seen through a microscope, they are too small to be seen
with the naked eye, we are making a hypothesis, not
stating a logical necessity of vision. It is a hypothesis that
what we see (when we look through a microscope) depends upon the microscope. We can imagine a world in
which on some days our visual experiences are what they

are now when "we look around with the unaided eye," and on other days are what we are now familiar with on looking through a microscope. What we have before our mind's eye when we ask if there are really microbes in a drop of water is an image of a clear drop of water beside an image of the same drop speckled with microbes; but looking at a drop of water and then looking at the same drop through a microscope is more like seeing a clear drop of water transform into, not a speckled drop, but a vessel of water filled with tiny creatures. That this vessel of water and the drop of water are the same thing is also only an hypothesis; that is to say, the form of expression "This vessel of water you see is really the drop of water seen through a microscope" expresses a purely arbitrary convention, one which we could abandon without denying any fact. Instead of saying that the microscope shows us the microbes (hidden) in the water, we could say that the microscope *transforms* the drop of water into an expanse of water filled with swimming creatures; of course, this change of expression (remember, it is not the facts we change) will entail other changes of expression. Instead of saying that a man has typhoid fever because the microscope reveals the presence of the typhoid bacillus in his blood, we should say that the microscope transformation of his blood contains the typhoid bacillus. And to the question "Surely there must be something already in the blood (before the microscope transformed it), else why is the man ill?" the answer is that to say the man is ill *because* of a microbe in his blood is only to make a hypothesis—a linguistic convention—which we can retain or abandon as we please. If the microscope transformation of my blood is found to contain the typhoid bacillus, I should unhesitatingly accept the treatment which I had observed in previous cases to be followed by a return to health, not because I had found out that "such and such a process *cures* typhoid" is more than a linguistic convention, but because that is how human beings behave.

It is sometimes said that, just as there are microbes too small to be seen by the unaided eye, so too there are electrons too small to be seen even by a microscope. This is rather like saying that something is seen which is not seen. The sentence "I see an electron" has not that relation to "I see a microbe" which this latter has to the sentence "I see a drop of water." If we ask a physicist to show us an electron he shows us pictures of white (or colored) lines on a black background and calls these pictures electron tracks; the physicist will say that he cannot show us single electrons, only streams of electrons, and will in fact show us not streams of anything, but just streams. It may be true that nowhere in the world can we find a single locust, that locusts are found only in swarms, but a swarm of locusts is specifically a swarm of *locusts*. The physicist tells us that he can distinguish one electron from another and in support of this shows us pictures which he calls streams of α-particles," "streams of β-particles," and so on, but it is not the contents of the streams by which these pictures differ. Again we are tempted to ask the familiar questions "Are electrons the framework of reality, is the world of electrons the real world behind the illusory world of the senses?" "Is the real chair that which we see and handle, buy and sell, cover with tapestry or chop up for firewood, or is the real chair an organization of electrons?" Is it a mark of ignorance to believe there are no electrons; does not the electric light prove the existence of electrons? Are there facts which we cannot describe without the use of the word electron (or a syntactically equivalent word)? If we say that the supposition that there are electrons explains the phenomenal world and enables us to predict the future so accurately that it is no longer possible to doubt the truth of the supposition, do we mean that because of this success (in foretelling the results of experiment, etc.) we have more confidence than before that we shall one day "isolate an electron" or do we only mean that we lose any temptation we may have had to abandon electron-language? After reading in the paper one morning that a certain man has taken his life and that beside his body a letter was found saying he was going to shoot himself because he had lost all his money, I might write a play in which a man immigrates to this country, works hard, makes a fortune, loses it, and shoots himself, and then find that I have described correctly in every detail the life of the man I read about in the paper. Suppose that I repeated the experiment many times, that each time I read of a suicide I write a play and then find I have correctly told the life story of the dead man. If I now say that I believe I have a second sight, will my success have proved the truth of my supposition? Of course, if we agree that "I have second sight" is just a form of expression for describing what I did, then to say I have second sight is just to say that I did what I did; but could we not dispute as to whether there is such a thing as second sight? And if someone says that *nothing* will convince him of the reality of second sight, is he denying the possibility of a certain experience or just refusing to use a certain form of expression? On the one hand I certainly did not *know* the life story of the man who took his life, yet I wrote that story correctly in every detail. The facts are not in dispute. I did not know the story but what I wrote turned out to be written just as if I had known the story. (The scientist does not know when there will be an eclipse, but what he says turns out to be true just as if he had known.) Shall we give a description of these facts which *stresses* the similarity of my writing to actual knowledge or shall we give a description which minimizes this similarity; that is the choice we make when we accept or reject the expression "second sight." If we grant the man who says he believes in survival after death any experience that he may desire, even a body walking the earth alike in all respects to that of one who has died, having all the memories of the dead man, speaking with the same voice, behaving in all respects like the dead man formerly behaved, must we say that the survivalist's belief has been proved true? Is there a fact in dispute if we argue whether we shall say the dead man has returned to earth or whether we shall say that the man who died has not returned but another exactly like him now walks in his place?

The word "reality" has whatever significance we choose to give it. To say that there is no correspondence of language with reality is to make the decision not to use the word "reality" and to express this decision with the air of making a new discovery about the nature of the world. And if we ask whether there is not some *Reality* behind the phenomenal world, a reality of which the world of our senses is but a shadow, we must answer that if we choose to change our language, and talk not of tables and chairs, but of shadows-of-tables and shadows-of-chairs and call what we now term "shadow" instead "shadow-of-a-shadow," then we perceive that "shadow-of-a-chair" is now a complex term, that for the word "chair" itself we have given no use and therefore "shadow-of-a-chair" is but a redundant form of expression for "chair."

6

OPERATIONISM, OBSERVATION, AND THEORETICAL TERMS:

Carl G. Hempel ·

PART I

Operationism, in its fundamental tenets, is closely akin to logical empiricism. Both schools of thought have put much emphasis on definite experiential meaning or import as a necessary condition of objectively significant discourse, and both have made strong efforts to establish explicit criterions of experiential significance. But logical empiricism has treated experiential import as a characteristic of statements —namely, as their susceptibility to test by experiment or observation—whereas operationism has tended to construe experiential meaning as a characteristic of concepts or of the terms representing them—namely, as their susceptibility to operational definition.

Basic ideas of operational analysis. An operational definition of a term is conceived as a rule to the effect that

· [Part I is taken from Hempel's "A Logical Appraisal of Operationism," from *The Validation of Scientific Theories,* P. Frank, Ed. (Boston: Beacon Press, Inc., 1956), pp. 52–8. Part II is from the same author's "Methods of Concept Formation in Science," *International Encyclopedia of Unified Science,* (Chicago: University of Chicago Press, 1953), pp. 23–38. We omit footnotes and cross-references. Reprinted by permission of Carl G. Hempel, the editors of *Science,* and the University of Chicago Press.]

CARL A. RUDISILL LIBRARY
LENOIR RHYNE COLLEGE

the term is to apply to a particular case if the performance of specified operations in that case yields a certain characteristic result. For example, the term "harder than" might be operationally defined by the rule that a piece of mineral, *x*, is to be called harder than another piece of mineral, *y*, if the operation of drawing a sharp point of *x* across the surface of *y* results in a scratch mark on the latter. Similarly, the different numerical values of a quantity such as length are thought of as operationally definable by reference to the outcomes of specified measuring operations. To safeguard the objectivity of science, all operations invoked in this kind of definition are required to be intersubjective in the sense that different observers must be able to perform "the same operation" with reasonable agreement in their results.

P. W. Bridgman, the originator of operational analysis, distinguishes several kinds of operation that may be invoked in specifying the meanings of scientific terms. The principal ones are (1) what he calls *instrumental operations*—these consist in the use of various devices of observation and measurement—and (2) paper-and-pencil operations, verbal operations, mental experiments, and the like—this group is meant to include, among other things, the techniques of mathematical and logical inference as well as the use of experiments in imagination. For brevity, but also by way of suggesting a fundamental similarity among the procedures of the second kind, I shall refer to them as *symbolic operations*.

The concepts of operation and of operational definition serve to state the basic principles of operational analysis, of which the following are of special importance.

1. "Meanings are operational." To understand the meaning of a term, we must know the operational criterions of its application, and every meaningful scientific term must therefore permit of an operational definition. Such definition may refer to certain symbolic operations and it always must ultimately make reference to some instrumental operation.

2. To avoid ambiguity, every scientific term should be defined by means of one unique operational criterion. Even when two different operational procedures (for instance, the optical and the tactual ways of measuring length) have been found to yield the same results, they still must be considered as defining different concepts (for example, optical and tactual length), and these should be distinguished terminologically because the presumed coincidence of the results is inferred from experimental evidence, and

CARL A. RUDISILL LIBRARY
LENOIR RHYNE COLLEGE

it is "not safe" to forget that the presumption may be shown to be spurious by new, and perhaps more precise, experimental data.

3. The insistence that scientific terms should have unambiguously specifiable operational meanings serves to insure the possibility of an objective test for the hypotheses formulated by means of those terms. Hypotheses incapable of operational test or, rather, questions involving untestable formulations, are rejected as meaningless: "If a specific question has meaning, it must be possible to find operations by which an answer may be given to it. It will be found in many cases that the operations cannot exist, and the question therefore has no meaning."

The emphasis on "operational meaning" in scientifically significant discourse has unquestionably afforded a salutary critique of certain types of procedure in philosophy and in empirical science and has provided a strong stimulus for methodological thinking. Yet, the central ideas of operational analysis as stated by their proponents are so vague that they constitute not a theory concerning the nature of scientific concepts but rather a program for the development of such a theory. They share this characteristic with the insistence of logical empiricism that all significant scientific statements must have experiential import, that the latter consists in testability by suitable data of direct observation, and that sentences which are entirely incapable of any test must be ruled out as meaningless "pseudo hypotheses." These ideas, too, constitute not so much a thesis or a theory as a program for a theory that needs to be formulated and amplified in precise terms.

An attempt to develop an operationist theory of scientific concepts will have to deal with at least two major issues: the problem of giving a more precise explication of the concept of operational definition; and the question whether operational definition in the explicated sense is indeed necessary for, and adequate to, the introduction of all nonobservational terms in empirical science.

I wish to present here in brief outline some considerations that bear on these problems. The discussion will be limited to the descriptive, or extralogical, vocabulary of empirical science and will not deal, therefore, with Bridgman's ideas on the status of logic and mathematics.

A broadened conception of operational definition and of the program of operational analysis. The terms "operational meaning" and "operational definition," as well as many of the pronouncements made in operationist writings, convey the suggestion that the criterions of application for any scientific term must ultimately refer to the outcome of some specified type of manipulation of the subject matter under investigation. Such emphasis would evidently be overly restrictive. An operational definition gives experiential meaning to the term it introduces because it enables us to decide on the applicability of that term to a given case by observing the response the case shows under specifiable test conditions. Whether these conditions can be brought about at will by "instrumental operations" or whether we have to wait for their occurrence is of great interest for the practice of scientific research, but it is inessential in securing experiential import for the defined term; what matters for this latter purpose is simply that the relevant test conditions and the requisite response be of such kind that different investigators can ascertain, by direct observation and with reasonably good agreement, whether, in a given case, the test conditions are realized and whether the characteristic response does occur.

Thus, an operational definition of the simplest kind—one that, roughly speaking, refers to instrumental operations only —will have to be construed more broadly as introducing a term by the stipulation that it is to apply to all and only those cases which, under specified observable conditions S, show a characteristic observable response R.

However, an operational definition cannot be conceived as specifying that the term in question is to apply to a given case only if S and R actually occur in that case. Physical bodies, for example, are asserted to have masses, temperatures, charges, and so on, even at times when these magnitudes are not being measured. Hence, an operational definition of a concept—such as a property or a relationship, for example—will have to be understood as ascribing the concept to all those cases that *would* exhibit the characteristic response if the test conditions *should* be realized. A concept thus characterized is clearly not "synonymous with the corresponding set of operations." It constitutes not a manifest but a potential character, namely, a disposition to exhibit a certain characteristic response under specified test conditions.

But to attribute a disposition of this kind to a case in which the specified test condition is not realized (for example, to attribute solubility-in-water to a lump of sugar that is not actually put into water) is to make a generalization, and this involves an inductive risk. Thus, the application of an operationally defined term to an instance of the kind here considered would have to be adjudged "not safe" in precisely the same sense in which Bridgman insists it is "not safe" to assume that two procedures of measurement that have yielded the same results in the past will continue to do so in the future. It is now clear that if we were to reject any procedure that involves an inductive risk, we would be prevented not only from using more than one operational criterion in introducing a given term but also from ever applying a disposition term to any case in which the characteristic manifest conditions of application are not realized; thus, the use of dispositional concepts would, in effect, be prohibited.

A few remarks might be added here concerning the non-instrumental operations countenanced for the introduction especially of theoretical terms. In operationist writings, those symbolic procedures have been characterized so vaguely as to permit the introduction, by a suitable choice of "verbal" or "mental" operations, of virtually all those ideas that operational analysis was to prohibit as devoid of meaning. To meet this difficulty, Bridgman has suggested a distinction between "good" and "bad" operations; but he has not provided a clear criterion for this distinction. Consequently, this idea fails to plug the hole in the operationist dike.

If the principles of operationism are to admit the theoretical constructs of science but to rule out certain other kinds of terms as lacking experiential, or operational, meaning, then the vague requirement of definability by reference to instrumental and "good" symbolic operations must be replaced by a precise characterization of the kinds of sentences that may be used to introduce, or specify the meanings of, "meaningful" nonobservational terms on the basis of the observational vocabulary of science. Such a characterization would eliminate the psychologistic notion of mental operations in favor of a specification of the logico-mathematical concepts and procedures to be permitted in the context of operational definition.

The reference just made to the observational vocabulary of science is essential to the idea of operational definition; for it is in terms of this vocabulary that the test conditions and the characteristic response specified in an operational definition are described and by means of which, therefore, the meanings of operationally defined terms are ultimately characterized. Hence, the intent of the original operationist insistence on intersubjective repeatability of the defining operations will be respected if we require that the terms included in the observational vocabulary must refer to attributes (properties and relationships) that are directly and publicly observable—that is, whose presence or absence can be ascertained, under suitable conditions, by direct observation, and with good agreement among different observers.

In sum, then, a precise statement and elaboration of the basic tenets of operationism require an explication of the logical relationships between theoretical and observational terms, just as a precise statement and elaboration of the basic tenets of empiricism require an explication of the logical relationships connecting theoretical sentences with observation sentences describing potential data of direct observation.

PART II

Definition vs. Reduction to an Experiential Basis

We now turn to a consideration of the connections between the technical terms of science and its observational vocabulary—connections which must exist if the technical terms are to have empirical content. Since the scientist has to introduce all his special terms on the basis of his observational vocabulary, the conjecture suggests itself that the former are defined in terms of the latter. Whether this is the case or not cannot be ascertained, however, by simply examining the writings and the pronouncements of scientists; for most presentations of science fail to state explicitly just what terms are taken to be defined and what others function as primitives. In general, only definitions of special importance will be stated, others will be tacitly taken for granted. Furthermore, the primitive terms of one presentation may be among the defined ones of another, and the formulations offered by different authors may involve various divergences and inconsistencies. The task of analyzing the logical relations among scientific terms is, therefore, one of rational reconstruction. Its ultimate objective is the construction of a language which is governed by well-determined rules, and in which all the statements of empirical science can be formulated. For the purposes of this monograph, it is not necessary to enter into the details of the complex problem—which is far from a complete solution—of how a rational reconstruction of the entire system of scientific concepts might be effected; it will suffice here to consider certain fundamental aspects of such a reconstruction.

The conjecture mentioned in the preceding paragraph may now be restated thus: Any term in the vocabulary of empirical science is definable by means of observation terms; i.e., it is possible to carry out a rational reconstruction of the language of science in such a way that all primitive terms are observation terms and all other terms are defined by means of them. This view is characteristic of the earlier forms of positivism and empiricism, and we shall call it the *narrower thesis of empiricism*. According to it, any scientific statement, however abstract, could be transformed, by virtue of the definitions of its constituent technical terms, into an equivalent statement couched exclusively in observation terms: Science would really deal solely with observables. It might well be mentioned here that among contemporary psychologists this thesis has been intensively discussed in reference to the technical terms of psychology; much of the discussion has been concerned with the question whether the so-called intervening variables of learning theory are, or should be, completely definable in terms of directly observable characteristics of the stimulus and response situations.

Despite its apparent plausibility, the narrower empiricist thesis does not stand up under closer scrutiny. There are at least two kinds of terms which raise difficulties: disposition terms, for which the correctness of the thesis is at least problematic, and quantitative terms, to which it surely does not apply. We will now discuss the status of disposition terms, leaving an examination of quantitative terms for the next section.

The property term "magnetic" is an example of a disposition term; it designates, not a directly observable characteristic, but rather a disposition, on the part of some physical objects, to display specific reactions (such as attracting small iron objects) under certain specifiable circumstances (such as the presence of small iron objects in the vicinity). The vocabulary of empirical science abounds in disposition terms, such as "elastic," "conductor of heat," "fissionable," "catalyzer," "phototropic," "recessive trait," "vasoconstrictor," "introvert," "somatotonic," "matriarchate"; the following comments on the term "magnetic" can be readily transferred to any one of them.

Since an object may be magnetic at one time and non-magnetic at another, the word "magnetic" will occur in contexts of the form "(object) x is magnetic at (time) t," and a contextual definition with this expression as definiendum has to be sought. The following formulation—which is deliberately oversimplified in matters of physical detail —might suggest itself:

(6.1) x is magnetic at $t =_{Df}$ if, at t, a small iron object is close to x, then it moves toward x.

But the conditional form of the definiens, while clearly reflecting the status of the definiendum as a disposition concept, gives rise to irksome problems. In formal logic the phrase "if . . . then ____" is usually construed in the sense of material implication, i.e., as being synonymous with "either not . . . or also ____"; accordingly, the definiens of (6.1) would be satisfied by an object x not only if x was actually magnetic at time t but also if x was not magnetic but no small iron object happened to be near x at time t.

This shows that if sentences of the form illustrated by (6.1) are to serve as definitions for disposition terms, the "if . . . then ____"clause in the definiens requires a different interpretation, whose import may be suggested by using the subjunctive mood:

(6.2) x is magnetic at $t =_{Df}$ if, at t, a small iron object should be close to x, then that object would move toward x.

Surely, the subjunctive conditional phrase cannot be interpreted in the sense of the material conditional; but before it can be accepted as providing an adequate formulation for the definition of disposition terms, the meaning of the phrase "if . . . then ____" in subjunctive clauses would have to be made explicit. This is a problem of great interest and importance, since the formulation of so-called counterfactual conditionals and of general laws in science calls for the use of "if . . . then ____" in the same sense; but despite considerable analytic efforts and significant partial results, no fully satisfactory explication seems available at present, and the formulation (6.2) represents a program rather than a solution.

An alternative way of avoiding the shortcomings of (6.1) has been suggested, and developed in detail, by Carnap. It consists in construing disposition terms as introduced, not by definition, but by a more general procedure, which he calls *reduction:* it amounts to partial, or conditional, definition and includes the standard procedure of explicit definition as a special case.

We will briefly explain this idea by reference to the simplest form of reduction, effected by means of so-called bilateral reduction sentences. A bilateral reduction sentence introducing a property term "Q" has the form

$$(6.3) \qquad P_1 x \supset \quad (Qx \equiv P_2 x).^1$$

Here, "$P_1 x$" and "$P_2 x$" symbolize certain characteristics which an object x may have; these may be more or less complex but must be stated in terms which are already understood.

In a somewhat loose paraphrase, which however suggests the scientific use of such sentences, (6.3) may be restated thus:

(6.31) If an object x has characteristic P_1 (e.g., x is subjected to specified test conditions or to some specified stimulus), then the attribute Q is to be assigned to x if and only if x shows the characteristic (i.e., the reaction, or the mode of response) P_2.

Now the idea that was to be conveyed by (6.1) may be restated in the following reduction sentence:

(6.4) If a small iron object is close to x at t, then x is magnetic at t if and only if that object moves toward x at t.

In reduction sentences, the phrase "if . . . then _____" is always construed as synonymous with "not . . . or _____," and "if and only if" is understood analogously; yet the

---

[1] [Read: If $P_1 x$, then Qx, if, and only if, $P_2 x$. The symbol "$\supset$" is the logical sign of implication, so that "_____ $\supset$ . . ." is read "if _____ then . . . ." The logical symbol "$\equiv$" is the sign of equivalence, so that "_____ $\equiv$ . . ." is read "_____ if, and only if, ..."]

difficulty encountered by (6.1) does not arise for (6.4): If no small iron object is close to x at t, then the whole statement (6.4) is true of x, but we cannot infer that x is magnetic at t.

A reduction sentence offers no complete definition for the term it introduces, but only a partial, or conditional, determination of its meaning; it assigns meaning to the "new" term only for its application to objects which satisfy specific "test conditions." Thus, e.g., (6.4) determines the meaning of "magnetic at t" only in reference to objects which meet the test condition of being close to some small iron body at t; it provides no interpretation for a sentence such as "Object x is now magnetic, but there is no iron whatever in its vicinity." Hence, terms introduced by reduction sentences cannot generally be eliminated in favor of primitives. There is one exception to this rule: If the expression, "P_1x," in (6.3) is analytic, i.e., is satisfied with logical necessity by any object x whatever (which is the case, for example, if "P_1x" stands for "x is green or not green"), then the bilateral reduction sentence is equivalent to the explicit definition "$Qx \equiv P_2x$"; hence, it fully specifies the meaning of "Qx" and permits its elimination from any context. This shows that reduction is actually a generalization of definition. To put the matter in a different way, which will be useful later: A set of reduction sentences for a concept Q lays down a necessary condition for Q and a sufficient one; but, in general, the two are not identical. A definition of Q, on the other hand, specifies, in the definiens, a condition which is both necessary and sufficient for Q.

The indeterminacy in the meaning of a term introduced by a reduction sentence may be decreased by laying down additional reduction sentences for it which refer to different test conditions. Thus, e.g., if the concept of electric current had been introduced previously, (6.4) might be supplemented by the additional reduction sentence:

(6.5) If x moves through a closed wire loop at t, then x is magnetic at t if and only if an electric current flows in the loop at t.

The sentences (6.4) and (6.5) together provide criteria of application for the word "magnetic" in reference to any object that satisfies the condition of at least one of them. But, since the two conditions are not exhaustive of all logical possibilities, the meaning of the word is still unspecified for many conceivable cases. On the other hand, the test conditions clearly are not logically exclusive: both may be satisfied by one and the same object; and for objects of this kind the two sentences imply a specific assertion, namely: Any physical object which is near some small iron body and moves through a closed wire loop will generate a current in the loop if and only if it attracts the iron body. But this statement surely is not just a stipulation concerning the use of a new term—in fact, it does not contain the new term "magnetic" at all; rather, it expresses an empirical law. Hence, while a single reduction sentence may be viewed simply as laying down a notational convention for the use of the term it introduces, this is no longer possible for a set of two or more reduction sentences concerning the same term, because such a set implies, as a rule, certain statements which have the character of empirical laws; such a set cannot, therefore, be used in science unless there is evidence to support the laws in question.

To summarize: An attempt to construe disposition terms as introduced by definition in terms of observables encounters the difficulties illustrated by reference to (6.1). These can be avoided by introducing disposition terms by sets of reduction sentences. But this method has two peculiar features: (1) In general, a set of reduction sentences for a given term does not have the sole function of a notational convention; rather, it also asserts, by implication, certain empirical statements. Sets of reduction sentences combine in a peculiar way the functions of concept formation and of theory formation. (2) In general, a set of reduction sentences determines the meaning of the introduced term only partially.

Now, as was noted in section 4, even an explicit nominal definition may imply a nondefinitional "justificatory" statement which has to be established antecedently if the definition is to be acceptable; thus, the first characteristic of introduction by reduction sentences has its analogue in the case of definition. But this is not true of the second characteristic; and it might seem that the partial indeterminacy of meaning of terms introduced by reduction sentences is too high a price to pay for a method which avoids the shortcomings of definitions such as (6.1). It may be well, therefore, to suggest that this second characteristic of reduction sentences does justice to what appears to be an important characteristic of the more fruitful technical terms of science; let us call it their *openness of meaning.* The concepts of magnetization, of temperature, of gravitational field, for example, were introduced to serve as crystallization points for the formulation of explanatory and predictive principles. Since the latter are to bear upon phenomena accessible to direct observation, there must be "operational" criteria of application for their constitutive terms, i.e., criteria expressible in terms of observables. Reduction sentences make it possible to formulate such criteria. But precisely in the case of theoretically fruitful concepts, we want to permit and indeed count on the possibility that they may enter into further general principles, which will connect them with additional variables and will thus provide new criteria of application for them. We would deprive ourselves of these potentialities if we insisted on introducing the technical concepts of science by full definition in terms of observables.

Theoretical Constructs and Their Interpretation

A second group of terms which fail to bear out the narrower thesis of empiricism are the metrical terms, which represent numerically measurable quantities such as length, mass, temperature, electric charge, etc. The term "length," for example, is used in contexts of the form "the length of the distance between points u and v is r cm." or briefly

(7.1) $$\text{length } (u, \ v) = r.$$

Similarly, the term "mass" occurs in contexts of the form "the mass of physical body x is s grams," or briefly

(7.2) $$\text{mass } (x) = s.$$

In the hypotheses and theories of physics, these concepts are used in such a way that their values— r or s, respectively—may equal any nonnegative number. Thus, e.g., in Newton's general law of gravitation, which expresses the force of the gravitational attraction between two physical bodies as a function of their masses and their distance, all these magnitudes are allowed to take any positive real-number value. The concept of length, therefore—and similarly that of mass, and any other metrical concept whose range of values includes some interval of the real-number system—provides for the theoretical distinction of an infinity of different possible cases, each of them corresponding to one of the permissible real-number values. If, therefore, the concept of length were fully definable in terms of observables, then it would be possible to state, purely in terms of observables, the meaning of the phrase "length $(u, v) = r$" for each of the permissible values of r. But this cannot be done, as we will now argue in two steps.

First, suppose that we try to define the characteristic of having a length of r cm. as tantamount to some specific combination (expressible by means of "and," "or," "not," etc.) of observable attributes. (In effect, this restricts the definiens to a molecular sentence in which all predicates are observation terms.) This is surely not feasible for every theoretically permissible value of r. For in view of the limits of discrimination in direct observation, there will be altogether only a finite, though large, number of observable characteristics; hence, the number of different complexes that can be formed out of them will be finite as well, whereas the number of theoretically permissible r-values is infinite. Hence, the assignment of a numerical r-value of length (or of any other measurable quantity) to a given object cannot always be construed as definitionally equivalent to attributing to that object some specific complex of observable characteristics.

Let us try next, therefore, to construe the assignment of a specified r-value to a given object as equivalent to a statement about that object which can be expressed by means of observation terms and logical terms alone. The latter may now include not only "and," "or," "not," etc., but also the expressions "all," "some," "the class of all things satisfying such and such a condition," etc. But even if definition in terms of observables is construed in this broad sense, the total number of defining expressions that can be formed from the finite vocabulary available is only denumerably infinite, whereas the class of all theoretically permissible r-values has the power of the continuum. Hence, a full definition of metrical terms by means of observables is not possible.

It might be replied, in a pragmatist or extreme operationist vein, that a theoretical difference which makes no observable difference is no significant difference at all and that therefore no metrical concept in science should be allowed to take as its value just any real number within some specified interval. But compliance with this rule would make it impossible to use the concepts and principles of higher mathematics in the formulation and application of scientific theories. If, for example, we were to allow only a discrete set of values for length and for temporal duration, then the concepts of limit, derivative, and integral would be unavailable, and it would consequently be impossible to introduce the concepts of instantaneous speed and acceleration and to formulate the theory of motion. Similarly, all the formulations in terms of real and complex functions and in terms of differential equations, which are so characteristic of the theoretically most powerful branches of empirical science, would be barred. The retort that all those concepts and principles are "mere fictions to which nothing corresponds in experience". is, in effect, simply a restatement of the fact that theoretical constructs cannot be definitionally eliminated exclusively in favor of observation terms. But it is precisely these "fictitious" concepts rather than those fully definable by observables which enable science to interpret and organize the data of direct observation by means of a coherent and comprehensive system which permits explanation and prediction. Hence, rather than exclude those fruitful concepts on the ground that they are not experientially definable, we will have to inquire what nondefinitional methods might be suited for their introduction and experiential interpretation.

Do reduction sentences provide such a method? The conjecture has indeed been set forth in more recent empiricist writings that every term of empirical science can be introduced, on the basis of observation terms, by means of a suitable set of reduction sentences. Let us call this assertion the *liberalized thesis of empiricism*.

But even for this thesis difficulties arise in the case of metrical terms. For, as was noted in section 6, a set of reduction sentences for a term t lays down a necessary and a (usually different) sufficient condition for the application of t. Hence, suitable reduction sentences for the phrase "length $(u, v) = r$" would have to specify, for every theoretically permissible value of r, a necessary and a sufficient condition, couched in terms of observables, for an interval (u, v) having a length of exactly r cm. But it is not even possible to formulate all the requisite sufficient conditions; for this would mean the establishment, for every possible value of r, of a purely observational criterion whose satisfaction by a given interval (u, v) would entail that the interval was exactly r cm. long. That a complete set of such criteria cannot exist is readily seen by an argument analogous to the one presented earlier in this section in reference to the limits of full definability in observational terms.

The metrical concepts in their theoretical use belong to the larger class of *theoretical constructs*, i.e., the often highly abstract terms used in the advanced stages of scientific theory formation, such as "mass," "mass point," "rigid body," "force," etc., in classical mechanics; "absolute temperature," "pressure," "volume," "Carnot process," etc., in classical thermodynamics; and "electron," "proton," "Ψ function," etc., in quantum mechanics. Terms of this kind are not introduced by definitions or reduction chains based on observables; in fact, they are not introduced by any piecemeal process of assigning meaning to them individually. Rather, the constructs used in a theory are introduced jointly, as it were, by setting up a theoretical system formulated in terms of them and by giving this system an experiential interpretation which in turn confers empirical meaning on the theoretical constructs. Let us look at this procedure more closely.

Although in actual scientific practice the processes of framing a theoretical structure and of interpreting it are not always sharply separated, since the intended interpretation usually guides the constructions of the theoretician, it is possible and indeed desirable, for the purposes of logical clarification, to separate the two steps conceptually.

A theoretical system may then be conceived as an uninterpreted theory in axiomatic form, which is characterized by (1) a specified set of primitive terms; these are not defined within the theory, and all other extralogical terms of the theory are obtained from them by nominal definition; (2) a set of postulates—we will alternatively call them primitive, or basic, hypotheses; other sentences of the theory are obtained from them by logical deduction.

As an example of a well-axiomatized theory which is of fundamental importance for science, consider Euclidean geometry. Its development as "pure geometry," i.e., as an uninterpreted axiomatic system, is logically quite independent of its interpretation in physics and its use in navigation, surveying, etc. In Hilbert's axiomatization, the primitives of the theory are the terms "point," "straight line," "plane," "incident on" (signifying a relation between a point and a line), "between" (signifying a relation between points on a line), "lies in" (signifying a relation between a point and a plane), and two further terms, for congruence among line segments and among angles, respectively. All other terms, such as "parallel," "angle," "triangle," "circle," are defined by means of the primitives: the term "parallel," for example, can be introduced by the following contextual definition:

(7.3) x is parallel to $y =_{Df} x$ and y are straight lines; there exists a plane in which both x and y lie; but there exists no point which is incident on both x and y.

The postulates include such sentences as these: For any two points there exists at least one, and at most one, straight line on which both are incident; between any two points incident on a straight line there exists another point which is incident on that line; etc. From the postulates, the other propositions of Euclidean geometry are obtained by logical deduction. Such proof establishes the propositions as theorems of pure mathematical geometry; it does not, however, certify their validity for use in physical theory and its applications, such as the determination of distances between physical bodies by means of triangulation, or the computation of the volume of a spherical object from the length of its diameter. For no specific meaning is assigned, in pure geometry, to the primitives of the theory (and, consequently, none to the defined terms either); hence, pure geometry does not express any assertions about the spatial properties and relations of objects in the physical world.

A physical geometry, i.e., a theory which deals with the spatial aspects of physical phenomena, is obtained from a system of pure geometry by giving the primitives a specific interpretation in physical terms. Thus, e.g., to obtain the physical counterpart of pure Euclidean geometry, points may be interpreted as approximated by small physical objects, i.e., objects whose sizes are negligible compared to their mutual distances (they might be pinpoints, the intersections of cross-hairs, etc., or, for astronomical purposes, entire stars or even galactic systems); a straight line may be construed as the path of a light ray in a homogeneous medium; congruence of intervals as a physical relation characterizable in terms of coincidences of rigid rods; etc. This interpretation turns the postulates and theorems of pure geometry into statements of physics, and the question of their factual correctness now permits—and, indeed, requires—empirical tests. One of these is the measurement made by Gauss of the angle-sum in a triangle formed by light rays, to ascertain whether it equals two right angles, as asserted by physical geometry in its Euclidean form. If the evidence obtained by suitable methods is unfavorable, the Euclidean form of geometry may well be replaced by some non-Euclidean version which, in combination with the rest of physical theory, is in better accord with observational findings. In fact, just this has occurred in the general theory of relativity.

In a similar manner, any other scientific theory may be conceived of as consisting of an uninterpreted, deductively developed system and of an interpretation which confers empirical import upon the terms and sentences of the latter. The term to which the interpretation directly assigns an empirical content either may be primitives of the theory, as in the geometrical example discussed before, or may be defined terms of the theoretical system. Thus, e.g., in a logical reconstruction of chemistry, the different elements might be defined by primitives referring to certain characteristics of their atomic structure; then, the terms "hydrogen," "helium," etc., thus defined might be given an empirical interpretation by reference to certain gross physical and chemical characteristics typical of the different elements. Such an interpretation of certain defined terms of a system confers mediately, as it were, some empirical content also upon the primitives of the system, which have received no direct empirical interpretation. This procedure appears well suited also for Woodger's axiomatization of biology, in which certain defined concepts, such as division and fusion of cells, permit of a more direct empirical interpretation than some of the primitives of the system.

An adequate empirical interpretation turns a theoretical system into a testable theory: The hypotheses whose constituent terms have been interpreted become capable of test by reference to observable phenomena. Frequently the interpreted hypotheses will be derivative hypotheses of the theory; but their confirmation or disconfirmation by empirical data will then mediately strengthen or weaken also the primitive hypotheses from which they were derived. Thus, for example, the primitive hypotheses of the kinetic theory of heat concern the mechanical behavior of the microparticles constituting a gas; hence, they are not capable of direct test. But they are indirectly testable because they entail derivative hypotheses which can be formulated in certain defined terms that have been interpreted by means of such "macroscopic observables" as the temperature and the pressure of a gas.

The double function of such interpretation of defined terms—to indirectly confer empirical content upon the primitives of the theory and to render its basic hypotheses capable of test—is illustrated also by those hypotheses in physics or chemistry which refer to the value of some magnitude at a space-time point, such as the instantaneous speed and acceleration of a particle; or the density, pressure, and temperature of a substance at a certain point: none of these magnitudes is capable of direct observation, none of these hypotheses permits of direct test. The connection with the level of possible experimental or observational findings is established by defining, with the help of mathematical integration, certain derived concepts, such as those of average speed and acceleration in a certain time interval, or of average density in a certain spatial region, and by interpreting these in terms of more or less directly observable phenomena.

A scientific theory might therefore be likened to a complex spatial network: Its terms are represented by the knots, while the threads connecting the latter correspond, in part, to the definitions and, in part, to the fundamental derivative hypotheses included in the theory. The whole system floats, as it were, above the plane of observation and is anchored to it by rules of interpretation. These might be viewed as strings which are not part of the network but link certain points of the latter with specific places in the plane of observation. By virtue of those interpretive connections, the network can function as a scientific theory: From certain observational data, we may ascend, via an interpretive string, to some point in the theoretical network, thence proceed, via definitions and hypotheses, to other points, from which another interpretive string permits a descent to the plane of observation.

In this manner an interpreted theory makes it possible to infer the occurrence of certain phenomena which can be described in observational terms and which may belong to the past or the future, on the basis of other such phenomena, whose occurrence has been previously ascertained. But the theoretical apparatus which provides these predictive and postdictive bridges from observational data to potential observational findings cannot, in general, be formulated in terms of observables alone. The entire history of scientific endeavor appears to show that in our world comprehensive, simple, and dependable principles for the explanation and prediction of observable phenomena cannot be obtained by merely summarizing and inductively generalizing observational findings. A hypothetico-deductive-observational procedure is called for and is indeed followed in the more advanced branches of empirical science: Guided by his knowledge of observational data, the scientist has to invent a set of concepts—theoretical constructs, which lack immediate experiential significance, a system of hypotheses couched in terms of them, and an interpretation for the resulting theoretical network; and all this in a manner which will establish explanatory and predictive connections between the data of direct observation.

Is it possible to specify a generally applicable form in which the interpretive statements for a scientific theory can be expressed? Let us note, to begin with, that those statements are not, in general, tantamount to full definitions in terms of observables. We will state the reasons by reference to the physical interpretation of geometrical terms. First, some of the expressions used in the interpretation, such as "light ray in a homogeneous medium," are not observation terms but at best disposition terms which can be partially defined through observables by means of chains of reduction sentences. Second, even if all the terms used in interpreting geometry were accepted as observation terms, the interpretive statements still would not express conditions which are both necessary and sufficient for the interpreted terms; hence, they would not have the import of definitions. If, e.g., it were necessary and sufficient for a physical point to be identical with, or at least at the same place as, a pinpoint or an intersection of cross-hairs or the like, then many propositions of geometry would be clearly false in their physical interpretation; among them, for example, the theorem that between any two points on a straight line there are infinitely many other points. Actually, no geometrical theory is rejected in physics for reasons of this type; rather, it is understood that comparatively small physical bodies constitute only approximations of points in the sense of physical geometry. The term "point" as used in the theoretical physics is a construct and does not denote any objects that are accessible to direct observation.

But an interpretation is not even generally tantamount to a set of reduction sentences: The interpretation of a theoretical term may well make use of expressions which are introducible by means of a set of reduction sentences based on observation predicates; but those expressions again will, as a rule, be used not to specify necessary and sufficient conditions for the theoretical term in question but only to provide a partial assignment of empirical content to it. Consider the case mentioned before of a reconstruction of chemistry in which the elements are theoretically defined in terms of their atomic structure and empirically interpreted by reference to their gross physical and chemical characteristics: Some of the latter, such as solubility in terms is achieved.

As a consequence, an interpreted scientific theory cannot be equivalently translated into a system of sentences whose constituent extralogical terms are all either observation predicates or obtainable from observation predicates by means of reduction sentences; and *a fortiori* no scientific theory is equivalent to a finite or infinite class of sentences describing potential experiences.

7

MEASUREMENT:

Ernest Nagel ·

I

The occasion and conditions for measurement. Measurement has been defined as the correlation with numbers of entities which are not numbers. As practiced in the developed sciences this is a sufficiently comprehensive, though cryptic, statement of the object of measurement. But in a larger sense, in a sense to include most of those acts of identification, delimitation, comparison, present in everyday thought and practise, numerical measurement is only infrequently used. *"This* is the missing book," or "He had a *good* sleep," or "The cake is *too* sweet," are judgments making no explicit reference to number. From this larger point of view, measurement can be regarded as the delimitation and fixation of our ideas of things, so that the determination of what it is to be a man or to be a circle is a case of measurement. The problems of measurement merge, at one end, with the problems of predication.

There are indeed vast domains of reflection and practice where numbers have taken little hold. Prior to Descartes, geometry was not established on a thoroughgoing numerical basis, and many branches of mathematics, like symbolic logic or projective geometry, may be pursued without introducing

· [This selection is reprinted from *Erkenntnis*, II Band, Heft 5, 1932, pp. 313–33. We omit only the footnotes of the original. Reprinted by permission of Ernest Nagel.]

numbers. In arts like cookery, measurement is not primarily numerical, and the operations used are very often controlled by disciplined judgments on the qualitative alterations of the subject matter.

But the difficulty and uncertainty often experienced in obtaining desired consequences when vaguely defined ideas and crude methods of applying them are used soon lead wherever possible to the introduction of more or less refined mathematical processes. The immediate, direct evaluation of subject matter secures too little uniformity to be of much value; and direct judgments, e.g., of lengths by the eye, are consequently replaced by more complicated and indirect operations, such as the transporting of unit lengths along the lines to be compared. It is, indeed, because less error, that is, greater uniformity, is obtained in judgments of spatial coincidences than, e.g., in judgments of differences of length or color, that spatial congruence plays so large a role in laboratory practice. The *raison d'être* of numbers in measurement is the elimination of ambiguity in classification and the achievement of uniformity in practice.

It is generally only after numerical measurements have been established and standardized that references to the "real" properties of things begin to appear: those properties, that is, which appear in circumstances allowing for most facility in their measurement. The "real" shape of the penny is round, because from the point of view from which the penny is round, measurements and correlations of other shapes can be carried on most easily. Nevertheless, it must not be overlooked that a numerical evaluation of things is only one way of making evaluations of certain selected characters, although it is so far the best. It is pre-eminently the best, because in addition to the obvious advantage they have as a universally recognized language, numbers make possible a refinement of analysis without loss of clarity; and their emotionally neutral character permits a symbolic rendering of invariant relations in a manifold of changing qualities. Mathematics expresses the recognition of a necessity which is not human.

From this last point of view, therefore, the search for a unified body of principles in terms of which the abrupt, the transitory, the unexpected are to be exhibited and in a measure controlled is the most conscious guiding principle in the application of numerical science. If the search for mathematical equations is the aim of physics, other activities such as experiment, classification, or measurement are subservient to this aim and are to be understood only in relation to it. Consequently, if we inquire why we measure in physics, the answer will be that if we do measure, and measure in certain ways, then it will be possible to establish the equations and theories which are the goal of inquiry.

It is relevant, therefore, to demand the logical foundations of the mathematical operations which physics constantly uses. For if mathematics is applicable to the natural world, the formal properties of the symbolic operations of mathematics must also be predicable of many segments of that world. And if we can discover what these formal properties are, since mathematics *is* relevant to the exploration of nature, a physical interpretation *must* be found for them. That physical interpretation will constitute, whenever it can be found, the conditions for the measurement of that subject matter. Consequently, if we ask why in measurement we attend to certain characters of objects to the exclusion of others, the answer will be that the selected characters are precisely those with which applied mathematics can cope. It is only by a reference to the function which the numerical measures or magnitudes of things have in equations that one can remove the apparent arbitrariness in selecting one rather than another set of conditions as fundamental for measurement.

In recent years the formal conditions of their science have been much discussed by mathematicians. The properties which magnitudes must have in order to be capable of the kind of elaboration which the mathematics of physics requires, have been variously formulated as axioms of quantity. The following set, with some modifications, is taken from Hoelder.

1. Either $a > b$, or $a < b$, or $a = b$.
2. If $a > b$, and $b > c$, then $a > c$.
3. For every a there is an a' such that $a = a'$.
4. If $a > b$, and $b = b'$, then $a > b'$.
5. If $a = b$, then $b = a$.
6. For every a there is a b such that $a > b$ (within limits).
7. For every a and b there is a c such that $c = a + b$.
8. $a + b > a'$.
9. $a + b = a' + b'$.

10. $a + b = b + a$.

11. $(a + b) + c = a + (b + c)$.

12. If $a < b$, there is a number n such that $na > b$ (also within limits).

How much more perspicacious such an axiomatic or functional analysis of magnitudes can be than definitions in terms of private, intrinsic properties (e.g., "quantity is the relation between the existence and the nonexistence of a certain kind of being"); how much more successfully it satisfies the demand for a formulation which, true for *every* instance of quantity, should not be the exhaustive statem ent of *any one* instance, will be evident from the sequel. Even Meinong's definition of magnitude as "whatever is capable of being limited toward zero" or as "that which is capable of having interpolations between itself and its contradictory," has little clarity to recommend it. Later on a distinction will be made between magnitudes which satisfy all twelve axioms and those which satisfy only the first six. A magnitude in the most complete sense, however, is whatever is capable of verifying the whole set.

II

Order and equality. The illustration of these relations by indicating some of the empirical procedure involved in measurement is the next portion of our task. At the very outset it must be pointed out, however, that an adequate interpretation of the axioms must inevitably lead out of the laboratory where measurements are usually made, and lead on to a consideration of the manufacture of the laboratory *instruments*. When a laboratory experiment is studied behavioristically, the measurements performed consist in the observation of the movement of a pointer on a scale, or of the superposition of lengths. How natural, therefore, to suppose that measurement consists only in the observation of space-time coincidences! It is important to remember, however, that the experimenter, working with marked or calibrated instruments, assumes that the calibrations indicate various qualitative continuities not *explicitly* present. The process of measurement has not been fully exhibited until all those operations of calibration have been noted. When a weight is attached to a spring balance, and the position of a marker on the scale read, only a very small fraction of the process actually necessary to estimate the weight as five pounds has been observed; the operations

entering into the construction and *correlation* of scale and spring must be included. It is of the essence of an experiment that it be repeatable. Therefore it is not the particular instrument used any more than it is the unique experiment which has such an overwhelming importance in science; it is rather the repeatable process capable of producing the markings on the instrument which is. Every marked instrument implies the construction and existence of some standard series of magnitudes, correlation with which constitutes the calibration. A wholehearted recognition of this reference of instruments to something beyond themselves, is a recognition that other characters of existence besides the spatial are capable of, and are involved in, the process of measurement.

The relation $>$, or its converse $<$, is a transitive assymetrical relation. It finds its exemplification in some discovered qualitative domain which is sufficiently homogeneous to allow identification as a well-defined range of a single quality. Within this domain the character studied must be capable of such a serial gradation that a transitive assymetrical relation can be discovered to hold between the discriminated elements. So we find the character of density which liquids manifest in relation to one another to be such a relation. This character may be defined, with somewhat more care than is shown here, as the capacity of a liquid to float upon other liquids. Liquid a will be said to be more dense than b if b can float on a but a cannot float on b. And it can and *must* be shown *experimentally* that, for a set of liquids distinguishable from each other by all sorts of physical and chemical properties, the relation $>$ (more dense) is a transitive assymetrical relation: if liquid a is more dense than b (i.e., b floats on a) and if b is more dense than c, then a is more dense than c (i.e., c floats on a).

The relation of equality ($=$) can be defined in terms of $>$. We say that $a = b$, if a is not $> b$, and a is not $< b$, and if $a \leqslant c$, then also $b \leqslant c$. Equality of density may therefore, be defined thus: c has a density equal to that of d if c does not float on d and d does not float on c; and if c floats on e so does d.

The experimental establishment of series of this kind involving the first six axioms is the first step in the introduction of number. The function of the experiments is the careful exhibition of physical relations symbolized by these axioms; without such an experimental exploration of the subject matter, it may turn out that the relation between the objects under survey will not generate the transitive assymetric sequence. If, to take an absurd example, we compare the lengths of elastic rubber bands by superposition, without specifying further the manner in which this is to be done, and if we define x as longer than y when x extends beyond y, it may well be that axiom two will not be satisfied.

Numbers may of course be introduced merely for purposes of identification, and many numerical designations have no more arithmetical significance than do the names of individuals. Thus, the policemen of a large city are often known by their number; but the policeman with number 500 is not thereby known to be stronger or more efficient or more handsome or wealthier or older than the one numbered 475.

This kind of out-and-out arbitrariness can be considerably reduced if a qualitative series is first established. The numbers assigned in the operations of science are more than a conventional tag; it is desirable that an object numbered 50 occupy a position higher or lower in a qualitative series as determined above, than one marked 40. So, for example, the liquids gasoline, alcohol, water, glycerine, hydrochloric acid, carbon bisulphide, and mercury are arranged in the order of increasing density as defined above; we can establish a one-to-one correspondence between these liquids and a series of real numbers such that the order of numbers will be symbolic of the order of densities. We may assign any one of the following sets of numbers to the series of liquids: (a) 1, 2, 3, 4, 5, 6, 7, or (b) 100, 90, 88, 85, 80, 60, 10, or (c) 22.5, 20, 19.6, 11.2; 10.5 8.9; or (d) .75, .79, 1, 1.26, 1.27, 1.29, 13.6. If, however, we specify further that the order of increasing numerical magnitude must correspond with the order of increasing density, the sets of numbers (b) and (c) are no longer available.

Nevertheless, there is still very much that is arbitrary and often misleading in assigning the numbers, say, 1 to 7 to the above sets of liquids. In choosing the set (a) instead of (d) or other sets having the same order, we exhibit the arbitrariness. The choice becomes positively misleading if, without further definition and experimental confirmation, we suppose that because alcohol in this scheme has a density of two and gasoline that of one, there is involved a physical meaning (a physical operation defined in terms of density) in talking of alcohol as *twice* as dense as gasoline, or of *adding* densities of gasoline to obtain the density of alcohol. The operational interpretation of the axioms assigns, so far, physical meaning only to the *order* in which numbers are employed; there is no such meaning as yet for numerical *differences*.

It is just such misunderstandings, however, that are at the basis of many of the confusions in psychological and social measurements. Bogoslovsky's attempt to measure the proportion of "mental activity elements" in various tasks, is one instance of such confusions. He presented to several people twenty descriptions of different situations involving mental and physical activity and obtained their estimate of the proportion of mental activity "elements" to physical activity "elements" in each. The judges were asked first to arrange the descriptions in order of increasing mental activity (an attempt to generate a qualitative series) and then to express the numerical percentage of mental activity "elements" in each. But "percentage of mental activity elements" has a well-defined meaning only on the assumption that the situation can be regarded as the *summed* total of elements; and that assumption must be justified both by an adequate criterion for an "element" and by the exhibition of a process of *addition* for them. Without that assumption and its justification, the results obtained indicate nothing. How little the nature of measurement is understood by the author is clear from the defense he makes for his procedure: "All our scales are arbitrary. There are no special intrinsic reasons for dividing an hour into sixty minutes." An hour may, of course, be divided into any number of intervals. But it is the possibility of definite operations defining more or less time and the addition of intervals, that makes the division of an hour into sixty parts valuable, and the nonexistence of such operations which makes valueless the computation of mental activity percentages.

When, therefore, numbers are correlated with some qualitative spectrum, it is not obvious and not always true that the differences between the numbers represent differences between qualities definable otherwise than ordinally. Since none of the operations exhibited so far in connection with density have defined anything besides "greater than" and "equality," it is meaningless to talk at this stage of addition.

III

Addition. "At this stage" must be amended in the case of some properties to read "ever." For it is a well-established character of existence that, although many qualities can be serially ordered and so numbered in accordance with an arbitrary plan, a few of these qualities (and a limited few they are) possess also a capacity for "addition" which the rest do not. This cleavage between additive or extensive qualities, and nonadditive or intensive qualities, is of fundamental importance in the philosophy of physical measurement.

Consequently, new operations and experiments must be introduced to define addition. And for density, defined as above, such operations are not obtainable, since there is no clear sense in which two liquids equally dense could be added to produce a liquid twice as dense, and so obtain a "sum" which would possess the formal properties listed in the last six axioms. Other physical properties must be used to exhibit these new operations.

"Illumination" is a very important photometric property which is capable of addition when defined as follows. It will be assumed, in the first place, that the immediate but disciplined judgments, with respect to perceived inequality or equality of the brightness of certain surfaces, can be obtained with sufficient uniformity. Brightness thus forms a qualitative domain within which more or less bright can be distinguished; equality of brightness may therefore be defined in conformity to the formal characters already specified. The surfaces used will have the same shape, same color, and the same reflection and diffusion coefficients. Surfaces will be said to form a "pair" if, when their positions are interchanged and everything else remains the same, no disturbance can be noted in the equality of the brightness of the surfaces.

A pair of surfaces will be said to have equal *illumination* when they are judged to be equally bright under specified circumstances; e.g., the lines which join the two surfaces to the eye must make equal angles with the perpendiculars to the surfaces. Many more specified conditions must be introduced in practice. When some body can be found such that, by altering its physical state or of the medium between it and the surfaces, the brightness of the surfaces is changed, the body is defined as the *source* of the illumination. It can now be shown experimentally that, if a pair of surfaces form an equally illuminated pair under a certain source, a second pair will also be equally illuninated if substituted for the first pair, even though a member of the first set does not form a "pair" with a member of the second set. This is the reason why illumination comes to conditions under which they are placed; these conditions include, as a minimum, the nature of the source and the position of the surfaces with respect to it.

Addition of illumination can now be defined. The illumination of a surface S from sources A *and* B is defined to be equal to the *sum* of the illumination of S from A alone and the illumination from B alone, if A and B remain in the same physical state and relative position to S. If we use sources of the same color (strictly, only monochromatic light can be used), it can be shown that axioms 8, 9, and 11 receive an experimental confirmation; but for heterochromatic light, addition in this complete sense no longer exists.

With physical addition defined, numbers can now be introduced, so that all arbitrariness in assigning them, except in the choice of a unit, is removed. Some constant source B_1 is chosen and placed at a fixed, convenient position with respect to the surface S_2, one of the pair S_1 and S_2. The illumination thus obtained is taken as unity. Next, two sources A_1 and A_1' are found and placed on a cone whose axis is perpendicular to S_1, so that either alone makes the illumination on S_1 equal to that on S_2 under B_1, and gives therefore unit illumination on S_1. Now letting A_1 and A_1' illuminate S_1 together, and extinguishing B_1, a source B_2 is found such that, placed with respect to S_2, it makes the illumination on S_2, equal to that on S_1 under both A_1 and A_1'. A source A_2 is found and placed on the cone so that the illumination of S_1 under A_2 is equal to that of S_2 under B_2. This illumination on S_1 is two, and it now has a clear physical meaning to speak of this illumination as *twice* that under A_1. This method of assigning numbers can be extended indefinitely for integral as well as fractional values, so illustrating the last axiom. To define fractional values we must find n sources placed in such positions on the cone that any one of them makes the illumination on S_2 equal to that on S_2 under a constant source, and such that all n together make the illumination on S_1 equal to a unit illumination. Each of these n sources gives an illumination equal to $\frac{1}{n}$ of the unit illumination.

The construction of such a series of standards, both integral and fractional, in terms of explicit physical operations which take note of qualitative homogeneities and differences, is the logical prius to any other mode of physical measurement. Only now can the theorem, that illumination is inversely proportional to the square of the distance from the source, be given experimental confirmation. Only after the physical meaning of numerical operations has been thus fixed may mathematical variables be introduced to denote unambiguously portions of subject matter. Only then may the movements of pointers be taken as signs for qualitative differences.

Clearly, the most important of the operations used in the definition of magnitude are those fixing the meaning of addition. Operations for defining physical addition can be found for mass, length, period, electrical resistance, area, volume, force, and about a dozen others; for these, processes of fundamental measurement can be found, while other properties studied in physics are measurable only in terms of them, that is, derivatively. The example chosen makes clear, as Helmholtz pointed out long ago, how experimental a concept addition is, valid only insofar as axioms 9, 10, and 11 are verified. It should, moreover, help expose the dogma that measurement consists in the observation of pointer coincidences, as well as the belief that addition is exclusively spatial juxtaposition and division. Undoubtedly, spatial juxtaposition is the primitive meaning in the addition of lengths; but in the example used addition involves *conjoint activity* of sources; in measurement of weights, it means the establishment of *rigid connections* between solids; in the estimation of time periods, it requires the *temporal repetition* of certain rhythms; in the evaluation of volumes it signifies the discovery of liquids which *fill containers* without implying spatial contiguity. The presence of spatial relations is not a sufficient condition for addition; there is necessary a distinctive qualitative context, inclusion in which identifies different instances of addition as addition of the *same* characters.

When once the standard sets of different magnitudes are constructed, the measurement of even those properties whose standards these sets are is indirect and consists in the comparison of the properties with their standards. The comparisons are very often circuitous, because advantage is taken of the relations between variations in the fundamentally measured magnitudes and the variations in the position of a pointer with which they are in some physical connection. It is easier to make the correlation between pointers and weights once for all than to engage in fundamental measurement whenever one is estimating the tonnage of an elephant.

IV

Some objections examined. The preceding analysis and exposition (1) assumed without much question that measurement was the evaluation of the empirical relations between physical objects diversely qualified; and (2) stressed the importance of the distinctions between extensive and intensive qualities. Both of these doctrines have met some opposition.

1. Impressed, no doubt, by the profound difference in cognitive status between the unmeasured and measured qualitative world, Russell converts that difference, achieved in terms of the processes already examined, into a difference between a concrete actuality and a realm of essences: this latter realm is understood not as the ordered relations of and between existences, but as a domain of immaterial entities having no necessary reference to existence. For Russell, therefore, actual foot-rules are quantity, their lengths are magnitudes. It is only by an ellipsis that two quantities can be said to be equal: they are equal because they possess the same magnitude; and it is improper to say that one of two quantities is greater than the other: what is meant is that the magnitude which the first quantity possesses is greater than the second magnitude. Only quantities can be said to be equal, by having the same magnitude; two magnitudes cannot be equal, since there is only one of each kind.

Russell's first objection to the relative view of quantity (the view that $>$, $<$, and $=$, are relations holding directly between physical things), and his espousal of the absolute theory (for which things must first be referred to an otherwise undefined realm of magnitudes in order to be measured), is based upon the observation that in any proposition asserting $>$, $<$, or $=$, an *equal* quantity may always be substituted anywhere, without altering the truth value of the proposition. It is not the *actual* quantity but some character which it has with other quantities that is of importance.

It will be granted that this point is well taken if possession of relations like equality is interpreted without reference to the specific process which defines equality. When two weights are equal, that relation holds by virtue of the way the two weights enter into a complicated evaluating process. Two weights are not equal "in themselves"; they are equal as a consequence of the manipulation to which they are subjected. Of course, once having specified the defining operation, whether it is actually performed or not, the things measured have a nature prior to the actual performance which conditions their behavior in it. This observation may be verbal only: if equality is defined in terms of the process, quantities can be called equal prior to the process only proleptically; unless at *some* time the process eventuates, we cannot know that there is such a property as equality.

But it is one thing to say that relations like equality hold between two objects only in specified contexts, and another thing to convert those relations into possession of some third entity or common essence, incapable of every empirical verification. That third entity is the reification of a relation. The absolute space which haunted physics is just such a hypostatization of relations; space and time may be construed more simply as pervasive relations between events rather than as containers, extrinsic and outside the changing qualities. So when magnitudes, which are always found to be relations exhibited in the physical operations of things, are invoked as the locus of those operations, it seems legitimate to ask what empirical difference their existence or nonexistence as "common essences" would make.

Russell's second point is that every transitive symmetrical relation is analyzable into a complex of two assymetric relations and a third term, and that since equality is such a relation, it should be analyzable into the possession of a common magnitude by two quantities. "The decision between the absolute and relative theories can be made at once by appealing to a certain general principle, the principle of abstraction. Whenever a relation of which there are instances is symmetric and transitive, then the relation is not primitive, but analyzable into sameness of relation to some other term, and this common relation is such that there is only one term at most to which a given term can be so related, though many terms may be so related to a given term."

If the analysis given above is sound, all measurement which is not fundamental in the sense defined, or which is not surrogative in the manner to be explained below, consists in the direct or indirect correlation of quantities to be measured with the standard series. It is correct to say, therefore, that two equal foot-lengths are equal because they possess a common magnitude, *if* this means that they are compared, ultimately, with the same member of a standard series. But in establishing equal magnitudes *within* the standard series itself, no referrence to a "common term" was necessary. Equality, it is true, was not taken as a fundamental character, since it defined in terms of two transitive assymetrical relations. But those relations held or did not hold between *qualities*, and did not relate to some third term *outside* the qualitative series. The weights *a* and *b* are equal, because with respect to the relation "greater than" which defines the series of weights (it may be defined in terms of the sinking or rising of the arms of a lever), a is neither greater than nor less than *b*, and if c is any other *weight* (a member of the *series*, not *outside* of it), then if *a* is greater or less than *c* so also is *b*. No unique third term outside the physical domain is involved in defining equality; if Occam's razor still can cut, the magnitudes demanded by the absolute theory may be eliminated.

2. The doctrine that magnitudes are essences and therefore not divisible or additive even though it is only between them that the relation "greater than" can hold, leads very naturally to the view that the distinction between extensive and intensive magnitudes is purely conventional. Additiveness belongs, on the absolute theory, only indirectly to magnitudes, as a manner of speaking of the addition of quantities whose magnitudes they are. For "addition" of two magnitudes yields two magnitudes, not a new magnitude, while the addition of two quantities does give a new single whole, "provided the addition is of the kind which results from logical addition by regarding classes as the wholes formed by their terms." Addition, for Russell, thus

always refers to the conjunction of collections, and to the enumeration of the number of parts in the new whole. And even in the logical addition of classes there is no clear warrant, he believes, for affirming that the "divisibility" of a sum of n units is n-fold that of one unit. "We can only mean that the sum of two units contains twice as many parts, which is an arithmetical, not a quantitative judgment, and is adequate only in the case when the number of parts is finite, since in other cases the double of a number is in general equal to it. Thus even the measurement of divisibility by numbers contains an element of convention."

Now, indeed, if magnitudes express the results of physical measurement, it is not the magnitudes which are added, just as the measure of anything measured is not itself measured. If magnitudes have a logical status, then surely it is only logical addition of which they are capable. For *magnitudes,* therefore, the distinction between extensive and intensive has no *meaning.* Nevertheless, on Russell's theory, it is magnitudes which are measured, and it is because he takes "logical sum" to be the primary sense of addition that he can find only a convention in the addition of spatial distances or time intervals. How the transition from the conceptual to the existential order is effected, how "logical addition" may receive an interpretation in terms of physical operations, is a consideration omitted from his analysis. Is it not, however, more perspicacious to think of mathematical "addition" as a *universal,* whose variable empirical content will be *cases* of addition, but which will require further specific definition and experimental proof of the presence of those formal characters which make those empirical contents instances of that universal?

Nevertheless, the unusual sense in whch addition is sometimes used should not be overlooked. The order generated by the relation "male ancestor" may be measured in the following fashion: Suppose a is the father of b, b the father of c, c the father of d; then the "relation-distance" father-of is "equal" in all the pairs $a\,b$, $b\,c$ and $c\,d$, and a has the relation of "great-grand-father-of" to d. By an obvious convention, we could express the ancestral relation of a to d as three times the relation of a to b; and we could say that the relation of a to c is the sum of the relations of a to b and b to c. It is clear, however, that the "addition" here defined does not possess *all* the formal properties demanded by the axioms; it does not obey, for example, the commutative rule. The addition here defined is not very much more than the ordinal arrangement of relations. It is the failure to recognize the necessity of obtaining all the formal characters in fundamental measurement which makes so unsatisfactory the attempt of Spaier to defend the measurement of nonspatial properties, and which enables him so easily to minimize the distinction between intensive and extensive qualities. The introduction of numbers has a function more inclusive than the *identification* of quality.

v

Surrogative measurement. In the light of what has been said, the dichotomy between primary and secondary qualities becomes more illuminating if we view this distinction not as between objective and subjective, efficient and otiose, pervasive and local, permanent and evanescent, but as between those qualities which are capable of fundamental measurement and those which are not.

No science, certainly not physics, can dispense with qualities that are incapable of addition in the fullest sense, and the progress of modern science has consisted very largely in bringing nonadditive qualities like density, temperature, hardness, viscosity, compressibility, under the sway of numerical determination. There is of course one obvious way, already suggested, how this could be done. That way is to place qualities like density into a serial order, and to assign numbers to points of this qualitative spectrum. It is characteristic of modern science, however, that such is *not* the method which has been adopted, just as in zoology it is with bats and not with fish that whales are classified. For it is the particular virtue of modern science not to be concerned with the grouping of the most obvious qualities, thereby treating them as isolated from and unconnected with other groups; that virtue resides in the persistent attempt to obtain well-defined connections, expressed mathematically wherever possible, between qualities measured or measurable fundamentally and those incapable of such measurement.

Unfortunately, the correlation of qualities has been often interpreted as the production of secondary qualities by the primary ones: the latter alone have been endowed with causal efficacy, the former degraded as otiose and epiphenomenal. Thus, a distinction which in *operation* is a practical and logical one has been converted into a distinction between grades of reality, on the ground that causes are more real than their supposed effects. Mathematical physics has been understood to make nonsense of the poet's cry—"Natur hat weder Kern noch Schale."—Nonetheless, all that the equations of physics and the method of establishing them do imply is that nonadditive qualities are inextricably interwoven with additive ones. This dependence is existentially mutual; from the point of view of the *logic* of measurement, it is assymetrical. It is because of this dependence, expressible in the form of numerical laws, that numbers may be correlated unambiguously with nonadditive qualities; it is because of such laws for density that, of the four sets of numbers entertained on a previous page, only the last set is adopted.

How nonadditive qualities may be unambiguously denoted will be clear from an example. In the case of density it is discovered that the weight of an object is intimately connected with its volume, a connection exhibited in the uniform association of these characters. Weight and volume are measurable fundamentally, so that, independently of the numerical relations which affirm their uniform association, numbers can be assigned to them. There is no special theoretical difficulty, although there may be many practical ones, in determining the value of the constant which expresses this uniform association and which mathematically is the ratio of the numerical value of the mass to the numerical value of the volume. The *form* which the mathematical equation will take is, of course, dictated only partly by the measurements on the properties studied in any *one* instance: more general considerations will come into play arising from the desire to make the many numerical equations themselves interconnected and parts of a unified doctrine.

In most cases, the order of the constants or ratios which are determined for several objects can be shown to be the same order as the serial order of some nonadditive quality which the objects possess in addition to those already measured fundamentally. So the order of the ratios of mass to volume is identically the order of the density of liquids as defined by their floating capacities relative to one another. Consequently, the same set of numbers may be used to denote both the uniform association of mass and volume, and the relative buoyancies. It goes without saying that the numbers thus obtained for qualities from numerical equations are not always amenable to a physical interpretation of addition. When one body is said to be thirteen times as heavy as another, a different meaning must be given to such a statement from the meaning of the statement that mercury is thirteen times as dense as water; only in terms of the numerical law connecting mass and volume has the latter proposition significance.

All equations which define a constant, to be identified perhaps with some property capable of definition independently of the equation, require therefore that the other terms of the equation be measurable without reference to the defining of the constant. In the sense that the constants are defined, not *all* magnitudes can be defined without leading to a circle; there must be an ultimate reference to magnitudes obtained by fundamental measurement. The equation $pv = RT$ has meaning only if $p, v, T,$ have a meaning outside of this equation; only then may R be determined experimentally. If $p, v, T,$ are not measurable fundamentally there must be a chain of equations connecting them with magnitudes which are. It is a testimony to the endless *complexity* of nature, not to her poverty of qualities, that only six independent fundamentally measured magnitudes are required for the investigations of physics. "There are only a few independent magnitudes in physics. But between these and the countless number of independent magnitudes appearing in human life, there is no sharp separation." Strength of wind would be a genuine aspect of some events even if strength of wind were completely definable, which it is not yet, in terms of the velocity and force of air particles.

Moreover, the power of all symbols, and especially of numerical symbols, to refer simultaneously to several contexts must be recognized if mystification is to be avoided. The unification and identification in statement that follows from the introduction of mathematical methods is due to the pervasiveness of certain formal characters in situations qualitatively different, which are as a consequence capable of a unified treatment. In the interpretation of equations as the literal identification of different qualitative continua, and as the attribution of intrinsic, nonrelational common characters to diverse subject matter, lies the force of most of the petulant criticism of science. Let us, for example, study the equilibrium conditions of a beam balance. If x, y, z represent certain bodies A, B, C, then the equation $x + y = z$ will mean that A and B on the same pan will balance C on the other, and it will also mean that the numerical measure of the weight of C is equal to the sum of the measures of A and B. The perhaps less relevant case of a chemical equation like $2H_2 + O_2 = 2H_2O$ represents theoretical conceptions such as atom, and valence, physical operations such as passing a spark through a mixture of two gases, and numerical relations between the measures of weights and volumes.

The confusions which arise from the failure to note how complex the functions of symbols may be is illustrated in a recent criticism of the achievements of science. The principle of the lever, as expressed in the form of a proportion, is the climax of an extended critique, but this special discussion is reproduced in full.

"It will be best to point out that it is the result of two apparently unjustified leaps of imagination. . . . A double leap it is, and the reader can supply whatever theory of revelation, reincarnation, or conventional fiction he prefers, to account for it.

"To say that $W_1 : W_2 :: D_2 : D_1$, is by itself ambiguous. Perhaps it only means that certain numbers stand to each other this way: $2 : 4 :: 3 : 6$. In that case it is merely a happy discovery in arithmetic. But W stands for weight and D stands for distance. It may therefore mean that the relation between two weights is the same as the relation between two distances. But this is not true for many relations; for instance 'heavier than' is a relation between two weights, but not between two distances. The only relation that works is a hybrid combination of these two.

"The combination is evidently derived from two previous proportions, namely: $W_1 : W_2 :: 2 : 4$ and $D_2 : D_1 :: 3 : 6$. Then because we already know in arithmetic that $2 : 4 : 3 : 6$ we can finally see how it is that $W_1 : W_2 :: D_2 : D_1$. But why weights and distances are like numbers, to use the simile, has still to be explained. The only answer that I know is that some poet of the commonplace was playing with words, and somebody took him literally."

It cannot be pretended that the actual history of the principle of the lever is being reported. As a deduction or validation of an important numerical law, however, it merits a conspicuous place in some future Budget of Paradoxes. The difficulties which are raised seem to arise partly from a dogma that numbers cannot be the numbers of anything without losing caste, and partly from the failure to realize that in the statement of the law at least two relations are symbolized. In the first place, the relation $W_1 : W_2 : : 2 : 4$ can be intelligibly interpreted as meaning that four weights each equal to W_1 are equal to two weights each equal to W_2, where "equal" is defined in some unambiguous way. Secondly, it must be observed that the *symbol* : : stands for both a *numerical* relation between numbers assigned in the way suggested and a *physical* relation into which the lever enters in a very specific way. The proportion as it stands expresses *two* sets of relations, and we can use the same *symbol* to represent both because the relations have certain formal properties which are *identical*. Numbers are not like weights, indeed, but numbers are, and numerals express, definite properties of weights. It is a great sin to *compare* the statement of a relation with the relation itself. If discourse cannot be literally compared with what it is about, is it not wisdom to recognize that discourse expresses it? The equation, in every case, is a symbolic statement, pointing to several aspects of the subject matter. When once the plural referents of the symbols are made explicit, and when numbers are not regarded either as common qualities or as chaste platonic beings, but rather as the expression of relations or operations between qualities, belief in the power and validity of mathematical physics need not be superstition.

As there are critics who find the application of numbers to additive properties a puzzle, so there are other critics who challenge the validity of the application of numbers to nonadditive ones. It is never the nonadditive qualities that are measured, it is said; velocity has a unique existential quale as a velocity, and to express it as the ratio of space and time is to measure space and to measure time, but it is not to measure velocity. A twofold reply may be made.

1. There are many qualities which, as a matter of practice, are measured as derived magnitudes by means of numerical equations, but which can be measured fundamentally. Bridgeman has shown how this may be done for velocity. Areas, volumes, or electric charges, are in the same position: they are usually measured as derived magnitudes, but are capable of fundamental evaluation. Nevertheless,

even when they enter numerical equations derivatively and measured therefore in their relation to other characters, *they* are measured.

2. It is true that most qualities, being incapable of addition, must be measured in terms of their "surrogates" in numerical equations. If the term "measurement" is restricted only to such qualities which are fundamentally measurable, it must be acknowledged that density and acceleration are incapable of measurement. But by calling the process of assigning numerical values to density some other name, the *significance* of what is done is not destroyed. What is beyond much doubt, is that the measure numbers of those characters incapable of addition, or even incapable of sensuous intuition such as magnetism, are not mere numerals or formulae for nominal combinations of additive characters; they represent rather certain coordinated qualities or certain relational properties of the systems studied. If it is the expansion of mercury that we actually measure in the more restricted sense, the measurement is performed because there is a uniform association between this expansion and qualitative temperature changes.

Several modes of surrogative measurement may be obtainable for the same property. So we may define the temperatures of black bodies by using the well known Stefan-Boltzmann law of energy radiation. Two temperatures will then be equal if the energy of radiation which the surfaces of black bodies send out in a given time into a given space is the same for the two temperatures; two temperature-differences will be equal if the differences of energies radiated are the same. Except for the zero point and unity, the temperature scale is defined. Comparison of this scale with the gas thermometer scale would show that the scales cannot be made directly congruent. However, by a proper choice of the zero point, the numbers of the gas thermometer are found proportional to the fourth roots of the numbers of the energy scale; if the fourth roots of the energy scale are used to define the temperature of the black body, the two scales can be used interchangeably. Similarly, velocity may be measured not in terms of space and time, but in terms of the resistance which a given body meets when moving through a specified medium.

It is by discovering the recurrence of certain constants in different numerical laws that the ideal of a unified science is progressively realized.

8

ON THE THEORY OF SCALES OF MEASUREMENT

S. S. Stevens ·

For seven years a committee of the British Association for the Advancement of Science debated the problem of measurement. Appointed in 1932 to represent Section A (Mathematical and Physical Sciences) and Section J (Psychology), the committee was instructed to consider and report upon the possibility of "quantitative estimates of sensory events"— meaning simply: Is it possible to measure human sensation? Deliberation led only to disagreement, mainly about what is meant by the term measurement. An interim report in 1938 found one member complaining that his colleagues "came out by that same door as they went in," and in order to have another try at agreement, the committee begged to be continued for another year.

For its final report (1940) the committee chose a common bone for its contentions, directing its arguments at a concrete example of a sensory scale. This was the Sone scale of loudness (S. S. Stevens and H. Davis. *Hearing.* New York: Wiley, 1938), which purports to measure the subjective magnitude of an auditory sensation against a scale having the formal properties of other basic scales, such as those used to measure length and weight. Again the nine-

· [This selection is reprinted from *Science*, Vol. 103, No. 2684, 1946. Reprinted by permission of S. S. Stevens and the editors of *Science*.]

teen members of the committee came out by the routes they entered, and their views ranged widely between two extremes. One member submitted "that any law purporting to express a quantitative relation between sensation intensity and stimulus intensity is not merely false but is in fact meaningless unless and until a meaning can be given to the concept of addition as applied to sensation" (Final Report, p. 245).

It is plain from this and from other statements by the committee that the real issue is the meaning of measurement. This, to be sure, is a semantic issue, but one susceptible of orderly discussion. Perhaps agreement can better be achieved if we recognize that measurement exists in a variety of forms and that scales of measurement fall into certain definite classes. These classes are determined both by the empirical operations invoked in the process of "measuring" and by the formal (mathematical) properties of the scales. Furthermore—and this is of great concern to several of the sciences—the statistical manipulations that can legitimately be applied to empirical data depend upon the type of scale against which the data are ordered.

A CLASSIFICATION OF SCALES OF MEASUREMENT

Paraphrasing N. R. Campbell (Final Report, p. 340), we may say that measurement, in the broadest sense, is defined as the assignment of numerals to objects or events according to rules. The fact that numerals can be assigned under different rules leads to different kinds of scales and different kinds of measurement. The problem then becomes that of making explicit (a) the various rules for the assignment of numerals, (b) the mathematical properties (or group structure) of the resulting scales, and (c) the statistical operations applicable to measurements made with each type of scale.

Scales are possible in the first place only because there is a certain isomorphism between what we can do with the aspects of objects and the properties of the numeral series. In dealing with the aspects of objects we invoke empirical operations for determining equality (classifying), for rank-ordering, and for determining when differences and when ratios between the aspects of objects are equal. The conventional series of numerals yields to analogous operations: We can identify the members of a numeral series and classify them. We know their order as given by convention. We can determine equal differences, as $8 - 6 = 4 - 2$, and equal ratios, as $8/4 = 6/3$. The isomorphism between these properties of the numeral series and certain empirical operations which we perform with objects permits the use of the series as a *model* to represent aspects of the empirical world.

The type of scale achieved depends upon the character of the basic empirical operations performed. These operations are limited ordinarily by the nature of the thing being scaled and by our choice of procedures, but, once selected, the operations determine that there will eventuate one or another of the scales listed in Table 1.

TABLE 1

Scale	Basic Empirical Operations	Mathematical Group Structure	Permissible Statistics (invariantive)
NOMINAL	Determination of equality	*Permutation group* $x' = f(x)$ $f(x)$ means any one-to-one substitution	Number of cases Mode Contingency correlation
ORDINAL	Determination of greater or less	*Isotonic group* $x' = f(x)$ $f(x)$ means any monotonic increasing function	Median Percentiles
INTERVAL	Determination of equality of intervals or differences	*General linear group* $x' = ax + b$	Mean Standard deviation Rank-order correlation Product-moment correlation
RATIO	Determination of equality of ratios	*Similarity group* $x' = ax$	Coefficient of variation

The decision to discard the scale names commonly encountered in writings on measurement is based on the ambiguity of such terms as "intensive" and "extensive." Both ordinal and interval scales have at times been called intensive, and both interval and ratio scales have sometimes been labeled extensive.

It will be noted that the column listing the basic operations needed to create each type of scale is cumulative: to an operation listed opposite a particular scale must be added all those operations preceding it. Thus, an interval scale can be erected only provided we have an operation for determining equality of intervals, for determining greater or less, and for determining equality (not greater and not less). To these operations must be added a method for ascertaining equality of ratios if a ratio scale is to be achieved.

In the column which records the group structure of each scale are listed the mathematical transformations which leave the scale-form invariant. Thus, any numeral, x, on a scale can be replaced by another numeral, x', where x' is the function of x listed in this column. Each mathematical group in the column is contained in the group immediately above it.

The last column presents examples of the type of statistical operations appropriate to each scale. This column is cumulative in that *all* statistics listed are admissible for data scaled against a ratio scale. The criterion for the appropriateness of a statistic is *invariance* under the transformations in Column 3. Thus, the case that stands at the median (midpoint) of a distribution maintains its position under all transformations which preserve order (isotonic group), but an item located at the mean remains at the mean only under transformations as restricted as those of the linear group. The ratio expressed by the coefficient of variation remains invariant only under the similarity transformation (multiplication by a constant). (The rank-order correlation coefficient is usually deemed appropriate to an ordinal scale, but actually this statistic assumes equal intervals between successive ranks and therefore calls for an interval scale.)

Let us now consider each scale in turn.

NOMINAL SCALE

The *nominal scale* represents the most unrestricted assignment of numerals. The numerals are used only as labels or type numbers, and words or letters would serve as well. Two types of nominal assignments are sometimes distinguished, as illustrated (a) by the "numbering" of football players for the identification of the individuals, and (b) by the "numbering" of types or classes, where each member of a class is assigned the same numeral. Actually, the first is a special case of the second, for when we label our football players we are dealing with unit classes of one member each. Since the purpose is just as well served when any two designating numerals are interchanged, this scale form remains invariant under the general substitution or permutation group (sometimes called the symmetric group of transformations). The only statistic relevant to nominal scales of Type A is the number of cases, e.g., the number of players assigned numerals. But once classes containing several individuals have been formed (Type B), we can determine the most numerous class (the mode), and under certain conditions we can test, by the contingency methods, hypotheses regarding the distribution of cases among the classes.

The nominal scale is a primitive form, and quite naturally there are many who will urge that it is absurd to attribute to this process of assigning numerals the dignity implied by the term measurement. Certainly there can be no quarrel with this objection, for the naming of things is an arbitrary business. However we christen it, the use of numerals as names for classes is an example of the "assignment of numerals according to rule." The rule is: Do not assign the same numeral to different classes or different numerals to the same class. Beyond that, anything goes with the nominal scale.

ORDINAL SCALE

The *ordinal scale* arises from the operation of rank-ordering. Since any "order-preserving" transformation will leave the scale form invariant, this scale has the structure of what may be called the isotonic or order-preserving group. A classic example of an ordinal scale is the scale of hardness of minerals. Other instances are found among scales of intelligence, personality traits, grade or quality of leather, etc.

As a matter of fact, most of the scales used widely and effectively by psychologists are ordinal scales. In the strictest propriety the ordinary statistics involving means and standard deviations ought not to be used with these scales, for these statistics imply a knowledge of something more than the relative rank-order of data. On the other hand, for this "illegal" statisticizing there can be invoked a kind of pragmatic sanction: In numerous instances it leads to fruitful results. While the outlawing of this procedure would probably serve no good purpose, it is proper to point out that means and standard deviations computed on an ordinal scale are in error to the extent that the successive intervals on the scale are unequal in size. When only the rank-order of data is known, we should proceed cautiously with our statistics, and especially with the conclusions we draw from them.

Even in applying those statistics that are normally appropriate for ordinal scales, we sometimes find rigor compromised. Thus, although it is indicated in Table 1 that percentile measures may be applied to rank-ordered data, it should be pointed out that the customary procedure of assigning a value to a percentile by interpolating linearly within a class interval is, in all strictness, wholly out of bounds. Likewise, it is not strictly proper to determine the mid-point of a class interval by linear interpolation, because the linearity of an ordinal scale is precisely the property which is open to question.

INTERVAL SCALE

With the *interval scale* we come to a form that is "quantitative" in the ordinary sense of the word. Almost all the usual statistical measures are applicable here, unless they are the kinds that imply a knowledge of a "true" zero point. The zero point on an interval scale is a matter of convention or convenience, as is shown by the fact that the scale form remains invariant when a constant is added.

This point is illustrated by our two scales of temperature, Centigrade and Fahrenheit. Equal intervals of temperature are scaled off by noting equal volumes of expansion; an arbitrary zero is agreed upon for each scale; and a numerical value on one of the scales is transformed into a value on the other by means of an equation of the form $x' = ax + b$. Our scales of time offer a similar example. Dates on one calendar are transformed to those on another by way of this same equation. On these scales, of course, it is meaningless to say that one value is twice or some other proportion greater than another.

Periods of time, however, can be measured on ratio scales and one period may be correctly defined as double another. The same is probably true of temperature measured on the so-called Absolute Scale.

Most psychological measurement aspires to create interval scales, and it sometimes succeeds. The problem usually is to devise operations for equalizing the units of the scales— a problem not always easy of solution but one for which there are several possible modes of attack. Only occasionally is there concern for the location of a "true" zero point, because the human attributes measured by psychologists usually exist in a positive degree that is large compared with the range of its variation. In this respect these attributes are analogous to temperature as it is encountered in everyday life. Intelligence, for example, is usefully assessed on ordinal scales which try to approximate interval scales, and it is not necessary to define what zero intelligence would mean.

RATIO SCALE

Ratio scales are those most commonly encountered in physics and are possible only when there exist operations for determining all four relations: equality, rank-order, equality of intervals, and equality of ratios. Once such a scale is erected, its numerical values can be transformed (as from inches to feet) only by multiplying each value by a constant. An absolute zero is always implied, even though the zero value on some scales (e.g., Absolute Temperature) may never be produced. All types of statistical measures are applicable to ratio scales, and only with these scales may we properly indulge in logarithmic transformations such as are involved in the use of decibels.

Foremost among the ratio scales is the scale of number itself—cardinal number—the scale we use when we count such things as eggs, pennies, and apples. This scale of the numerosity of aggregates is so basic and so common that it is ordinarily not even mentioned in discussions of measurement.

It is conventional in physics to distinguish between two types of ratio scales: *fundamental* and *derived*. Fundamental scales are represented by length, weight, and electrical resistance, whereas derived scales are represented by density, force, and elasticity.

These latter are *derived* magnitudes in the sense that they are mathematical functions of certain fundamental magnitudes. They are actually more numerous in physics than are the fundamental magnitudes, which are commonly held to be basic because they satisfy the criterion of *additivity*. Weights, lengths, and resistances can be added in the physical sense, but this important empirical fact is generally accorded more prominence in the theory of measurement than it deserves. The so-called fundamental scales are important instances of ratio scales, but they are only instances. As a matter of fact, it can be demonstrated that the fundamental scales could be set up even if the physical operation of addition were ruled out as impossible of performance. Given three balances, for example, each having the proper construction, a set of standard weights could be manufactured without it ever being necessary to place two weights in the same scale pan at the same time. The procedure is too long to describe in these pages, but its feasibility is mentioned here simply to suggest that physical addition, even though it is sometimes possible, is not necessarily the basis of all measurement. Too much measuring goes on where resort can never be had to the process of laying things end-to-end or of piling them up in a heap.

Ratio scales of psychological magnitudes are rare but not entirely unknown. The Sone scale discussed by the British committee is an example founded on a deliberate attempt to have human observers judge the loudness ratios of pairs of tones. The judgment of equal intervals had long been established as a legitimate method, and with the work on sensory ratios, started independently in several laboratories, the final step was taken to assign numerals to sensations of loudness in such a way that relations among the sensations are reflected by the ordinary arithmetical relations in the numeral series. As in all measurement, there are limits imposed by error and variability, but within these limits the Sone scale ought properly to be classed as a ratio scale.

To the British committee, then, we may venture to suggest by way of conclusion that the most liberal and useful definition of measurement is, as one of its members advised, "the assignment of numerals to things so as to represent facts and conventions about them." The problem as to what is and is not measurement then reduces to the simple question: What are the rules, if any, under which numerals are assigned? If we can point to a consistent set of rules, we are obviously concerned with measurement of some sort, and we can then proceed to the more interesting question as to the kind of measurement it is. In most cases a formulation of the rules of assignment discloses directly the kind of scale involved. If there remains any ambiguity, we may seek the final and definitive answer in the mathematical group-structure of the scale form: In what ways can we transform its values and still have it serve all the functions previously fulfilled? We know that the values of all scales can be multiplied by a constant, which changes the size of the unit. If, in addition, a constant can be added (or a new zero point chosen), it is proof positive that we are not concerned with a ratio scale. Then, if the purpose of the scale is still served when its values are squared or cubed, it is not even an interval scale. And finally, if any two values may be interchanged at will, the ordinal scale is ruled out and the nominal scale is the sole remaining possibility.

This proposed solution to the semantic problem is not meant to imply that all scales belonging to the same mathematical group are equally precise or accurate or useful or "fundamental." Measurement is never better than the empirical operations by which it is carried out, and operations range from bad to good. Any particular scale, sensory or physical, may be objected to on the grounds of bias, low precision, restricted generality, and other factors, but the objector should remember that these are relative and practical matters and that no scale used by mortals is perfectly free of their taint.

9

ELEMENTARY AND ABSTRACT TERMS:
Rudolf Carnap ·

We find among the concepts of physics—and likewise among those of the whole of empirical science—differences of abstractness. Some are more elementary than others, in the sense that we can apply them in concrete cases on the basis of observations in a more direct way than others. The others are more abstract; in order to find out whether they hold in a certain case, we have to carry out a more complex procedure, which, however, also finally rests on observations. Between quite elementary concepts and those of high abstraction there are many intermediate levels. We shall not try to give an exact definition for "degree of abstractness"; what is meant will become sufficiently clear by the following series of sets of concepts, proceeding from elementary to abstract concepts: bright, dark, red, blue, warm, cold, sour, sweet, hard, soft (all concepts of this first set are meant as properties of things, not as sense-data); coincidence; length; length of time; mass, velocity, acceleration, density, pressure; temperature, quantity of heat; electric charge, electric current, electric field; electric potential, electric resistance, coefficient of induction, frequency of oscillation; wave function.

· [This selection consists of Section 24 and 25 of Carnap's *Foundations of Logic and Mathematics*. This work is part of *The Encyclopedia of Unified Science*, Vol. III (Chicago: University of Chicago Press, 1937). Reprinted by permission of the University of Chicago Press.]

Suppose that we intend to construct an interpreted system of physics—or of the whole of science. We shall first lay down a calculus.[1] Then we have to state semantical rules of the kind SD for the specific signs, i.e., for the physical terms. (The SL-rules are presupposed as giving the customary interpretation of the logico-mathematical basis calculus.) Since the physical terms form a system, i.e., are connected with one another, obviously we need not state a semantical rule for each of them. For which terms, then, must we give rules, for the elementary or for the abstract ones? We can, of course, state a rule for any term, no matter what its degree of abstractness, in a form like this: "the term 'te' designates temperature," provided the metalanguage used contains a corresponding expression (here the word "temperature") to specify the designatum of the term in question. But suppose we have in mind the following purpose for our syntactical and semantical description of the system of physics: the description of the system shall teach a layman to understand it, i.e., to enable him to

[1] [By a "calculus," Carnap means "a system of formal rules which determine certain formal properties and relations of sentences, especially for the purpose of formal deduction." So construed, a calculus will furnish rules for constructing sentences (formation rules) and for deriving further sentences from some set of sentences taken as "primitive" (transformation rules). The sentences taken as primitive are analogous to the axioms in a deductive system, and indeed any deductive system will exhibit the features of a calculus if the required sorts of rules are made explicit, and the system is itself regarded purely from the point of view of the logical relations amongst its sentences. A calculus has to do with the syntactical features of such a system. Most deductive systems, historically, were considered as referring to some subject-matter or other: but it is possible to see these as consisting of a calculus *together with* a set of rules which relate the calculus to that subject-matter. These latter rules are, in Carnap's terms, *semantical* rules; and a calculus with a set of semantical rules is a semantical system, in contrast to a syntactical system which is *just* the calculus. A sentence, considered as part of a syntactical system, is simply a string of uninterpreted signs: it becomes a true (or false) proposition when meanings are assigned to its terms via semantic rules. Signs are of two sorts: logical signs and nonlogical signs. Accordingly, there are two sorts of semantic rules: rules of "the kind SD" which assign designata to the nonlogical terms of a calculus, i.e., state what things and what properties of things the names and predicates of the calculus are to designate; and rules of "the kind SL" which interpret the logical signs of the calculus.]

apply it to his observations in order to arrive at explanations and predictions. A layman is meant as one who does not know physics but has normal senses and understands a language in which observable properties of things can be described (e.g., a suitable part of everyday nonscientific English). A rule like "the sign '*P*' designates the property of being blue" will do for the purpose indicated; but a rule like "the sign '*Q*' designates the property of being electrically charged" will not do. In order to fulfill the purpose, we have to give semantical rules for elementary terms only, connecting them with observable properties of things. For our further discussion we suppose the system to consist of rules of this kind, as indicated in the following diagram.

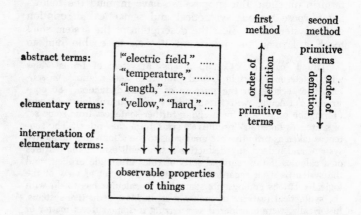

Now let us go back to the construction of the calculus. We have first to decide at which end of the series of terms to start the construction. Should we take elementary terms as primitive signs, or abstract terms? Our decision to lay down the semantical rules for the elementary terms does not decide this question. Either procedure is still possible and seems to have some reasons in its favor, depending on the point of view taken. The *first method* consists in taking elementary terms as primitive and then introducing on their basis further terms step by step, up to those of highest abstraction. In carrying out this procedure, we find that the introduction of further terms cannot always take the form of explicit definitions; conditional definitions must also be used (so-called reduction sentences).[2] They describe a method of testing for a more abstract term, i.e., a procedure for finding out whether the term is applicable in particular cases, by referring to less abstract terms. The first method has the advantage of exhibiting clearly the connection between the system and observation and of making it easier to examine whether and how a given term is empirically founded. However, when we shift our attention from the terms of the system and the methods of empirical confirmation to the laws, i.e., the universal theorems, of the system, we get a different perspective. Would it be possible to formulate all laws of physics in elementary terms, admitting more abstract terms only as abbreviations? If so, we would have that ideal of a science in sensationalistic form which Goethe in his polemic against Newton, as well as some positivists, seems to have had in mind. But it turns out—this is an empirical fact, not a logical necessity —that it is not possible to arrive in this way at a powerful and efficacious system of laws. To be sure, historically, science started with laws formulated in terms of a low level of abstractness. But for any law of this kind, one nearly always later found some exceptions and thus had to confine it to a narrower realm of validity. The higher the physicists went in the scale of terms, the better did they succeed in formulating laws applying to a wide range of phenomena. Hence we understand that they are inclined to choose the *second method*. This method begins at the top of the system, so to speak, and then goes down to lower and lower levels. It consists in taking a few abstract terms as primitive signs and a few fundamental laws of great generality as axioms. Then further terms, less and less abstract, and finally elementary ones, are to be introduced by definitions; and here, so it seems at present, explicit definitions will do. More special laws, containing less abstract terms, are to be proved on the basis of the axioms. At least, this is the direction in which physicists have been striving with remarkable success, especially in the past few decades. But at the present time, the method cannot yet be carried through in the pure form indicated. For many less abstract

[2] [These are discussed in Hempel's paper, reprinted in this volume, on concept formation in empirical science.]

terms no definition on the basis of abstract terms alone is as yet known; hence those terms must also be taken as primitive. And many more special laws, especially in biological fields, cannot yet be proved on the basis of laws in abstract terms only; hence those laws must also be taken as axioms.

Now let us examine the result of the interpretation if the first or the second method for the construction of the calculus is chosen. In both cases the semantical rules concern the elementary signs. In the first method these signs are taken as primitive. Hence, the semantical rules give a complete interpretation for these signs and those explicitly defined on their basis. There are, however, many signs, especially on the higher levels of abstraction, which can be introduced not by an explicit definition but only by a conditional one. The interpretation which the rules give for these signs is in a certain sense incomplete. This is due not to a defect in the semantical rules but to the method by which these signs are introduced; and this method is not arbitrary but corresponds to the way in which we really obtain knowledge about physical states by our observations.

If, on the other hand, abstract terms are taken as primitive—according to the second method, the one used in scientific physics—then the semantical rules have no direct relation to the primitive terms of the system but refer to terms introduced by long chains of definitions. The calculus is first constructed floating in the air, so to speak; the construction begins at the top and then adds lower and lower levels. Finally, by the semantical rules, the lowest level is anchored at the solid ground of the observable facts. The laws, whether general or special, are not directly interpreted, but only the singular sentences. For the more abstract terms, the rules determine only an *indirect interpretation,* which is—here as well as in the first method—incomplete in a certain sense. Suppose "B" is defined on the basis of "A"; then, if "A" is directly interpreted, "B" is, although indirectly, also interpreted completely; if, however, "B" is directly interpreted, "A" is not necessarily also interpreted completely (but only if "A" is also definable by "B").

To give an example, let us imagine a calculus of physics constructed, according to the second method, on the basis of primitive signs like "electromagnetic field," "gravitational field," "electron," "proton," etc. The system of definitions will then lead to elementary terms, e.g., to "Fe," defined as a class of regions in which the configuration of particles fulfills certain conditions, and "Na-yellow" as a class of space-time regions in which the temporal distribution of the electromagnetic field fulfills certain conditions. Then semantical rules are laid down stating that "Fe" designates iron and "Na-yellow" designates a specified yellow color. (If "iron" is not accepted as sufficiently elementary, the rules can be stated for more elementary terms.) In this way the connection between the calculus and the realm of nature, to which it is to be applied, is made for terms of the calculus which are far remote from the primitive terms.

Let us examine, on the basis of these discussions, the example of a derivation D_2.[3] The premises and the conclusion of D_2 are singular sentences, but most of the other sentences are not. Hence the premises and the conclusion of this as of all other derivations of the same type can be directly interpreted, understood, and confronted with the results of observations. More of an interpretation is not necessary for a practical application of a derivation. If, in confronting the interpreted premises with our observations, we find them confirmed as true, then we accept the conclusion as a prediction and we may base a decision upon it. The sentences occurring in the derivation between premises and conclusion are also interpreted, at least indirectly. But we need not make their interpretation explicit in order to be able to construct the derivation and to apply it. All that is necessary for its construction are the formal rules of the calculus. This is the advantage of the method of formalization, i.e., of the separation of the calculus as a formal system from the interpretation. If some persons want to come to an agreement about the formal correctness of a given derivation, they may leave aside all differences of opinion on material questions of interpretation. They simply have to examine whether or not the given series of formulas fulfills the formal rules of the calculus. Here again, the function of calculi in empirical science becomes clear as instruments for transforming the expression of what we know or assume.

Against the view that for the application of a physical calculus we need an interpretation only for singular sentences, the following objection will perhaps be raised. Be-

[3] [D_2 is a derivation carried out in Section 23 of Carnap's *Foundations of Logic and Mathematics*. We feel that the discussion is clear without having to reproduce the details of D_2.]

fore we accept a derivation and believe its conclusion we must have accepted the physical calculus which furnishes the derivation; and how can we decide whether or not to accept a physical calculus for application without interpreting and understanding its axioms? To be sure, in order to pass judgment about the applicability of a given physical calculus we have to confront it in some way or other with observation, and for this purpose an interpretation is necessary. But we need no explicit interpretation of the axioms, nor even of any theorems. The empirical examination of a physical theory given in the form of a calculus with rules of interpretation is not made by interpreting and understanding the axioms and then considering whether they are true on the basis of our factual knowledge. Rather, the examination is carried out by the same procedure as that explained before for obtaining a prediction. We construct derivations in the calculus with premises which are singular sentences describing the results of our observations, and with singular sentences which we can test by observations as conclusions. The physical theory is indirectly confirmed to a higher and higher degree if more and more of these predictions are confirmed and none of them is disconfirmed by observations. Only singular sentences with elementary terms can be directly tested; therefore, we need an explicit interpretation only for these sentences.

"UNDERSTANDING" IN PHYSICS

The development of physics in recent centuries, and especially in the past few decades, has more and more led to that method in the construction, testing, and application of physical theories which we call *formalization,* i.e., the construction of a calculus supplemented by an interpretation. It was the progress of knowledge and the particular structure of the subject matter that suggested and made practically possible this increasing formalization. In consequence it became more and more possible to forego an "intuitive understanding" of the abstract terms and axioms and theorems formulated with their help. The possibility and even necessity of abandoning the search for an understanding of that kind was not realized for a long time. When abstract, nonintuitive formulas, as, e.g., Maxwell's equations of electromagnetism, were proposed as new axioms, physicists endeavored to make them "intuitive" by constructing a "model," i.e., a way of representing electromagnetic microprocesses by an analogy to known macroprocesses, e.g., movements of visible things. Many attempts have been made in this direction, but without satisfactory results. It is important to realize that the discovery of a model has no more than an aesthetic or didactic or at best a heuristic value, but is not at all essential for a successful application of the physical theory. The demand for an intuitive understanding of the axioms was less and less fulfilled when the development led to the general theory of relativity and then to quantum mechanics, involving the wave function. Many people, including physicists, have a feeling of regret and disappointment about this. Some, especially philosophers, go so far as even to contend that these modern theories, since they are not intuitively understandable, are not at all theories about nature but "mere formalistic constructions," "mere calculi." But this is a fundamental misunderstanding of the function of a physical theory. It is true that a theory must not be a "mere calculus," but possess an interpretation, on the basis of which it can be applied to facts of nature. But it is sufficient, as we have seen, to make this interpretation explicit for elementary terms; the interpretation of the other terms is then indirectly determined by the formulas of the calculus, either definitions or laws, connecting them with the elementary terms. If we demand from the modern physicist an answer to the question what he means by the symbol "Ψ" of his calculus, and are astonished that he cannot give an answer, we ought to realize that the situation was already the same in classical physics. There the physicist could not tell us what he meant by the symbol "E" in Maxwell's equations. Perhaps, in order not to refuse an answer, he would tell us that "E" designates the electric field vector. To be sure, this statement has the form of a semantical rule, but it would not help us a bit to understand the theory. It simply refers from a symbol in a symbolic calculus to a corresponding word expression in a calculus of words. We are right in demanding an interpretation for "E," but that will be given indirectly by semantical rules referring to elementary signs together with the formulas connecting them with "E." This interpretation enables us to use the laws containing "E" for the derivation of predictions. Thus we understand "E," if "understanding" of an expression, a sentence, or a theory means capability of its use for the description of known facts or the prediction of new facts. An "intuitive understanding" or a direct translation of "E" into terms referring to observable properties is neither necessary nor possible. The situation of the modern physicist is not essentially different. He knows how to use the symbol "Ψ" in the calculus in order to derive predictions which we can test by observations. (If they have the form of probability statements, they are tested by statistical results of observations.) Thus the physicist, although he cannot give us a translation into everyday language, understands the symbol "Ψ" and the laws of quantum mechanics. He possesses that kind of understanding which alone is essential in the field of knowledge and science.

10

THEORETICAL TERMS AND
A MODEST EMPIRICISM:
Israel Scheffler •

THE PROBLEM OF THEORETICAL OR TRANSCENDENTAL
TERMS

Theoretical terms, unlike dispositional predicates, do not
generally purport to apply to entities within the range of
application of our clearly observational terms. They are typically nonobservational and beyond the reach even of reduction sentences. It is generally claimed that they are required not because of their usefulness in expressing available observational evidence, but rather because, by their
introduction in the context of certain developed theories,
comprehensive relationships become expressible in desirable
ways on the observable level.

• [This selection is excerpted from Israel Scheffler's "Prospects of a
Modest Empiricism," *The Review of Metaphysics*, Vol. X, Nos. 3–4,
1957. Scheffler's "modest empiricism" comes to this. A language
E—an empiricist language—is supposed which contains, in addition
to logical terms, only a finite set of observation terms. It was at
one time thought that translatability into *E* constitutes a criterion
of empirical meaningfulness for all sentences. But earlier in his
article Scheffler shows difficulties in such a program, and this leads
to his revised empiricism. According to it, we may say that every
sentence translatable into *E* is indeed empirically meaningful.
But it does not follow that every sentence *not* translatable into *E* is
therefore meaningless. So translatability into *E* is a sufficient, but

Such theories seem to commit us to a new range of entities as values of variables to which their transcendental terms may be attached in existentially quantified statements, e.g., "There is an electron," "Something is a positron." For the entities here required are not such as are qualifiable by our hitherto accepted observational predicates. We have, for example, no clearly true sentence such as "x is an electron and x is red," or "x is an electron and x is non-red," for any value of "x." Historically, this is perhaps related to the distinction between primary and secondary qualities, a distinction which, in some form, it is dangerous to overlook in the interpretation of modern scientific theories. Thus, it is by now well known that confusion results both from the popularization of advanced theories through pictorial description in the common language of observation, and from the ascription of exclusive reality to the entities presupposed by such of these theories as we deem true. But to maintain the relevant distinction among ranges seems clearly to mean the abandonment of even our modest, revised empiricism. For the predicates appropriate to one of these ranges are nonobservational, and to admit the necessity of theories couched in such terms in order for an empiricist language E to be adequate is to admit that no adequate, purely observational E exists which is even a sufficient condition of cognitive significance. (Thus those who insist on some such distinction by saying that "theoretical entities" have only such properties as are attributed to them by their respective theoretical contexts are, if they let the matter rest here, abandoning even our modest version of empiricism.) Furthermore, aside from empiricism, the perpetuation of a distinction among ranges seems to have generally puzzling aspects, which have troubled philosophers of science recurrently: (1) If adequacy requires that clearly nonobservational terms be eligible for admission into the language of science, then, since these include terms ordinarily deemed meaningless, *what* are we believing in committing ourselves to science? (2) If science explains by

not a necessary, condition for empirical meaningfulness. And the meaningfulness of sentences not translatable into E must be determined on independent grounds. In the present selection the author considers a number of attempts at assessing the meaningfulness of sentences embodying "theoretical" terms. Reprinted by permission of Israel Scheffler and the editor of *The Review of Metaphysics*.]

providing *true* premises from which the relevant problematic data may be derived, how can theories that are *meaningless* in the ordinary sense be said to explain? In short, *even if we are not interested in relating cognitive significance to observationality*, but are concerned with constructing some weakest language adequate for formulating some specified segment of our scientific beliefs, we may be troubled to find ourselves explicitly allowing clearly meaningless units to be built into our language structure, in some ordinary sense of "meaningless."

PRAGMATISM

The qualification embodied in the final phrase of the last sentence is a clue to one widespread attempt to cope with the troubles discussed: the view which takes the *system* to be the unit of significance, and adopts a wider notion of meaningfulness in deference to scientific practice. This view I shall label "pragmatism." The alternative reaction, which I shall discuss in later sections, I call "fictionalism."[1] Both views may be considered independently of the issue of empiricism . . . For, however we delimit the terms initially admissible (whether by reference to observation or not), we face the problem of interpreting all the others which seem to be required in increasing numbers with the theoretical development of science. Nevertheless,

[1] The labels I introduce here and in following selections are related to, but not intended as names of, specific philosophies associated with familiar historical movements or individual thinkers. They refer rather to characteristic trends, somewhat oversimplified and idealized, perhaps, in comparison to actually held philosophies. Nevertheless, they are influential and salient trends and will be recognizable, I hope, as elements of much of the recent literature in philosophy of science and theory of knowledge. As recent illustrations (in a loose sense) of pragmatism see R. Carnap, "Empiricism, Semantics, and Ontology," *Revue Internationale de Philosophie*, Vol. XI, 1950, reprinted in L. Linsky, *Semantics and the Philosophy of Language* (Urbana, Ill.: University of Illinois Press, 1952); and W. V. Quine, "Two Dogmas of Empiricism," *Philosophical Review*, 1951, included in W. V. Quine; *From a Logical Point of View* (Cambridge: Harvard University Press, 1953); of instrumentalistic fictionalism, see S. E. Toulmin, *The Philosophy of Science* (London: University Library, Hutchinson, 1953). Regarding vacillation between the latter two trends, see Nagel's discussion of Dewey in *Sovereign Reason* (Glencoe, Ill.: University of Illinois Press, 1954), pp. 110–115.

a consideration of this problem in abstraction from empiricism will bear rather directly on it as embodied in our revised form: pragmatism will negate this empiricism, while fictionalism will render it at least possible.

Pragmatism, then (in my terminology), accepts as fact that no initial listing of admissible terms is sufficient for the formulation of our scientific beliefs, and that the admission of any term is conceivable (hence legitimate) on the grounds of its utility in prediction and theoretical simplification. It admits, furthermore, that some such terms are meaningless, *in one usual sense*. But here it takes the bull by the horns, claiming that this sense is irrelevant for analyzing our scientific beliefs and practices. For any sense of "meaningless" which renders what is predictively useful meaningless is inadequate for philosophy of science, however relevant it may be in other contexts. If science finds, e.g., transcendental theories fruitful within whole systematic contexts, our notions of cognitive significance must reflect this fact. If science introduces terms not only by reference to prescientific usage or explicit test-methods, but within the network of whole theoretical frameworks justified by their predictive utility in subsequent inquiry, this is a *bona fide* fact about cognitive significance, not a problem. We must, accordingly, for the pragmatists, admit the *significance* of whole systems with unrestricted vocabularies, provided that they are, at some points, functionally tied to our initially specified language. Since, however, this proviso excludes no term at all, and virtually no system at all (every system meets this requirement by addition of one conjunct in the initial language, and every term is part of some system meeting this requirement), pragmatism supplements it by stressing some simplicity factor which presumably is to eliminate certain systems, but which is not to be so stringent as to eliminate every system which overflows the bounds of the initially specified language. In no account is the treatment of simplicity very precise, but in some accounts it is intended as a matter of degree so that cognitive significance is broadened correspondingly. It is, further, not very clear how considerations of simplicity are to be applied in determination of *confirmedness* or *truth* as distinct from *significance*. Nevertheless, the pragmatist reaction to the problem of interpreting transcendental terms and their theoretical contexts is clearly to accept their fruitfulness and to defend, in consequence, a broader notion of significance applicable to whole systems. This systematic emphasis is supported also by reference to well-known analyses of testing which show the theoretical revisability of every segment of a system when any segment is ostensibly under review. A corollary of this pragmatist treatment is its insistence that questions of ontology are scientific questions, since it takes the range of significant ontological assertion to be solely a function of scientific utility in practice and denies all independent language restrictions based on intuitive clarity or observationality. And rejecting such independent restrictions, it solves the two initial difficulties noted above (at the end of section 13) by (a) denying that we believe meaningless assertions in committing ourselves to science and by (b) affirming the possible truth and explanatory power of transcendental theories.

To what extent is the pragmatist position in favor of a broader notion of significance positively supported by the arguments it presents? Its strong point is obviously its congruence with the *de facto* scientific use of transcendental theories and with the interdependence of parts of a scientific system undergoing test. These facts are, however, not in themselves *conclusive* evidence for significance, inasmuch as many kinds of things are used in science with no implication of cognitive significance, i.e., truth-or-falsity; and many things are interdependent under scientific test without our feeling that they are therefore included within the cognitive system of our assertions. Clearly "is useful," "is fruitful," "is subject to modification under test," etc., are applicable also to nonlinguistic entities, e.g., telescopes and electronic computers. On the other hand, even linguistic units judged useful and controllable via empirical test may conceivably be construed as nonsignificant machinery, and such construction is not definitely ruled out by pragmatist arguments. Thus, even if we accept pragmatism's positive grounds, we *need* not broaden our original notion of literal significance. And it further follows that our revised empiricism is not refuted by pragmatism.

PRAGMATISM AND FICTIONALISM

But if not refuted, our empiricism remains beset with the problem of interpreting transcendental terms and theories. If pragmatism's positive grounds do not, that is, *establish* the literal significance of transcendental theories, it is not thereby demonstrated that they are eliminable or otherwise interpretable as nonbeliefs, i.e., mere instruments. Any view which takes them to be either I call "fictionalism." Clearly if fictionalism can show how transcendental terms are eliminable from our corpus of scientific beliefs, it will have removed transcendental theories from the domain of beliefs which need to be encompassed in E, and it will have destroyed a major obstacle to our revised empiricism. Short of showing eliminability, if fictionalism can plausibly construe transcendental theories as mere machinery without literal meaning, it will avoid the need for expressing such theories in E, and again make way for our revised empiricism.

INSTRUMENTALISTIC FICTIONALISM

Perhaps the easiest and by far the most popular type of fictionalism is one which simply disavows the belief-character of transcendental theories without claiming their eliminability from scientific discourse. Indeed such a fictionalism often goes with a positive indifference to the question of their eliminability, or even champions their ineliminability; we might aptly label this type "instrumentalism," and note in passing that some writers have vacillated between pragmatism and instrumentalism (in our present terminology) or have confused the two. Instrumentalistic fictionalism, then, holds that some scientific theories are not significant, but that they are moreover not intended as formulations of belief or as truths, being employed simply as mechanical devices for coordinating or generating *bona fide* assertions. Hence, again, transcendental theories are said to pose no problem; since they do not represent *beliefs*, we need not worry about including them within any deliberate statement of our beliefs in some restricted language. Our problem, it will be recalled, was that clearly meaningless terms seem required for adequate expression of our scientific beliefs. Whereas pragmatism's answer is to deny that any terms usefully employed in science are meaningless in the relevant sense, fictionalism's answer is to deny that our objectionable terms are required for expression of *beliefs*, though they may be otherwise required. And our instrumentalistic variant supports this denial not by showing how to eliminate such terms from scientific language, but rather by stipulating how "belief" is to be understood. Correspondingly, certain further stipulations are generally accepted as corollaries, e.g., that transcendental theories be said to *hold* or *fail* rather than to be *true* or *false,* that they are adopted or abandoned rather than believed or denied, etc. Thus instrumentalism takes care of the difficulties mentioned (a) by insisting that we do not strictly *believe* but *hold* or *employ* some statements in science and (b) by generalizing the concept of explanation to allow such held theories to serve as explanatory grounds.

If pragmatism's positive grounds seemed to us unconvincing, instrumentalism's positive grounds seem to consist just in the intuitive meaninglessness of transcendental theories. But the point at issue is whether science requires us to believe such theories, and this point is not met but begged by arguing that the answer is negative since the theories are intuitively meaningless. We can, however, be more generous to both pragmatism and instrumentalism by taking them not as arguments but as decisions or resolutions: pragmatism's denial of the meaninglessness of transcendental theories represents a decision to apply to them the ordinary language of truth and falsity, and this, coupled with denial of the need for further interpretation, involves a rejection of even a modified empiricism, as we have above formulated it. Instrumentalism's denial of the belief-character of transcendental theories represents a decision to talk about such theories in different and special ways without any further changes. Taken as basic decisions, there would seem to be no way of refuting either position, and to this extent at least, ontology is independent of science. There is no way to refute the instrumentalist's denial of the belief-character of various theories which he continues to employ. We may charge his implicit conception of the nature of belief with being tenuous and merely verbal, and we may declare his disavowels of belief to be rather hollow unless he gives up using the sentences which he claims intellectually to disavow. Yet, if he sticks to his guns, and continues to remind us that we all *use* all kinds of objects which we hold meaningless, and feel no guilt upon reflection in continuing to use them, then he is secure. Ontology, then, is relative to the person, and independent of the used language. Just as our common use of available technology does not commit us all equally to the same beliefs, so our common use of scientific language does not dictate that we should all draw the same line between literal sense and nonsense therein.

Coming back to our modified empiricism now, it appears that if pragmatism, in choosing to deny it, does not thereby refute it, instrumentalism renders it trivial. For if the range of our *beliefs* is freely specifiable by intellectual decision independently of the *content of our discourse,* we can always guarantee E's adequacy by simply deciding to exclude recalcitrant sentences from this range. Our judgments of recalcitrance will, of course, vary; but one consistent with our modified empiricism is trivially always possible.

If, however, we interpret our modified empiricist problem more stringently and more objectively, i.e., as not allowing for such a trivial answer, we must require of the empiricist fictionalist not simply that he appropriately adjust his terminology of belief but that he provide a method for eliminating transcendental terms and theories from scientific *discourse,* or of treating them within his discourse otherwise than as significant.

SYNTACTIC FICTIONALISM

One such course open to the fictionalist is to provide a syntax for transcendental theories. Goodman and Quine [2] have in part thus dealt with the problem of treating mathematics nominalistically. Unable, at the time of their study, to translate all of mathematics into a nominalistic language, they developed a nominalistic syntax language enabling them to talk *about* and deal with the untranslated residue, thus *independently* supporting the claim that this residue could be treated as mere machinery without literal significance. Though, in one sense, they did not eliminate this residue, they did go considerably beyond a mere statement that it might be considered as machinery only. For they provided an alternative language without the (to them at that time) objectionable features of the original, such that it was capable of doing much the same job. As they put their view, "our position is that the formulas of platonistic mathematics are, like the beads of an abacus, convenient computational aids which need involve no question of truth. What is meaningful and true in the case of platonistic mathematics as in the case of the abacus is not the apparatus itself, but only the description of it: the rules by which it is

[2] N. Goodman and W. V. Quine, "Steps Toward a Constructive Nominalism," *Journal of Symbolic Logic,* Vol. XII, 1947, pp. 105–22.

constructed and run. These rules we do understand, in the strict sense that we can express them in purely nominalistic language. The idea that classical mathematics can be regarded as mere apparatus is not a novel one among nominalistically minded thinkers; but it can be maintained only if one can produce, as we have attempted to above, a syntax which is itself free from platonistic commitments. At the same time, every advance we can make in finding direct translations for familiar strings of marks will increase the range of the meaningful language at our command" (p. 122).

Such a syntactical approach has relevance far beyond the question of platonistic mathematics. It is in general open to the fictionalist who wishes to disavow the belief-character of some segment of received scientific discourse in more than the trivial sense discussed above in connection with instrumentalism. In the special case of nominalism, it was by no means initially obvious that a syntax could be constructed without platonistic features. Having such a syntax for mathematics, it seems possible to extend it to specified parts of empirical science by addition of predicates applicable to the extralogical notation contained therein. In particular, such syntax could be developed for transcendental theories which the fictionalist cannot eliminate through translation but which he finds it objectionable to take as significant. For the nonnominalist who objects to taking as significant some particular transcendental theory, the task is, of course, much easier, for he has available all the tools of platonistic syntax. In a less trivial sense than that of instrumentalism, then, our modified empiricism may be feasible through syntactic construction. Note again, incidentally, that ontology turns out independent of our received scientific discourse, through the possibility of variable syntactic reinterpretation, and that only such elements as are needed for the applicability of syntactic predicates may be sufficient in the extreme case.

ELIMINATIVE FICTIONALISM

We may, finally, require our modified empiricism to show how transcendental terms may be eliminated from scientific discourse in favor of some other object-language discourse which is equivalent in some appropriate sense. Here it is well to recall that transcendental theories are justified generally as making possible the statement of comprehensive relationships (in desirable ways) on the observable level. Thus, if a way could be shown of appropriately stating these observational relationships in some theory, S, which otherwise differed from its transcendental counterpart only by lacking sentences with any transciendental term, S would be, in a reasonable sense, equivalent to that counterpart.

One such method is that of Craig, who states as one of his results, " . . . if K is any recursive set of non-logical (individual, function, predicate) constants, containing at least one predicate constant, then there exists a system whose theorems are exactly those theorems of T in which no constants other than those of K occur. In particular, suppose that T expresses a portion of a natural science, that the constants of K refer to things or events regarded as 'observable,' and that the other constants do not refer to 'observables' and hence may be regarded as 'theoretical' or 'auxiliary.' Then there exists a system which does not employ 'theoretical' or 'auxiliary' constants and whose theorems are the theorems of T concerning 'observables.' "[3]

Professor Hempel, discussing Craig's method, states concisely what is involved and what sense of "equivalence" is here relevant: "Craig's result shows that no matter how we select from the total vocabulary V_T' of an interpreted theory T' a subset V_B of experiential or observational terms, the balance of V_T', constituting the 'theoretical terms,' can always be avoided in sense (c)." This sense, which Hempel distinguishes from definability and translatability, he calls "functional replaceability" and describes as follows, "The terms of T might be said to be avoidable if there exists another theory T_B, couched in terms of V_B, which is 'functionally equivalent' to T in the sense of establishing exactly the same deductive connections between V_B sentences as T."

Professor Hempel offers, however, two reasons against the scientific use of Craig's method, "no matter how welcome the possibility of such replacement may be to the epistemologist." One reason is that the functionally equivalent replacing system constructed by Craig's method "always

[3] W. Craig, "On Axiomatizability Within a System," *Journal of Symbolic Logic*, Vol. XVIII, 1953, p. 31, text and n. 9. See also W. Craig, "Replacement of Auxiliary Expressions," *Philosophical Review*, Vol. LXV, 1956, pp. 38–55.

has an infinite set of postulates, irrespective of whether the postulate set of the original theory is finite or infinite, and that his result cannot be essentially improved in this respect. . . . This means that the scientist would be able to avoid theoretical terms only at the price of forsaking the comparative simplicity of a theoretical system with a finite postulational basis, and of giving up a system of theoretical concepts and hypotheses which are heuristically fruitful and suggestive—in return for a practically unmanageable system based upon an infinite, though effectively specified, set of postulates in observational terms."[4]

It should be obvious that any proposal like Craig's for meeting our present demand for elimination of transcendental terms will be judged in various ways in accordance with varying approval of its tools and subsidiary concepts. Moreover, such variation may be independent of the question of modified empiricism as such. In particular, a dissatisfaction with systems containing infinite, effectively specified sets of postulates may or may not be justified, but is at any rate independent of modified empiricism as we have formulated it. Further, though the relevant notions of heuristic fruitfulness and suggestiveness, simplicity, and practicality are not very precise, suppose it granted that Craig's functionally equivalent system is indeed inferior to its counterpart in all these respects. This is irrelevant to our modified empiricism. If Craig's replacing system renders such empiricism possible, this represents an intellectual gain no worse for the fact that the system is unwieldy and not likely to be used by the practicing scientist. The case is analogous to ordinary definition, where we try to minimize the complexity of our primitive basis at the cost of replacing short and handy definienda by cumbersome definientia in terms of a simple few primitives. Obviously, no one intends these definientia to be used in practice in place of their definienda, but neither does anyone seriously maintain that their formulation therefore represents less of an intellectual gain.

One may however, with Goodman,[5] suggest the infinity

4 C. G. Hempel, "Implications of Carnap's Work for the Philosophy of Science," to appear in the forthcoming Carnap volume of the *Library of Living Philosophers*.

5 This point was made by Goodman in correspondence with the present writer.

of postulates in Craig's replacing system not as representing a practical difficulty, but rather as indicating that the deductive character of the original system is not sufficiently reflected by its replacement. That is to say, if transcendental theories serve to enable finite postulation, no replacement is equivalent *deductively* in every relevant sense if it fails to serve thus also, even though it does accurately reflect the whole class of relevant postulates-or-theorems (assertions) of the original. If specific empiricist programs are to be interpreted in accord with this point of view, then, even granted Craig's result, they are not proven generally achievable, and continue to represent nontrivial problems in individual cases. It seems to me, however, that if we take these programs as requiring simply the reflection of nontranscendental assertions into replacing systems without transcendental terms, then we do not distort traditional notions of empiricism, and we have to acknowledge that Craig's result does the trick; the further cited problems remain but they are independent of empiricism as above formulated.

Professor Hempel's second reason against the scientific use of Craig's method is that "The application of scientific theories in the prediction and explanation of empirical findings involves not only deductive inference, i.e., the exploitation of whatever deductive connections the theory establishes among statements representing potential empirical data, but it also requires procedures of an inductive character, and some of these would become impossible if the theoretical terms were avoided." He illustrates in terms of the following four sentences, where "magnet" is taken to be a theoretical, i.e., nonobservational, term:

(5.1) The parts obtained by breaking a rod-shaped magnet in two are again magnets.
(5.2) If x is a magnet, then whenever a small piece y of iron filing is brought into contact with x, then y clings to x. In symbols:

$$Mx \supset (y) (Fxy \supset Cxy).$$

(5.3) Objects b and c were obtained by breaking object a in two, and a was a magnet and rod-shaped.
(5.4) If d is a piece of iron filing that is brought into contact with b, then d will cling to b.

Now, says Hempel, given (5.3) (and assuming (5.2)), we are able to deduce, with the help of (5.1), such sentences as (5.4). But (5.3) is nonobservational, containing *"Ma,"* itself not deducible from observational sentences via (5.2). which states only a necessary, but not a sufficient, condition for it. Thus, if (5.4) is to be connected by our theory here with other observational sentences, an *inductive* step is necessary, leading to (5.3), i.e., to *"Ma"* specifically, from observational sentences. E.g., *"Ma"* might be *inductively* based on a number of instances of *"Fay ⊃ Cay,"* assuming that we have no instance of *"Fay. ~ Cay."* This is so, since such instances confirm *"(y) (Fay ⊃ Cay),"* which, by (5.2), partially supports *"Ma."* Thus, our hypothesis (5.1) takes us, in virtue of (5.2), from some observational sentences, i.e., instances of *"Fay ⊃ Cay,"* to observational sentences such as (5.4), but the transition requires certain inductive steps along the way. But though Craig's functionally equivalent system retains all the deductive connections among observational sentences of the original system, it does not, in general, retain the inductive connections among such sentences. Hempel concludes, "the transition, by means of the theory, from strictly observational to strictly observational sentences usually requires inductive steps, namely the transition from some set of observational sentences to some non-observational sentence which they support inductively, and which in turn can serve as a premise in the strictly deductive application of the given theory."

With respect to this argument, we might question by what theory of confirmation *"(y) (Fay ⊃ Cay)"* supports *"Ma"*; it surely is not Hempel's satisfaction criterion of confirmation.[6] But this is irrelevant to the important point brought out by Hempel's argument, viz., that since functionally equivalent systems (of Craig's type) are not logically equivalent to their originals, they need not (on *any* likely view of confirmation) sustain the same confirmation relations as these originals, even emong purely observational sentences. And this despite the fact that they do preserve the same deductive relations among such sentences by retaining all original theorems couched in purely observational terms. Thus, if we do not attempt an observational reduction of the *whole* of our theoretical discourse in given scientific domains via definition and translation or syntactic con-

[6] "A Purely Syntactical Definition of Confirmation," *Journal of Symbolic Logic,* Vol. VIII, 1943, pp. 122–43. See also C. G. Hempel, "Studies in the Logic of Confirmation," *Mind,* N. S. Vol. LIV, 1945, pp. 1–26 and 97–121, especially pp. 107 ff.

struction, but aim merely to isolate the *observational part* of such discourse, we must be careful to construe this part adequately, i.e., as comprising not only a deductive network but also a wider confirmational range. Specific empiricist programs would then seem to be not achievable generally by means of Craig's result, in the light of Hempel's argument. . . .

SUMMARY AND CONCLUSION

If our journey has yielded no single, easy solution as a climax, its difficulty has nevertheless earned for us the right to stop and get our bearings. For we have traveled a long way from the conception of empiricism as a shiny, new philosophical doctrine for weeding out obscurantism and cutting down nonsense wherever they crop up. We have, furthermore, seen that even if we take empiricism as the proposal of a general meaning-criterion in terms of translatability into a chosen artificial language, we run into trouble. We have thus come to restrict the empiricist's job to providing merely an adequate sufficient condition of significance on an observational basis, in the form of an observational system capable of housing our scientific beliefs.

Even this restricted task has, however, turned out to have quite difficult obstacles before it. While the inclusion of needed disposition terms seemed to us not as formidable a problem as hitherto thought, we found theoretical terms to be generally resistant to straightforward empiricist interpretation. Considering this difficulty in the light of a number of recent approaches to philosophy of science, we found that the pragmatic rejection of our restricted empiricism does not constitute a refutation, while intrumentalism's easy solution fulfills such empiricism in only the most trivial sense. Taking empiricism's task as the provision of an appropriate modification of scientific discourse itself rather than simply of our notions of belief, we found the possibility of syntactic reinterpretation promising, though less intuitively satisfying then a direct reinterpretation of the object-language of science proper. Our final examination of Craig's method for eliminating theoretical terms wholly from such language while preserving its observational segment intact led to the conclusion that this method is, in itself, incapable of achieving the goal of our restricted empiricism.

It appears, in sum, that even a modest empiricism is presently a hope for clarification and a challenge to constructive investigation rather than a well-grounded doctrine, unless we construe it in a quite trivial way. Empiricists are perhaps best thought of as those who share the hope and accept the challenge—who refuse to take difficulty as a valid reason either for satisfaction with the obscure or for abandonment of effort.

PART TWO

LAWS AND THEORIES

INTRODUCTION

A law is a true sentence, and a theory is a system of sentences. This gross characterization of one difference between laws and theories may be objected to on at least two counts. First, "theory" is sometimes interchangeable with "hypothesis" in ordinary usage; a man may entertain the theory (hypothesis) that Bacon wrote Hamlet; but "Bacon wrote Hamlet." is a sentence, and accordingly some theories are just sentences, not systems of sentences. To this we merely reply that there may indeed be this sense of "theory," but that it is not sense which interests us. Secondly, it is sometimes argued that laws may be sentences but not *true* sentences. They are, rather, rules of inference, "inference tickets," and rules are either *useful* or not instead of being true or false. Our reply to this is that any argument in favor of regarding laws as rules of inference may be matched by equally good arguments in favor of regarding them as true sentences. Moreover it is scientific practice to speak of a purported law being falsified, and to regard laws as descriptive of regularities in the world.

Not every true sentence is a law, of course. Let us therefore introduce the term "lawlike." A law will then be a true lawlike sentence (a *lawful* sentence may be defined as a well-confirmed lawlike sentence); the problem is then to specify the conditions of lawlikeness. Intuitively, a sentence S is lawlike if it is general, spatially and temporally unrestricted, and nonaccidental. These conditions respectively rule out such true sentences as "Bacon was English," "All the persons in this room are philosophers," and "Every country in the world in 1959 has a name less than 150 syllables long." Unfortunately, the same conditions also rule out Kepler's laws and possibly even statistical laws. And indeed the correct analysis of lawlikeness is an unsolved problem in the philosophy of science. We should add that scientists employ the term "law" more loosely than our set of conditions would indicate.

Laws describe regularities and are employed in order to explain and predict particular occurences and phenomena. But often we wish an explanation of the regularity itself. One way of achieving this in science is to *deduce* the law which describes this regularity from some other law of a higher degree of generality, or a set of such laws. And typically, a whole family of laws, in our original sense, may be deduced from a very few laws of high generality. When this is achieved, these highly general laws will be a *theory* for the family of laws which are deducible from them, or for the regularities described by these laws. Roughly, we may say that a set of sentences $T_1 \ldots T_n$ is "the theory" for another set of sentences $S_1 \ldots S_m$ when the members of both sets of sentences are lawlike, the members of the set $S_1 \ldots S_m$ are deductive consequences of $T_1 \ldots T_n$ (when these are supplemented with suitably specified boundary conditions) and where members of the set $T_1 \ldots T_m$ are more general than the members of the set $S_1 \ldots S_m$. Sometimes the sentences in the theory will include variables which range over unobservables, so there is a connection between "theoretical terms" (as these were discussed in our first introduction), and theories in the present sense. We are only indicating here some of the conditions a theory must satisfy, not explicating these conditions. The notion of "more general than," in particular, calls for analysis, but this goes beyond the scope of our introduction.

We have already remarked that our characterization of theories differs from the ordinary sense in which "theory" is interchangeable with "hypothesis." But it is fair to point out that it differs from a number of scientific usages as well. Thus scientists sometimes employ the term "theory" to designate a sketch of the general laws they anticipate will be highly confirmed. A great many theories in the social sciences are theories in this sense. Again, we sometimes refer to a whole body of sentences from a given branch of science as constituting a theory, e.g., we speak of Newtonian mechanics as a theory. In connection with this latter usage, the question arises whether or not theories ought to be put into axiomatic or formalized shape. Euclid's geometry is a fair example of an axiomatized theory, and it is indeed often taken as the paradigm for scientific theories. But it is well known by now that Euclid's system is defective as it stands, making use of concepts it does not specify and axioms which are not listed. Axiom systems do not generally include explicit reference to the rules—the so-called formation and transformation rules—which specify what signs are admissible in the system and what operations on these signs are allowable. A system in which all this apparatus is made explicit is a *formalized* system. The best examples of formalized systems are to be found in the field of mathematical logic; but some philosophers have contended that formalization, or at the very least axiomatization, is a *desideratum* for scientific progress. Just as many philosophers, perhaps, are convinced that formalization is a luxury which science may well do without. But this is a quarrel we need not enter upon here.

Returning to laws, we have said that laws are employed to predict and explain phenomena and events. But many philosophers of science are convinced that something will *count* as an explanation only if it employs one or more laws. Explanation consists, according to them, of the exhibition of some sentence which *describes* the event to be explained as a logical consequence of a set of sentences which contains one or more laws. But then explanation and prediction are logically isomorphic: to be able correctly to explain is to be able correctly to predict a given event or phenomenon. Explanations of course must satisfy conditions other than employment of some law among the premises and deduction of the sentence which describes the event to be explained; but these are the central features of this theory of explanation, and it is these which received particular criticism. At least three objections have been raised: (A) Often we are able successfully to predict events and phenomena without employing general laws at all. (B) Often, perhaps even typically in history, satisfactory explanations of historical events do not make use of general laws—and even in science it might be argued that explanations which employ general laws or satisfy the deductive requirements are rare; (C) Intuitively, it seems that a pattern of sentences exactly satisfying the deductive model of explanation might still not be accepted as an explanation, e.g., a person demanding an explanation of Jones's death might reject "Jones was a man and all men are mortal" as in any significant sense explanatory.

The logic of explanation is very much under discussion these days, but at least some replies to the above objections are worth making. (*A'*) It is true that we may successfully predict without employing general laws, e.g., we may make a lucky guess. But there is a difference between correct predictions and *warranted* predictions: the predictions of science are presumably warranted predictions; and it is not at all clear that we can classify a prediction as warranted without appealing to some general law. (*B'*) It is true that historical explanations frequently, even typically, make no use of general laws; but such explanations may be given in a context of tacitly held statistical generalizations and so may require at least statistical laws. A statistical law cannot, of course be used to *deduce* the required sentence; but it is feasible that at least an *inductive* model for historical explanation might be furnished which still employs laws. But very little progress has been as yet made along these lines. (*C'*) Reference to human mortality may not count as explanatory to a person already familiar with the law which describes it, and will not at any rate explain why Jones died when he did. But a suitable description of what one wants to have explained, e.g., why Jones died at such and such a time and place, may very well be explained via a general law or—assuming the inductive model of explanation mentioned above—via some set of statistical laws. But in the end the objection under (*C*) may count for very little, since it may be argued, no matter how paradoxical it might seem that "All men are mortal" is a law, and not just a well-confirmed general sentence. We have suggested that not all highly confirmed general sentences are laws, and we have indicated that other conditions must be satisfied. We add that the history of science is replete with instances of a general sentence, which has proven useful for predicting events, nevertheless being contested on grounds of its incapacity to square with certain *a priori* beliefs regarding how the world must be, or certain regulative ideals concerning the way in which science is to be done. Thus the Cartesians objected to the concept of action-at-a-distance despite the explanatory and predictive power of theories which employed the concept. More recently, Einstein took a stand against the "orthodox interpretation" of Quantum Theory, not least of all because it was, according to him, a departure from the sort of ideals which characterized three centuries of scientific progress. None of this means, of course, that dissatisfaction with a given theory on whatever grounds may not stimulate the framing of new theories in accordance with more acceptable standards; but only that such new theories are to be accepted or rejected by the criterion of successful explanation and prediction.

When, however, each of a pair of theories is of equal explanatory and predictive power, other criteria may be invoked. A theory T may introduce a certain simplicity over another theory T' and considerations of economy may then lead to the adoption of T. As a special case of economy a theory T' is reduced to a theory T, e.g., thermodynamics to mechanics. Reduction means roughly that the phenomena describable with the vocabulary of T' may henceforth be explained and predicted on the basis of information about the phenomena describable with the vocabulary of T. It is this difference in vocabulary which formally distinguishes reduction from the cases we have spoken of in which a law is deduced from a theory; but it is sometimes argued that once supplementary definitions are *added* to T, the deduction goes through. It is worth pointing out that attempts to reduce T' to T often involve revisions of T'—so the logic of reduction is in fact an extremely complicated matter.

The problems which arise in connection with the concept of reduction are frequently philosophical; they are of the kind familiar in such time-honored distinctions as animate-inanimate, body-mind, etc., where some "higher" order phenomenon is sometimes claimed to be causally connected with a "lower" order phenomenon. The traditional Naturalist position is that physics is the basic science, in that all other theories are claimed to be reducible to physical theories. With this bit of belief we have no inclination either to agree or disagree. We only wish to suggest that careful treatment of many of these and similar issues must be along the lines of some of the papers included in this section.

1

PHYSICAL LAW:
Pierre Duhem ·

I. THE LAWS OF PHYSICS ARE SYMBOLIC RELATIONS

Just as the laws of common sense are based on the observation of facts by means natural to man, so the laws of physics are based on the results of physical experiments. Of course, the profound differences which separate the non-scientific ascertainment of a fact from the result of a physical experiment will also separate the laws of common sense from the laws of physics; thus, nearly everything we have said about the experiments of physics will extend to the laws that science states.

Let us consider one of the simplest and most certain of common-sense laws: All men are mortal. This law surely relates two abstract concepts, the abstract idea of man in general, rather than the concrete idea of this or that man in particular, and the abstract idea of death, rather than the concrete idea of this or that form of death; indeed, it is only on this condition, viz., that the concepts related are abstract, that the law can be general. But these abstractions are in no way theoretical symbols, for they merely extract what is universal in each of the particular cases to which

· [This selection is Chap. 5 of Part II of Duhem's *The Aim and Structure of Physical Theory*, trans. by Phillip Wiener, (Princeton: Princeton University Press, 1954), pp. 165–79. Some cross references are omitted. Reprinted by permission of Princeton University Press.]

the law applies. Thus, in each of the particular cases where we apply the law, we shall find concrete objects in which these abstract ideas are realized; each time we might wish to ascertain that all men are mortal we shall find ourselves aware of a certain individual man embodying the general idea of man, and of a certain particular death implying the general idea of death.

Let us take another law, . . . It is a law about an object belonging to the domain of physics, but it retains the form that the laws of physics had when this branch of knowledge existed only as a dependency of common sense without yet having acquired the dignity of a rational science.

Here is the law: We see the flash of lightning before we hear thunder. The ideas of lightning and thunder which this statement ties together are abstract and general ideas, but these abstractions are drawn so instinctively and naturally from particular data that with each bolt of lightning we perceive a glare and a rumbling in which we recognize immediately the concrete form of our ideas of lightning and thunder.

This is not, however, true of the laws of physics. Let us take one of these laws, Mariotte's law,[1] and examine its formulation without caring for the moment about the accuracy of this law. At a constant temperature, the volumes occupied by a constant mass of gas are in inverse ratio to the pressures they support; such is the statement of the law of Mariotte. The terms it introduces, the ideas of mass, temperature, pressure, are still abstract ideas. But these ideas are not only abstract; they are, in addition, symbolic, and the symbols assume meaning only by grace of physical theories. Let us put ourselves in front of a real, concrete gas to which we wish to apply Mariotte's law; we shall not be dealing with a certain concrete temperature embodying the general idea of temperature, but with some more or less warm gas; we shall not be facing a certain particular pressure embodying the general idea of pressure, but a certain pump on which a weight is brought to bear in a certain manner. No doubt, a certain temperature corresponds to this more or less warm gas, and a certain pressure corresponds to this effort exerted on the pump, but this correspondence is that of a sign to the thing signified and replaced by it, or of a reality to the symbol representing it.

[1] Translator's note: Boyle's law.

This correspondence is by no means immediately given; it is established with the aid of instruments and measurements, and this is often a very long and very complicated process. In order to assign a definite temperature to this more or less warm gas, we must have recourse to a thermometer; in order to evaluate in the form of a pressure the effort exerted by the pump, we must use a manometer, and the use of the thermometer and manometer imply . . . the use of physical theories.

The abstract terms referred to in a common-sense law being no more than whatever is general in the concretely observed objects, the transition from the concrete to the abstract is made in such a necessary and spontaneous operation that it remains unconscious; placed in the presence of a certain man or of a certain case of death, I associate them immediately with the general idea of man and with the general idea of death. This instinctive and unreflective operation yields unanalyzed general ideas, abstractions taken grossly, so to speak. No doubt, the thinker may analyze these general and abstract ideas, he may wonder what man is, what death is, and seek to penetrate the deep and full sense of these words. This inquiry will lead him to a better understanding of the reasons for the law, but it is not necessary to do that in order to understand the law; it is sufficient to take the terms related in their obvious sense in order to understand this law, which is clear to us whether we are philosophers or not.

The symbolic terms connected by a law of physics are, on the other hand, not the sort of abstractions that emerge spontaneously from concrete reality; they are abstractions produced by slow, complicated, and conscious work, i.e., the secular labor which has elaborated physical theories. If we have not done this work or if we do not know physical theories, we cannot understand the law or apply it.

According to whether we adopt one theory or another, the very words which figure in a physical law change their meaning, so that the law may be accepted by one physicist who admits a certain theory and rejected by another physicist who admits some other theory.

Take a peasant who has never analyzed the notions of man or of death and a metaphysician who has spent his life analyzing them; take two philosophers who have analyzed and adopted different irreconcilable notions of man and of death; for all, the law "All men are mortal" will be equally clear and true. In the same way, the law "We see the flash of lightning before we hear thunder" has for the physicist who knows thoroughly the laws of disruptive electrical discharge the same clarity and certainty as it had for the Roman plebeian who saw in a stroke of lightning the anger of Capitoline Jupiter.

On the other hand, let us consider the following physical law: "All gases contract and expand in the same manner"; and let us ask different physicists whether this law is or is not violated by iodine vapor. The first physicist professes theories according to which iodine vapor is a single gas, and draws from the foregoing law the consequence that the density of iodine vapor relative to air is a constant. Now, experiment shows that this density depends on the temperature and pressure; therefore, our physicist concludes that iodine vapor is not subject to the law stated. A second physicist will have it that iodine vapor is not a single gas but a mixture of two gases which are polymers of each other and capable of being transformed into each other; consequently, the law mentioned does not require the iodine-vapor density relative to air to be constant, but claims this density varies with the temperature and pressure according to a certain formula established by J. Willard Gibbs. This formula represents, indeed, the results of experimental determinations; our second physicist concludes that iodine vapor is not an exception to the rule which states that all gases contract and expand in the same manner. Thus our two physicists have entirely different opinions concerning a law which both enunciate in the same form: one finds fault with it because of a certain fact, the other finds that it is confirmed by that very fact. That is because the different theories they hold do not determine uniquely the meaning suited to the words "a single gas," so that though they both pronounce the same sentence, they mean two different propositions; in order to compare his proposition with reality each makes different calculations, so that it is possible for one to verify this law which the other finds contradicted by the same facts. This is plain proof of the following truth: A physical law is a symbolic relation whose application to concrete reality requires that a whole group of laws be known and accepted.

2. A LAW OF PHYSICS IS, PROPERLY SPEAKING, NEITHER TRUE NOR FALSE BUT APPROXIMATE

A common-sense law is merely a general judgment; this judgment is either true or false. Take, for instance, the law that everyday observation reveals: In Paris, the sun rises every day in the east, goes up in the heavens, then comes down and sets in the west. There you have a true law without conditions or restrictions. On the other hand, take this statement: The moon is always full. That is a false law. If the truth of a common-sense law is questioned, we can answer this question by yes or no.

Such is not the case with the laws that a physical science, come to full maturity, states in the form of mathematical propositions; such laws are always symbolic. Now, a symbol is not, properly speaking, either true or false; it is, rather, something more or less well selected to stand for the reality it represents, and pictures that reality in a more or less precise, a more or less detailed manner. But applied to a symbol the words "truth" and "error" no longer have any meaning; so, the logician who is concerned about the strict meaning of words will have to answer anyone who asks whether physics is true or false, "I do not understand your question." Let us comment on this answer, which may seem paradoxical but the understanding of which is necessary for anyone who claims to know what physics is.

The experimental method, as practiced in physics, does not make a given fact correspond to only one symbolic judgment, but to an infinity of different symbolic judgments; the degree of symbolic indetermination is the degree of approximation of the experiment in question. Let us take a sequence of analogous facts; finding the law for these facts means to the physicist finding a formula which contains the symbolic representation of each of these facts. The symbolic indetermination corresponding to each fact consequently entails the indetermination of the formula which is to unite these symbols; we can make an infinity of different formulas or distinct physical laws correspond to the same group of facts. In order for each of these laws to be accepted, there should correspond to each fact not *the* symbol of this fact, but some one of the symbols, infinite in number, which can represent the fact; that is what is meant when the laws of physics are said to be only approximate.

Let us imagine, for example, that we refuse to be satisfied

with the information supplied by the common-sense law about the sun's rising in the east, climbing the sky, descending, and setting in the west every day in Paris; we address ourselves to the physical sciences in order to have a precise law of the motion of the sun seen from Paris, a law indicating to the observer in Paris what place the sun occupies in the sky at each moment. In order to solve the problem, the physical sciences are not going to use sensed realities, say of the sun just as we see it shining in the sky, but will use symbols through which theories represent these realities: the real sun, despite the irregularities of its surface, despite the enormous protuberances it has, will be replaced in their theories by a geometrically perfect sphere, and it is the position of the center of this ideal sphere that these theories will try to determine; or rather, they will seek to determine the position that this point would occupy if astronomical refraction did not deviate the rays, and if the annual aberration did not modify the apparent position cf the heavenly bodies. It is, therefore, a symbol that is substituted for the sole sensible reality offered to our observation, for the shiny disk that our lens may sight. In order to make the symbol correspond to the reality, we must effect complicated measurements, we must make the edges of the sun coincide with the hairlines of a lens equipped with a micrometer, we must make many readings on divided circles, and subject these readings to diverse corrections; we must also develop long and complex calculations whose legitimacy depends on admitted theories, on the theory of aberration, and on the theory of atmospheric refraction.

The point symbolically called the center of the sun is not yet obtained by our formulas; they tell us only the coordinates of this point, for instance, its longitude and latitude, coordinates whose meaning cannot be understood without knowing the laws of cosmography, and whose values do not designate a point in the sky that you can indicate with your finger or that a telescope can sight except by virtue of a group of preliminary determinations: the determination of the meridian of the place, its geographical coordinates, etc.

Now, can we not make a single value for the longitude and a single value for the latitude of the sun's center correspond to a definite position of the solar disk, assuming the corrections for aberration and refraction to have been made? Indeed not. The optical power of the instrument used to sight the sun is limited; the diverse operations required of our experiment are of a limited sensitivity. Let the solar disk be in such a position that its distance from the next position is small enough, and we shall not be able to perceive the deviation. Admitting that we cannot know the coordinates of a fixed point on the celestial sphere with a precision greater than 1′, it will suffice, in order to determine the position of the sun at a given instant, to know the longitude and latitude of the sun's center to approximately 1′. Hence, to represent the path of the sun, despite the fact that it occupies only one position at each instant, we shall be able to give for each instant not one value alone for the longitude and only one value for the latitude, but an infinity of values for each, except that for a given instant two acceptable values of the longitude or two acceptable values of the latitude will not differ by more than 1′.

We now proceed to seek the law of the sun's motion, that is to say, two formulas permitting us to calculate at each instant of a period the value of the longitude and latitude, respectively, of the center of the sun. It is not evident that, in order to represent the path of the longitude as a function of the time, we shall be able to adopt not a single formula, but an infinity of different formulas provided that for a given instant all these formulas give us values for the longitude differing by less than 1′? And is not the same evident for the latitude? We shall then be able to represent equally well our observations on the path of the sun by an infinity of different laws; these diverse laws will be expressed by equations which algebra regards as incompatible, by equations such that if one of them is verified, no other is. They will each trace a different curve on the celestial sphere, and it would be absurd to say that the same point describes two of these curves at the same time; yet, to the physicist all these laws are equally acceptable, for all determine the position of the sun with a closer approximation than can be observed with our instruments. The physicist does not have the right to say that any of these laws is true to the exclusion of the others.

No doubt the physicist has the right to choose between these laws, and generally he will choose; but the motives which will guide his choice will not be of the same kind or be imposed with the same imperious necessity as those which compel him to prefer truth to error.

He will choose a certain formula because it is simpler than the others; the weakness of our minds constrains us to attach great importance to considerations of this sort. There was a time when physicists supposed the intelligence of the Creator to be tainted with the same debility, when the simplicity of these laws of nature was imposed as an indisputable dogma in the name of which any experimental law expressing too complicated an algebraic equation was rejected, when simplicity seemed to confer on a law a certainty and scope transcending those of the experimental method which supplied it. It was than that Laplace, speaking of the law of double refraction discovered by Huygens, said: "Until now this law has been only the result of observation, approximating the truth within the limits of error to which the most exact experiments are subject. Now the simplicity of the law of action on which it depends should make us consider it a rigorous law." That time no longer exists. We are no longer dupes of the charm which simple formulas exert on us; we no longer take that charm as the evidence of a greater certainty.

The physicist will especially prefer one law to another when the first follows from the theories he admits; he will, for example, ask the theory of universal attraction to decide which formulas he should prefer among all those which could represent the motion of the sun. But physical theories are only a means of classifying and bringing together the approximate laws to which experiments are subject; theories, therefore, cannot modify the nature of these experimental laws and cannot confer absolute truth on them.

Thus, every physical law is an approximate law. Consequently, it cannot be, for the strict logician, either true or false; any other law representing the same experiments with the same approximation may lay as just a claim as the first to the title of a true law or, to speak more precisely, of an acceptable law.

3. EVERY LAW OF PHYSICS IS PROVISIONAL AND RELATIVE
   BECAUSE IT IS APPROXIMATE

What is characteristic of a law is that it is fixed and absolute. A proposition is a law only because once true, always true, and if true for this person, then also for that one. Would it not be contradictory to say that a law is provisional, that it may be accepted by one person and rejected by another? Yes and no. Yes, certainly, if we mean by "laws" those that common sense reveals, those we can call true in the proper sense of the word; such laws cannot be true today and false tomorrow, and cannot be true for you and false for me. No, if we mean by "laws" the laws that physics states in mathematical form. Such laws are always provisional; not that we must understand this to mean that a physical law is true for a certain time and then false, but at no time is it either true or false. It is provisional because it represents the facts to which it applies with an approximation that physicists today judge to be sufficient but will some day cease to judge satisfactory. Such a law is always relative; not because it is true for one physicist and false for another, but because the approximation it involves suffices for the use the first physicist wishes to make of it and does not suffice for the use the second wishes to make of it.

We have already noticed that the degree of approximation is not something fixed; it increases gradually as instruments are perfected, and as the causes of error are more rigorously avoided or more precise corrections permit us to evaluate them better. As experimental methods gradually improve, we lessen the indetermination of the abstract symbol brought into correspondence with the concrete fact by physical experiment; many symbolic judgments which might have been regarded at one time as adequately representing a definite, concrete fact will no longer be accepted at another time as signifying this fact with sufficient precision. For example, the astronomers of one century will, in order to represent the position of the sun's center at a given instant, accept all the values of the longitude which do not differ from each other by more than 1′ and all the values of the latitude confined within the same interval. The astronomers of the next century will have telescopes with greater optical power, more perfectly divided circles, more minute and precise methods of observation; they will require then that the diverse determinations of the latitude, respectively, of the sun's center at a given instant agree within about 10″; an infinity of determinations which their predecessors were willing to permit would be rejected by them.

As the indetermination of experimental results becomes

narrower, the indetermination of the formulas used to condense these results becomes more restricted. One century would accept as the law of the sun's motion any group of formulas which gave for each instant the coordinates of the center of this star within approximately 1'; the next century will impose on any law of the sun's motion the condition that the coordinates of the sun's center be known within approximately 10"; an infinity of laws accepted by the first century will thus be rejected by the second.

This provisional character of the laws of physics is made plain every time we read the history of this science. For Dulong and Arago, Mariotte's [Boyle's] law was an acceptable form of the law of the compressibility of gases because it represented the experimental facts with deviations that remained less than the possible errors of the methods of observation used by them. When Regnault had improved the apparatus and experimental method, this law had to be rejected; the deviations of Mariotte's law from the results of observation were much greater than the uncertainties affecting the new apparatus.

Now, given two contemporary physicists, the first may be in the circumstances Regnault was in, whereas the second may still be working under conditions under which Dulong and Arago worked. The first possesses very precise apparatus and plans to make very exact observations; the second possesses only crude instruments and, in addition, the investigations he is making do not demand close approximation. Mariotte's law will be accepted by the latter and rejected by the former.

More than that, we can see the same physical law simultaneously adopted and rejected by the same physicist in the course of the same work. If a law of physics could be said to be true or false, that would be a strange paradox; the same proposition would be affirmed and denied at the same time, and this would constitute a formal contradiction.

Regnault, for example, is making inquiries about the compressibility of gases for the purpose of finding a more approximate formula to substitute for Mariotte's law. In the course of his experiments he needs to know the atmospheric pressure at the level reached by the mercury in his manometer; he uses Laplace's formula to obtain this pressure, and Laplace's formula rests on the use of Mariotte's law.

There is no paradox or contradiction here. Regnault knows that the error introduced by this particular employment of Mariotte's law is much smaller than the uncertainties of the experimental method he is using.

Any physical law, being approximate, is at the mercy of the progress which, by increasing the precision of experiments, will make the degree of approximation of this law insufficient: the law is essentially provisional. The estimation of its value varies from one physicist to the next, depending on the means of observation at their disposal and the accuracy demanded by their investigations: the law is essentially relative.

4. EVERY PHYSICAL LAW IS PROVISIONAL BECAUSE IT IS SYMBOLIC

Physical law is provisional not only because it is approximate, but also because it is symbolic: there are always cases in which the symbols related by a law are no longer capable of representing reality in a satisfactory manner.

In order to study a certain gas, for example, oxygen, the physicist has created a schematic representation of it which can be grasped in mathematical reasoning and algebraic calculation. He has pictured this gas as one of the perfect fluids that mechanics studies: it has a certain density, is brought to a certain temperature, and is subject to a certain pressure. Among these three elements, density, temperature, and pressure, he has established a certain relation that a certain equation expresses: that is the law of the compressibility and expansion of oxygen. Is this law definitive?

Let the physicist place some oxygen between the plates of a strongly charged electrical condenser; let him determine the density, temperature, and pressure of the gas; the values of these three elements will no longer verify the law of the compressibility and expansion of oxygen. Is the physicist astonished to find his law at fault? Not at all. He realizes that the faulty relation is merely a symbolic one, that it did not bear on the real, concrete gas he manipulates but on a certain logical creature, on a certain schematic gas characterized by its density, temperature, and pressure, and that this schematism is undoubtedly too simple and too incomplete to represent the properties of the real gas placed in the conditions given now. He then seeks to complete this schematism and to make it more representative of reality: he is no longer content to represent oxygen by means of its density, its temperature, and the pressure it supports; he introduces into the construction of the new schematism the intensity of the electrical field in which the gas is placed; he subjects this more complete symbol to new studies and obtains the law of the compressibility of oxygen endowed with dielectric polarization. This is a more complicated law; it includes the former as a special case, but it is more comprehensive and will be verified in cases where the original law would fail.

Is this new law definitive?

Take the gas to which it applies and place it between the poles of an electromagnet; you will see the new law falsified in its turn by the experiment. Do not think that this new falsity upsets the physicist; he knows that he has to deal with a symbolic relation and that the symbol he has created, though a faithful picture of reality in certain cases, cannot resemble it in all circumstances. Hence, without being discouraged, he again takes up the schematism by which he pictures the gas on which he is experimenting. In order to have this sketch represent the facts he burdens it with new features: it is not enough for the gas to have a certain density, a certain temperature, and a certain dielectric power, to support a certain pressure, and to be placed in an electrical field of a given intensity; in addition, he assigns to it a certain coefficient of magnetization; he takes into account the magnetic field in which the gas is and, connecting all these elements by a group of formulas, he obtains the law of the compressibility and expansion of the polarized and magnetized gas, a more complicated and more comprehensive law than those he had at first obtained, a law which will be verified in an infinity of cases where the former would be falsified; and yet it is a provisional law. Some day the physicist expects to find conditions in which this law will in its turn be faulty; on that day, he will have to take up again the symbolic representation of the gas studied, add new elements to it and enounce a more comprehensive law. The mathematical symbol forged by theory applies to reality as armor to the body of a knight clad in iron: the more complicated the armor, the more supple will the rigid metal seem to be; the multiplication of the pieces that are overlaid like shells assures more perfect contact between the steel and the limbs it protects; but no matter how numerous the fragments composing it, the armor will never be exactly wedded to the human body being modelled.

I know what is going to be said in objection to this. I shall be told that the law of compressibility and expansion formulated at the very first has not in any way been upset by the later experiments; that it remains the law according to which oxygen is compressed and dilated when all electrical and magnetic actions are eliminated; that the physicist's later inquiries have taught us only that it was suitable to join to this law, whose validity was unaffected, the law of the compressibility of an ionized gas and the law of the compressibility of a magnetized gas.

These same persons who take things so obliquely ought to recognize that the original law could lead to serious mistakes if taken without caution, for the domain it governs has to be delimited by the following double restriction: the gas studied is removed from all electrical action as well as magnetic action. Now the necessity for this restriction did not appear at first but was imposed by the experiments we have mentioned. Are such restrictions the only ones which should be imposed on the law's statement? Will not experiments done in the future indicate other restrictions as essential as the former? What physicist would dare to pronounce judgment on this and assert that the present statement is not provisional but final?

The laws of physics are therefore provisional in that the symbols they relate are too simple to represent reality completely. There are always circumstances in which the symbol ceases to picture concrete things and to announce phenomena exactly; the statement of the law must then be accompanied by restrictions which permit one to eliminate these circumstances. It is the progress of physics which brings knowledge of these restrictions; never is it permissible to affirm that we possess a complete enumeration of them or that the list drawn up will not undergo some addition or modification.

This task of continual modification by which the laws of physics avoid more and more adequately the refutations provided by experiment plays such an essential role in the development of the science that we may be permitted to insist somewhat further on its importance and to study its course in a second example.

Here is some water in a vessel. The law of universal

attraction teaches us what force acts on each of the particles of this water: this force is the weight of the particle. Mechanics indicates to us what shape the water should assume: whatever the nature and shape of the vessel are, the water should be bounded by a horizontal plane. Look closely at the surface bounding the water: horizontal at a distance from the edge of the vessel, it stops being so in the vicinity of the walls of glass, and rises along these walls; in a narrow tube the water rises very high and becomes altogether concave. There you have the law of universal attraction failing. In order to prevent capillary phenomena from refuting the law of gravitation, it will be necessary to modify it: we shall no longer have to regard the formula of the inverse ratio of the square of the distance as an exact formula but as an approximate one; we shall have to suppose that this formula shows with sufficient precision the attraction of two distant material particles but that it becomes very incorrect when the problem is to express the mutual action of two elements very close to each other; we shall have to introduce into the equations a complementary term which, while complicating them, will make them capable of representing a wider class of phenomena and will permit them to include the motions of heavenly bodies and capillary effects under the same law.

This law will be more comprehensive than Newton's law, but will not be, for all that, safe from all contradiction. At two different points of a liquid mass, let us insert the metallic wires coming from two poles of a battery: there you see the laws of capillarity in disagreement with observation. In order to remove this disagreement, we must again take up the formula for capillary action, and modify and complete it by taking into account the electrical charges carried by the fluid's particles and the forces acting among these ionized particles. Thus, this struggle between reality and the laws of physics will go on indefinitely: to any law that physics formulates, reality will oppose sooner or later the harsh refutation of a fact, but indefatigable physics will touch up, modify, and complicate the refuted law in order to replace it with a more comprehensive law in which the exception raised by the experiment will have found its rule in turn.

Physics makes progress through this unceasing struggle and the work of continually supplementing laws in order to include the exceptions. It was because the laws of weight were contradicted by a piece of amber rubbed by wool that physics created the laws of electrostatics, and because a magnet lifted iron despite these same laws of weight that physics formulated the laws of magnetism; it was because Oersted had found an exception to the laws of electrostatics and of magnetism that Ampère invented the laws of electrodynamics and electromagnetism. Physics does not progress as does geometry, which adds new final and indisputable propositions to the final and indisputable propositions it already possessed; physics makes progress because experiment constantly causes new disagreements to break out between laws and facts, and because physicists constantly touch up and modify laws in order that they may more faithfully represent facts.

5. THE LAWS OF PHYSICS ARE MORE DETAILED THAN THE LAWS OF COMMON SENSE

The laws that ordinary nonscientific experience allows us to formulate are general judgments whose meaning is immediate. In the presence of one of these judgments we may ask, "Is it true?" Often the answer is easy; in any case the answer is a definite yes or no. The law recognized as true is so for all time and for all men; it is fixed and absolute.

Scientific laws based on the experiments of physics are symbolic relations whose meaning would remain unintelligible to anyone who did not know physical theories. Since they are symbolic, they are never true or false; like the experiments on which they rest, they are approximate. The degree of approximation of a law, though sufficient today, will become insufficient in the future through the progress of experimental methods; sufficient for the needs of the physicist, it would not satisfy somebody else, so that a law of physics is always provisional and relative. It is provisional also in that it does not connect realities but symbols, and that is because there are always cases where the symbol no longer corresponds to reality; the laws of physics cannot be maintained except by continual retouching and modification.

The problem of the validity of the laws of physics hence poses itself in an entirely different manner, infinitely more complicated and delicate than the problem of the certainty of the laws of common sense. One might be tempted to draw the strange conclusion that the knowledge of the laws of physics constitutes a degree of knowledge inferior to the simple knowledge of the laws of common sense. We are content to reply to those who would deduce this paradoxical conclusion from the foregoing considerations by repeating for the laws of physics what we have said about scientific experiments: A law of physics possesses a certainty much less immediate and much more difficult to estimate than a law of common sense, but it surpasses the latter by the minute and detailed precision of its predictions.

Take the common-sense law "In Paris the sun rises every day in the east, climbs the sky, then comes down and sets in the west" and compare it with the formulas telling us the coordinates of the sun's center at each instant within about a second, and you will be convinced of the accuracy of this proposition.

The laws of physics can acquire this minuteness of detail only by sacrificing something of the fixed and absolute certainty of common-sense laws. There is a sort of balance between precision and certainty: one cannot be increased except to the detriment of the other. The miner who presents me with a stone can tell me without hesitation or qualification that it contains gold; but the chemist who shows me a shiny ingot, telling me, "It is pure gold," has to add the qualification "or nearly pure"; he cannot affirm that the ingot does not retain minute traces of impurities.

A man may swear to tell the truth, but it is not in his power to tell the whole truth and nothing but the truth. "Truth is so subtle a point that our instruments are too blunt to touch it exactly. When they do reach it, they crush the point and bear down around it, more on the false than on the true."[2]

[2] B. Pascal, *Pensées*.

PROBLEMS OF THE CONCEPT
OF GENERAL LAW:
Carl G. Hempel and P. Oppenheim *

From our general survey of the characteristics of scientific explanation, we now turn to a closer examination of its logical structure. The explanation of a phenomenon, we noted, consists in its subsumption under laws or under a theory. But what is a law, what is a theory? While the meaning of these concepts seems intuitively clear, an attempt to construct adequate explicit definitions for them encounters considerable difficulties. In the present section, some basic problems of the concept of law will be described and analyzed. . . .

The concept of law will be construed here so as to apply to true statements only. The apparently plausible alternative procedure of requiring high confirmation rather than truth of a law seems to be inadequate: It would lead to a relativized concept of law, which would be expressed by the phrase "sentence S is a law relatively to the evidence E." This does not seem to accord with the

* [This selection is extracted from Hempel and Oppenheim's "The Logic of Explanation," Part III, paragraph 6. This appeared originally in *Philosophy of Science*, Vol. 15, 1948; reprinted in Feigl and Brodbeck, *Readings in the Philosophy of Science* (New York: Appleton-Century-Crofts, 1953). References in footnotes are omitted. Reprinted by permission of the editors of *Philosophy of Science*.]

meaning customarily assigned to the concept of law in science and in methodological inquiry. Thus, for example, we would not say that Bode's general formula for the distance of the planets from the sun was a law relatively to the astronomical evidence available in the 1770's, when Bode propounded it, and that it ceased to be a law after the discovery of Neptune and the determination of its distance from the sun; rather, we would say that the limited original evidence had given a high probability to the assumption that the formula was a law, whereas more recent additional information reduced that probability so much as to make it practically certain that Bode's formula is not generally true, and hence not a law.[1]

Apart from being true, a law will have to satisfy a number of additional conditions. These can be studied independently of the factual requirement of truth, for they refer, as it were, to all logically possible laws, no matter whether factually true or false. Adopting a convenient term proposed by Goodman, we will say that a sentence is lawlike if it has all the characteristics of a general law, with the possible exception of truth. Hence, every law is a lawlike sentence, but not conversely.

Our problem of analyzing the concept of law thus reduces to that of explicating the meaning of "lawlike sentence." We shall construe the class of lawlike sentences as including analytic general statements, such as "A rose is a rose," as well as the lawlike sentences of empirical science, which have empirical content. It will not be necessary to require that each lawlike sentence permissible in explanatory contexts be of the second kind; rather, our definition of explanation will be so constructed as to guarantee the factual character of the totality of the laws—though not of every single one of them—which function in an explanation of an empirical fact.

What are the characteristics of lawlike sentences? First of all, lawlike sentences are statements of universal form, such as "All robins' eggs are greenish-blue," "All metals are conductors of electricity," "At constant pressure, any

[1] The requirement of truth for laws has the consequence that a given empirical statement S can never be definitely known to be a law; for the sentence affirming the truth of S is logically equivalent with S and is therefore capable only of acquiring a more or less high probability, or degree of confirmation, relatively to the experimental evidence available at any given time.

gas expands with increasing temperature." As these examples illustrate, a lawlike sentence usually is not only of universal but also of conditional form; it makes an assertion to the effect that universally, if a certain set of conditions, C, is realized, then another specified set of conditions, E, is realized as well. The standard form for the symbolic expression of a lawlike sentence is therefore the universal conditional. However, since any conditional statement can be transformed into a nonconditional one, conditional form will not be considered as essential for a lawlike sentence, while universal character will be held indispensable.

But the requirement of universal form is not sufficient to characterize lawlike sentences. Suppose, for example, that a certain basket, b, contains at a certain time t a number of red apples and nothing else. Then the statement

(S_1) Every apple in basket b at time t is red

is both true and of universal form. Yet the sentence does not qualify as a law; we would refuse, for example, to explain by subsumption under it the fact that a particular apple chosen at random from the basket is red. What distinguishes S_1 from a lawlike sentence? Two points suggest themselves, which will be considered in turn, namely, finite scope, and reference to a specified object.

First, the sentence S_1 makes, in effect, an assertion about a finite number of objects only, and this seems irreconcilable with the claim to universality which is commonly associated with the notion of law. But are not Kepler's laws considered as lawlike although they refer to a finite set of planets only? And might we not even be willing to consider as lawlike a sentence such as the following?

(S_2) All the sixteen ice cubes in the freezing tray of this refrigerator have a temperature of less than 10 degrees Centigrade.

This point might well be granted; but there is an essential difference between S_1 on the one hand and Kepler's laws as well as S_2 on the other: The latter, while finite in scope, are known to be consequences of more comprehensive laws whose scope is not limited, while for S_1 this is not the case.

Adopting a procedure recently suggested by Reichenbach, we will therefore distinguish between fundamental and derivative laws. A statement will be called a derivative law if it is of universal character and follows from some fundamental laws. The concept of fundamental law requires further clarification; so far, we may say that fundamental laws, and similarly fundamental lawlike sentences, should satisfy a certain condition of nonlimitation of scope.

It would be excessive, however, to deny the status of fundamental lawlike sentence to all statements which, in effect, make an assertion about a finite class of objects only, for that would rule out also a sentence such as "All robins' eggs are greenish-blue," since presumably the class of all robins' eggs—past, present, and future—is finite. But again, there is an essential difference between this sentence and, say, S_1. It requires empirical knowledge to establish the finiteness of the class of robins' eggs, whereas, when the sentence S_1 is construed in a manner which renders it intuitively unlawlike, the terms "basket b" and "apple" are understood so as to imply finiteness of the class of apples in the basket at time t. Thus, so to speak, the meaning of its constitutive terms alone—without additional factual information —entails that S_1 has a finite scope. Fundamental laws, then, will have to be construed so as to satisfy what we have called a condition of nonlimited scope; our formulation of that condition however, which refers to what is entailed by "the meaning" of certain expressions, is too vague and will have to be revised later. Let us note in passing that the stipulation here envisaged would bar from the class of fundamental lawlike sentences also such undesirable candidates as "All uranic objects are spherical," where "uranic" means the property of being the planet Uranus; indeed, while this sentence has universal form, it fails to satisfy the condition of nonlimited scope.

In our search for a general characterization of lawlike sentences, we now turn to a second clue which is provided by the sentence S_1. In addition to violating the condition of nonlimited scope, this sentence has the peculiarity of making reference to a particular object, the basket b; and this, too, seems to violate the universal character of law.[2] The restriction which seems indicated here, should however

[2] In physics, the idea that a law should not refer to any particular object has found its expression in the maxim that the general laws of physics should contain no reference to specific space-time points, and that spatiotemporal coordinates should occur in them only in the form of differences or differentials.

again be applied to fundamental lawlike sentences only; for a true general statement about the free fall of physical bodies on the moon, while referring to a particular object, would still constitute a law, albeit a derivative one.

It seems reasonable to stipulate, therefore, that a fundamental lawlike sentence must be of universal form and must contain no essential—i.e., uneliminable—occurrences of designations for particular objects. But this is not sufficient; indeed, just at this point, a particularly serious difficulty presents itself. Consider the sentence

(S_3) Everything that is either an apple in basket b at time t or a sample of ferric oxide is red.

If we use a special expression, say "x is ferple," as synonymous with "x is either an apple in b at t or a sample of ferric oxide," then the content of S_3 can be expressed in the form

(S_4) Everything that is ferple is red.

The statement thus obtained is of universal form and contains no designations of particular objects, and it also satisfies the condition of nonlimited scope; yet clearly, S_4 can qualify as a fundamental lawlike sentence no more than can S_3.

As long as "ferple" is a defined term of our language, the difficulty can readily be met by stipulating that after elimination of defined terms, a fundamental lawlike sentence must not contain essential occurrences of designations for particular objects. But this way out is of no avail when "ferple," or another term of the kind illustrated by it, is a primitive predicate of the language under consideration. This reflection indicates that certain restrictions have to be imposed upon those predicates—i.e., terms for properties or relations—which may occur in fundamental lawlike sentences.

More specifically, the idea suggests itself of permitting a predicate in a fundamental lawlike sentence only if it is purely universal, or, as we shall say, purely qualitative, in character; in other words, if a statement of its meaning does not require reference to any one particular object or spatiotemporal location. Thus, the terms "soft," "green," "warmer than," "as long as," "liquid," "electrically charged," "female," "father of" are purely qualitative predicates, while "taller than the Eiffel Tower," "medieval," "lunar," "arctic," "Ming" are not.[3]

Exclusion from fundamental lawlike sentences of predicates which are not purely qualitative would at the same time ensure satisfaction of the condition of nonlimited scope; for the meaning of a purely qualitative predicate does not require a finite extension; and indeed, all the sentences considered above which violate the condition of nonlimited scope make explicit or implicit reference to specific objects.

The stipulation just proposed suffers, however, from the vagueness of the concept of purely qualitative predicate. The question whether indication of the meaning of a given predicate in English does or does not require reference to some one specific object does not always permit an unequivocal answer since English as a natural language does not provide explicit definitions or other clear explications of meaning for its terms. It seems therefore reasonable to attempt definition of the concept of law not with respect to English or any other natural language, but rather with respect to a formalized language—let us call it a model language, L—which is governed by a well-determined system of logical rules, and in which every term either is characterized as primitive or is introduced by an explicit definition in terms of the primitives.

This reference to a well-determined system is customary in logical research and is indeed quite natural in the context of any attempt to develop precise criteria for certain logical distinctions. But it does not by itself suffice to overcome the specific difficulty under discussion. For while it is now readily possible to characterize as not purely qualitative all those among the defined predicates in L whose definiens contains an essential occurrence of some indivi-

[3] The above characterization of purely universal predicates seems preferable to a simpler and perhaps more customary one, to the effect that a statement of the meaning of the predicate must require no reference to particular objects. For this formulation might be too exclusive since it could be argued that stating the meaning of such purely qualitative terms as "blue" or "hot" requires illustrative reference to some particular object which has the quality in question. The essential point is that no one specific object has to be chosen; any one in the logically unlimited set of blue or of hot objects will do. In explicating the meaning of "taller than the Eiffel Tower," "being an apple in basket b at the time t," "medieval," etc., however, reference has to be made to one specific object or to some one in a limited set of objects.

dual name, our problem remains open for the primitives of the language, whose meanings are not determined by definitions within the language but rather by semantical rules of interpretation. For we want to permit the interpretation of the primitives of L by means of such attributes as blue, hard, solid, warmer, but not by the properties of being a descendant of Napoleon, or an arctic animal, or a Greek statue; and the difficulty is precisely that of stating rigorous criteria for the distinction between the permissible and the nonpermissible interpretations. Thus the problem of setting up an adequate definition for purely qualitative attributes now arises again; namely, for the concepts of the metalanguage in which the semantical interpretation of the primitives is formulated. We may postpone an encounter with the difficulty by presupposing formalization of the semantical metalanguage, the meta-metalanguage, and so forth; but somewhere, we will have to stop at a nonformalized metalanguage, and for it a characterization of purely qualitative predicates will be needed and will present much the same problems as nonformalized English, with which we began. The characterization of a purely qualitative predicate as one whose meaning can be made explicit without reference to any one particular object points to the intended meaning but does not explicate it precisely, and the problem of an adequate definition of purely qualitative predicates remains open.

3

LAWS AND THEORIES IN
THE PHYSICAL SCIENCES:
C. F. Presley ·

I

The complexity of the procedures and arguments used in
the sciences, and the vagueness of the terms "law" and
"theory," make it difficult to say anything which is both
informative and general. Although this discussion is restricted
to the physical sciences, I do not claim that my remarks
apply to all the laws and all the theories in this field. I
intend to describe some of the definitive characteristics of
a certain kind of law, to indicate that there are some laws
of this kind and some which are different, and to consider
the way in which laws of this kind function in a science.
I shall then consider theories in the same way. Statements
of laws and theoretical statements are sometimes contrasted with factual, material object, or observation statements, which, it is implied, are pure and simple. If this
purity and simplicity are only apparent, the contrast loses
much of its force. Consequently, I shall begin with a brief

· [This selection is reprinted, with references omitted, from *The
Australasian Journal of Philosophy*, Vol. XXXII, No. 2, 1954, pp.
79–103. Reprinted by permission of C. F. Presley and the editors of
The Australasian Journal of Philosophy.]

discussion of the kind of statements upon which laws and theories are based: a discussion which is intended, primarily, to make explicit what is assumed in the rest of this paper.

Some material object statements are the result of inference, while others are the result of inspection. In the first case, the evidence upon which the statement was based could be described, but in the second it would be unusual to speak of evidence. A statement based on inspection may turn out to be false: the man who made the statement may later admit that he was mistaken, deluded, or the victim of an illusion. To admit this, however, is to admit that some statements are more certain than others. Furthermore, it is possible to guard against mistakes. Some material object statements are less fallible than others because they make a smaller claim. Compare "Metals expand when heated," "This metal expands when heated," "This metal was heated, and it expanded," and "A piece of metal was heated, and it expanded." There are some material object statements which we describe as certain, and of which we say that we know them to be true. It is admitted that they could conceivably turn out to be false, but in saying that they are certain or known to be true, part of our meaning is that no further tests would increase our confidence in them, and that we have no reason to expect that they will be falsified.

Now, consider what the physicist or chemist does when he takes a reading: he records the number which is opposite an engraved mark, a pointer, or a column of liquid, or he writes down the numbers which are stamped on the weights that he has used. Taking a reading is not always as simple as this, but it often is and in designing experiments every effort is made to make it so. These readings may be said to make a minimum claim: to be correct they have to satisfy only one condition.

The development of an experimental technique is partly the development of a procedure which is such that, first, a mistake is not likely to be made, and secondly, if a mistake is made, then it will be detected. Liquids are colored so that they may easily be seen; small scales are read through telescopes; verniers and other devices are used in measurement, and where changes of color are important, color charts are attached to the apparatus. Simple rules of procedure are adopted in order to reduce the chance of error. A single reading is not accepted unless it is impossible to take more, and this repetition is one of the ways of detecting mistakes. When a new technique is being developed, the apparatus is modified until consistent readings can be obtained, and until this is possible the results are not accepted. The difficulty of obtaining consistent readings emphasizes the importance of exactly specifying the conditions in which they were obtained.

The numbers which are written in a notebook are correct or incorrect readings, but beyond the context in which they were written, these numbers depend for their meaning on such expressions as "millimeters of mercury" or "degrees Centigrade" which are written after them, and this is to say that they have meaning within a system of measurement or with reference to a theory. I shall refer to a reading together with an expression of this kind as an observation, and to a statement that a certain observation was made under certain conditions as an observation statement. The physicist or chemist must know not only how to take readings and how to interpret them but also what readings to take and when to take them, and this depends on his knowledge of accepted techniques, systems of measurement and theories, and of their relevance to the work he is doing. Furthermore, the apparatus used in making observations is the result of the application of theories and techniques. To quote Mr. Mackie: "Observation includes thinking and relies on background knowledge."

In the event of a change in a system of measurement, or of the adoption of a new theory, readings would have to be reinterpreted. It might be the case that they could no longer be interpreted because a factor which was not taken into account at the time had been found to be relevant, but they would not become incorrect. Observation statements are not falsified by subsequent developments, but they may cease to be useful or interesting. These statements make a claim greater than readings, but still very limited: that a particular observation was made in conditions of a certain kind—conditions which were examined and recorded with care. They are the result of methods which are designed to eliminate errors, and consequently they are among those statements which are certain or known to be true, in the sense which I have specified.

II

Laws of the type which I shall discuss are usually called empirical laws. Scientists normally apply this term to a law which is based on observed regularities, but which has not been explained by a theory. I shall consider as an empirical law any law which was *originally* based on observations, as distinct from being derived from a theory. Thus, in saying that a law is an empirical law, I imply that scientists did describe or would have described it as an empirical law, but not that they do so now. The second characteristic of an empirical law is that the statement of the law has no terms which do not appear in the observation statements on which it is based. Boyle's law, for example, might be described, provisionally, as a generalized observation statement. A further necessary characteristic of an empirical law is that values of its variable terms may be determined independently of each other, and without presupposing the law. Boyle's law, Hooke's law, and Snell's law satisfy these three criteria. In contrast, Stokes's law is not an empirical law, because it was the result of theoretical work; Avogadro's law does not satisfy the second condition, since it refers to particles which cannot be directly observed, and Newton's second law is excluded because force and mass are not independent in the required sense.

To the question, "Is an empirical law which is accepted within a science true?" at least four answers have been given. First: that such a law could be true, and could be known to be true. Second: that such a law is true, but in a sense different from the sense in which observation statements, for example, are true. Third: it is held that we cannot know an established law to be true, but that we are justified in asserting it to be true, in the only sense of "true." Fourth: it is said that an empirical law is neither true nor false. This list is neither exhaustive nor detailed, but many of the proposed answers to this question fall under one or more of these headings, and the list will serve as a basis for a discussion of the question.

The belief that empirical laws could be known to be true has led to the search for a principle which would reduce induction to deduction. I shall not discuss views of this kind here, as I think that it can be shown, first, that even if it were possible to formulate such a principle, it would not be possible to establish its truth, and secondly, that it is not possible to state the principle in a way that would guarantee any particular empirical law.

As an example of the second kind, I have in mind the view expressed by Dr. Waismann when he wrote: "A law of nature is never true in the same sense in which, say, 'There is a fire burning in this room' is," but I should add that I do not know whether he still holds such a view, nor do I know whether he meant by a "law of nature" what I mean by "an empirical law." It may be argued that the word "true" is used in quite different ways when we speak of true statements on the one hand, and of true Christians on the other; that it is necessary, in order to avoid certain logical paradoxes, to say that "true" as applied to statements also has different senses, and it seems obvious that if empirical laws are ever true, they are true in a sense different from that in which observation statements are true. If I look at a pointer, see that it points to the figure 5, and say that this is so, I should be at a loss to say on what evidence my statement was based, and if I were asked to carry out additional tests I should not know what to do. If I am later convinced that my statement was false, then I have to admit that I was mistaken or deceived. If, on the other hand, I say that an empirical law is true, I am not claiming to have seen that all gases behave in a certain way, for example, but rather that all the available evidence supports the law, and that consequently the law would be used with confidence in order to make predictions. It is always possible to make additional tests, although this may be held to be unnecessary. If the prediction fails, it does not follow that someone must have been mistaken or deceived.

One of the consequences of saying that an empirical law is true if it is supported by all the available evidence, is that we might have to say of a law that it *was* true, but that it *is* false. This might be regarded as an objection, or it might be offered as an additional reason for saying that laws are true or false in a special sense. The truth of statements about statements may be different from the truth of statements, but from this alone it does not follow, and of course Waismann has never suggested that it does follow, that a law statement and an observation statement are true in different senses. Indeed, even if there are different levels of language, the fact that the terms in a law state-

ment are exactly those in the relevant observation statements suggests that both are on the same level.

A further consequence of this view may be that if two
statements, true or false in different senses, are related, then
the statement of this relation is true or false in a third sense.
I am not sure of this because, although it is clear that "the
known relations of logic" do not hold between statements
at different levels, the nature of the "looser" relations which
do hold is obscure. The premises of a syllogism may suggest
the correct conclusion to some people, and an incorrect
one to others. One statement may suggest or invite us to
accept another, and this may be because the statements
are related in a certain way, but to say that the one suggests the other is not to describe the logical relation between
them. A "looser" relation must be either a relation which is
not a logical relation, or a logical relation which has not
yet been specified. But the former view is untenable in this
context, because it implies that although certain observation statements may suggest a law, the truth or falsity of
the law is quite independent of the truth or falsity of the
observation statements. Consequently, to hold this second
view is to assert, first, that no satisfactory account of the
relation between an empirical law and the observation
statements on which it is based has yet been given, and
secondly, that no such account could be given in terms of
"the known relations of logic." The difficulties in this position
arise, here, from the attempt to explain one fact. When a
law is used for prediction, it appears to function as the
premise in a deductive argument, and yet if the prediction
fails, the law is seldom rejected. These difficulties may not
be insuperable, but I think that they can be avoided, and
that an adequate account of empirical laws and of their relations to observation statements can be given without multiplying the senses of "true," and without introducing unspecified relations.

The third position is that since an empirical law is an
unrestricted generalization we cannot know it to be true,
but that if the law has been properly established we are
justified in asserting it to be true. It is maintained that the
law, together with a number of statements to the effect
that the law applies in certain conditions, and a statement
of the initial conditions, implies a certain outcome. The list
of boundary conditions is not complete. If the prediction
fails, then the protasis is falsified, but since it is a conjunc-

tion of an indefinite number of statements, it is always possible to retain the law. We may say either that one of the specified boundary conditions was not satisfied, or, if we think that they all were, that there is an unspecified condition which was not satisfied. Later we may be able to specify this condition and add it to the list.

It seems that in choosing between this position and the last one, we have to choose between an unspecified relation between precise statements, and a strict relation between two statements, one of which can never be completely stated. It is also important to note that to assert a law to be true when it is admitted that it is not known to be true, is merely to announce the intention of using it for prediction: what is known to be true is that the law has been found to apply in certain conditions.

This analysis does not go far enough to do the job for which it was designed. The statements of boundary conditions are separated from the statement of the law in the protasis, so that we may still assert the law to be true if the apodosis is found to be false. But the history of Boyle's law, for example, shows not only that we have increased and refined our knowledge of the pressures and temperatures at which it has been found to apply but also that we have changed our ideas about what it applies to. Originally it was said to apply to the air, later to gases, and since then our notion of what is to count as a gas has been continually modified. At very low pressures the law applies to all gases; at pressures nearer normal it applies, at any given temperature, to some gases and not to others; in some cases it applies exactly, in others approximately, and in others not at all. To state the law as applying only in those conditions in which it applies exactly to all gases, would not do justice to the way in which the law is used. If this is taken into account, the analysis would involve not only the separate statement of the conditions in which the law applies, but also statements that in certain conditions it applies only to certain gases, and in other conditions to others. The statements of conditions cannot be separated from statements about what the law applies to in these conditions. In order to explain the persistence of Boyle's law, and in order to enable us to retain this law, it is necessary to separate from the law statements not only of the conditions in which the law applies, but also of what it applies to in any of these conditions. But to do this is to empty the law of all content, leaving only a formula or equation which by itself could be neither true nor false, and which, consequently, could never function as the premise in an argument. The only thing about Boyle's law which has remained unchanged, except possibly in notation, is "$PV = K$," and this, by itself, is neither true nor false, any more than "$x^2 + y^2 = 3$" or "All S is P" is true or false. This conclusion, which is the basis of the fourth position which I shall consider, implies that an empirical law cannot function as a premise. This consequence is, I think, in accord with practice in the sciences. When a problem is solved, or a prediction made by means of an empirical law, the premises are the initial conditions, and the conclusion the final conditions; the law is used as a formula or rule of inference, and if the prediction fails, it is concluded, not that the law is false, but that conditions were such that it did not hold.

The collection of statements which is normally described as the exposition of an empirical law is to be analyzed as, first, a formula or equation which is satisfied by the observations which led to the formulation of the law, and which, by itself, is neither true nor false, and secondly, statements of conditions in which the observations were taken, and statements of what was being examined when they were taken—samples of air, steel springs or glass blocks, for example. For brevity, I shall treat both kinds of statements as stating conditions. These observation statements are known to be true.

Many experiments are such that in adjusting the apparatus in order to take a fresh reading, any marked irregularity in the rate of change of possible readings would be noticed. Now any given set of observations will satisfy large numbers of different equations, but these equations are such that, within the range of the given observations, they do not differ by an amount that could be detected, for if this were not so, it would be easy to eliminate some of them. Consequently the difference between the equations will become significant only when we extrapolate beyond the given observations. It should be noted here that laws are very seldom applied in conditions different from those in which they have previously been found to hold. The formulation of a law leads to further investigation of the conditions in which it holds, and this work may be carried out just in order to see whether it can be applied in certain conditions. There remains, however, the question of choosing between different equations which are satisfied by the given observations. I shall not consider this here. I say only that it appears that the simplest equation is chosen, and that this choice was based on a belief about the nature of the world, but that it is now a matter of economy of effort. The relation between any set of observations and any equation is unambiguous, and to say that, given certain observations, a certain equation is chosen, may be to imply something about the equation, but it is not to describe any additional relation between the two. There might be reasons for describing this relation as mathematical rather than logical, but there is no reason to describe it as a loose relation.

Despite these limitations of the use of a law for prediction, it is still the case, of course, that laws are applied in situations numerically different from those in which they were established, and in conditions which, although they appear to be the same as those in which the law has been found to hold, are not known to be so. It might be contended that when a law is so applied, it is inferred that the law will hold, and that this inference is based on some general premise, such as: "If a law has held in certain conditions, then in exactly similar conditions it will always hold." But this is a disguised tautology, for although we have independent criteria for similar conditions, one of our criteria for judging whether two sets of conditions are exactly the same is that the same laws hold in both cases. If a law applied in one case and not in the other, then we should say that the conditions must have been different, even though we may not be able to say what the difference was. Subsequent investigation might show that a factor which had not been taken into account was relevant, but if it did not, then it would be concluded that some of the terms in the observation statements were not sufficiently precise. The making more precise of such terms would involve a new way of interpreting readings. If a scientist or an engineer makes any inference before applying a law, his conclusion is not that a certain law must hold, but that a certain law is the correct one to apply. This conclusion would follow from some such suppressed premise as this: "The correct law to apply in any given situation is the law which has been found to apply in situations in which the conditions known to be relevant are known to be the same as those in the given situation." This, to borrow Max Born's expression, is a "rule of craft."

This procedure is justified by its success in the past. Those who have suggested that this is no justification have not, as far as I know, been able to say what would be a justification. No such justification could be given in the seventeenth century, of course, and this is why belief in the uniformity and the simplicity of nature is important in the history of science, although not in its logic. It is sometimes asked whether this procedure is rational. This is, in effect, to ask whether, when making predictions, it is rational to take into account all the most carefully collected and examined evidence which is believed to be relevant, and the answer is that this is just what we mean by "rational" in this context. A physicist, a chemist, or an engineer may have more confidence in one prediction than in another. It is possible to say that in certain cases a certain degree of confidence is reasonable, and where it is important to be able to do so, methods of assessing this degree of confidence have been developed, but these methods are themselves based on what is known to have happened in the past.

To say that empirical laws are neither true nor false is to state this fourth position too crudely, for although "$PV = K$" is neither true nor false, this formula by itself is not Boyle's Law. The law is a formula together with a large number of statements of conditions. The terms in these statements may be modified, and the list of statements may be increased. To treat the law as a generalization about the way in which all gases behave in certain conditions, and to ask if this general statement is true or false, is to invite confusion. The scope of the generalization is such that we could not possibly know it to be true in the way in which we know an observation statement to be true. But the fact that the law is still used nearly three hundred years after its original formulation suggests that it must be at least partly true. On the other hand, the continual modification of the law suggests that previous formulations have been, and that the present formulation might be, found to be false. We *could* say that empirical laws are true in a sense different from that in which observation statements are true, but we should then have to give an account of the logical relations between statements which are true or false in different senses. If the distinction is not made between inferring that a certain law is the correct one to apply in a certain situation, and making inferences in accordance with the law, then the relation between laws and observation statements appears to be loose and difficult to specify. This fourth analysis does not introduce inferences which cannot be justified, relations which are not specified, or premises that cannot be stated. Instead of representing the scientist as asserting to be true what cannot be known to be true, or as establishing truths of a special kind, it represents him as discovering formulae which apply in certain conditions; as investigating these conditions, and as predicting by means of these formulae, and this is, I suggest, more closely in accordance with the practice of scientists, although it may differ from what some of them preach. Empirical laws, however, are a small part of the physical sciences, and an analysis of them must take account of the way in which they are related to theories.

III

The statement of an empirical law contains no terms which do not appear in the observation statements from which it was derived. In contrast to this, it is a necessary characteristic of the kind of theory with which I am concerned that it shall have terms which do not appear in the empirical laws, or, consequently, in the observation statements on which it is based. I shall take as an example a theory which is simple and well known: the kinetic theory of gases. The empirical laws upon which this theory was based were Boyle's law and Charles's law, which refer only to the observed pressures, volumes, and temperatures of enclosed gases. The theory, on the other hand, refers to very small elastic particles: a term which does not appear in either of the laws. It is because of this feature of some theories that, although industry may be necessary in the sciences, it is not sufficient. Major contributions to the sciences have been made only by men of imagination, and Bacon was quite wrong in supposing that the sciences could ever be developed without such men.

The terms which appear in the theory but not in the laws are not precisely defined. Gas particles are very small, perfectly elastic, and they and their environment are such that the laws of classical mechanics apply to them exactly. This is an example of one of the ways in which two theories may be related. In collisions these particles behave as if they were spherical, but whether they are spherical or not is not stated. Their velocity, mass, size, shape, and any other properties that they may have are not specified. This "open texture," to borrow Waismann's term, gives the theory a flexibility such that it may be developed and modified in order to take account of observations subsequent to its formulation. Those who advocated that theories should be constructed with a precision that would preclude metaphysical speculation failed to see that this would also preclude theoretical speculation, which is essential to the development of science.

Whether the terms peculiar to a theory refer to postulated entities or whether they refer only, although in a special way, to the entities to which the relevant observation statements refer, has been debated for many years. Is the Kinetic Theory, for example, to be interpreted as implying that there are gas particles, or only that gases behave as if they were collections of elastic particles? This issue is raised when it is asked whether electrons were discovered or invented, and whether it is reasonable to suppose that mesons are really there. It is not only philosophers who are interested in these questions: Glasstone, for example, in his *Textbook of Physical Chemistry*, describes the Brownian movement as "One of the most striking and important pieces of evidence in favor of the kinetic theory and of the real existence of molecules." It is striking because it would enable any one of us to see, just as Ostwald saw, the molecules in action. But what exactly did Ostwald see? Small grains of powder moving erratically in a liquid, as if they were being bombarded by very small particles, which he did *not* see. To show that the observed motion of these grains of powder is just what it would be if they were being agitated by the impacts of particles which have the properties of those particles which are used to explain the behavior of gases and liquids, to show this, it was necessary to refer to many other observations and to make elaborate calculations. This was the work of Perrin and Einstein. As Schrödinger says of observations which are, in the same way, striking evidence for the real existence of mesons: "In their apparent simplicity they appeal to the vivid imagination of an intelligent child. They would have set any of the old warriors for the cause of atomism, from Democritus down to Dalton and Boltzmann, gasping with joyful excitement. Yet they are not as simple as they seem. This is witnessed by the pages and pages of intricate formalism that is often devoted to account for even the simplest of them." Now, while I do not wish to join Schrödinger in patting the intelligent Democritus on the head, I think it is important to realize that these striking phenomena are evidence direct only in comparison with the other evidence on which the relevant theories are based. Are we to say, then, that what we actually see are columns of mercury, specks of powder moving in liquids, and marks on photographic plates, and that we invent molecules and mesons in order to deal economically with a great variety of such observations?

Mr. Thornton has suggested that if we say that the electron was invented in 1897, then we must also say that Neptune was invented in 1846. The calculations of Adams and Leverrier are comparable in complexity with those of Einstein, and what was seen through the telescope would have been as meaningless to the layman as the photographic plates which show the path of a meson. Despite the similarity of these two cases, there is an important difference between them, a difference which will show the second characteristic of the kind of theory with which I am concerned. If it is asked what Galle discovered in 1846, we can say that he discovered that there are eight planets, not seven: that a region of space which was previously thought to be comparatively empty was found to contain a very large spherical object. This issue is sometimes raised in connection with micro-organisms, and in this context, too, we can say that it was discovered that the air contains not only insects and particles of dust but also very small organisms. But consider the so-called discovery of gas particles: we have not discovered that there is something where we had thought that there was nothing, nor have we discovered that gases contain something when we had thought that they contained nothing. We have not discovered that, in addition to tables, benches, flasks, and gases, there are also molecules. If it is accepted that a gas is a collection of molecules, then to satisfy oneself that a cylinder really does contain a gas is to satisfy oneself that the molecules are really there. Clearly this does not answer the question, but it shows that it may be dealt with by considering the function of such statements as "A gas is a collection of molecules." Furthermore, I can see no other way of dealing with the question, for those who disagree on this matter seldom dispute about the reliability of the relevant evidence, nor do they suggest that further experiments should be made. Statements of this kind are characteristic of the exposition of theories of the type with which I am concerned: theories which are sometimes described as being about the structure of matter. The body of theories about the structure of molecules and atoms and the properties of fundamental particles have the two related characteristics which I have described, and the kinetic theory of gases is a simple example of such theories. I shall use the word "theory" to refer only to theories of this kind. Theories about the habits of birds, the origin of species, the cause of a disease, or the function of an organ are not theories of this kind, although they may be related to such theories. And there are theories which are such that it would be difficult to decide whether they are of the kind with which I am concerned, or not.

It is sometimes asked whether a theory is true, and it is suggested that this is an important question, because it appears that if we knew, for example, that "A gas is a collection of particles" is true, or that it is reasonable to believe that it is true, then the real existence of these particles would be established, or at least made probable. But some theories which are accepted cannot be true. Incompatible theories and theories which are not self-consistent are common in the sciences. Although difficulties of this kind are usually resolved, there is no reason to suppose that they will not continue to arise. Indeed it is to be hoped that they will, for they are among the most powerful stimuli to scientific inquiry. To say that, because one of the two incompatible theories is better supported than the other, the first is true and the second false, would be undesirable. . . . If, because two theories are incompatible, they are both said to be false, then it is necessary to explain why they are used rather than any other false theories. If they are retained because they work, I suggest that it is more important to distinguish theories that work from those that do not, and go on to see what it means to say that a theory works than to speak of them as true or false. I suggest, too, that it is misleading to describe as false a theory which is of value in pure science and reliable in practice, and that it is misleading to speak of the vast majority of theories as being false. I think it is possible to give a satisfactory account of theories, of the relation between theories and empirical laws, and of the status of submicroscopic entities, without describing theories in terms of truth and falsity.

Many of the characteristics of a theory are revealed if it

is considered as a language. I want to make it quite clear that I am not saying that a theory *is* an artificial language. If I may be allowed a further analogy: an artificial language is rigid and sterile, like a wax flower, but a theory, on the other hand, is more like a hot-house plant. Its development is controlled more or less successfully by skillful pruning and careful attention. If it lives, it grows more rapidly than a normal plant, it is more fertile, and it dies sooner. The vocabulary of a theory is partly its own, partly that of other theories, and of mathematics, and partly that of ordinary language. In a theory many of the features of natural languages are exaggerated.

I shall call observation statements, including complex statements of the conditions in which empirical laws have been observed to hold, O-statements. Statements in the language of theory are T-statements. Some O-statements can be exactly translated into T-statements, but others cannot. That a gas is yellow-green or that it has an acrid smell, for example, cannot be expressed in terms of the kinetic theory of gases. Some T-statements cannot be translated into O-statements. This feature is present, although to a smaller extent, in natural languages. Some T-statements are logically related to others, and some O-statements are logically related to other O-statements. But the pattern of the logical relations in a theory is different from that among the O-statements. By this I mean that there will be statements such that O_1 and O_2 is a conjunction, while the translations T_1 and T_2 are the terms of an implication. As well as T-statements and O-statements, there are other statements which I shall call translation rules.

It is usually difficult to say precisely when a theory began. We might say that the kinetic theory was formulated by Maxwell, or Clausius, or Bernouilli, but more than a hundred years earlier Bacon had said that heat is the restrained and expansive motion of the smallest parts of bodies. "Atom" is now a scientific term and in the time of Democritus it was not, but when did atomism become a theory? Theories are not constructed; they grow out of earlier theories and doctrines just as a language develops imperceptibly out of earlier languages. In the history of theories, however, there are critical periods when a theory is "formulated," or "reformulated," or "put on a scientific basis," and it is such a period that I shall consider. When the kinetic theory of gases was formulated it was proposed that a gas should be regarded as a collection of particles with the properties which I have already described. It was further proposed that the rate of change of the momentum of the particles per unit area at the walls of the container be regarded as the observed pressure of the gas, and the mean kinetic energy of the particles as a measure of the temperature of the gas. These proposals, if the theory is adopted, become translation rules.

The particles are so described that it follows that the rate of change of their momentum per unit area multiplied by the volume in which they move is constant, provided that their mean kinetic energy remains constant. It also follows that if the rate of change of momentum per unit area is constant, the mean kinetic energy can increase only if the volume increases. Now, if we apply the translation rules to these two theoretical statements, we have, first, Boyle's law, and secondly, Charles's law. The statement O_1, that this is a certain mass of hydrogen at such-and-such a temperature, and O_2, that this gas obeyed Boyle's law within a certain pressure range, are merely an observed conjunction, but their translations are such that T_1 implies T_2. This is the sense in which the kinetic theory explains the gas laws. Empirical laws are said to be explained when they are related to a theory and thus related to other laws and to other observations. The establishment of such relations increases the confidence with which we apply the laws. This is not the only sense of "explanation," even within the sciences, but it is one of the most common, and it is unobjectionable, because there is no suggestion of finality in it. It is objectionable, however, to project the logical necessity which holds within the theory onto the world, and to talk of discovering the necessity which underlies phenomena. To do this is to overlook the way in which the logical structure of a theory is constantly changed.

In order to take account of additional or more accurate observations a theory is changed in a number of ways. The translation rules are modified: the observed pressure of a gas becomes the rate of change of momentum of the particles per unit area less the cohesion pressure, and the observed volume becomes the theoretical volume plus the volume of the particles. Here the particles have been given the additional property of attracting each other, and, in certain conditions, their volume is specified. The open texture of the term "gas particle" makes changes of this kind possible. Not only may the theoretical terms be modified but also the terms in the observation statements, and this is why, as I have pointed out, changes in a theory may lead to the reinterpretation of readings. The logical relations between T-statements is often based on other laws and theories, and this is a further source of change. The behavior of large numbers of gas particles was treated by classical statistics, but quantum statistics have been found to be more appropriate in certain contexts. When changes in a theory are made, the old rules are not completely discarded. Gas particles attract each other, but at very low pressures this attraction is negligible. In this way, levels of sophistication, comparable with those in ordinary language, develop in a theory, and we talk of the simple kinetic theory and the developed theory, and of statements as being of different orders of accuracy.

As the logical structure of a theory is developed, and as the fundamental terms are more precisely defined, it is possible to work out implications which were not foreseen when the theory was formulated. There may be translation rules for these implied T-statements, or it may be necessary to formulate new ones. Yukawa, for example, worked out that, according to the accepted theories, there should be a free particle about one hundred and fifty times as great as the electron. Such a particle, one of the mesons, was later detected. This is the way in which a theory may lead to genuine discoveries.

I want to consider now some of the conditions which lead to a theory being described as unsatisfactory. The development of a theory consists of changes of four kinds, changes which are not independent: first, the terms in the theory may be modified or made more precise; secondly, the rules of inference within the theory may be changed; thirdly, the translation rules may be changed; and fourthly, the terms in the relevant observation statements may be modified. Because O-statements are related to, or might even be described as a part of, ordinary language, the possibility of modification here is restricted. Consequently the development of a theory will consist mainly of changes of the first two kinds. The difficulties which may arise from the continual modification of the fundamental terms in a theory are exemplified by the theory of the ether. To quote Chalmers: "The more the ether was studied, the more extensive and remarkable became the properties with

which it had to be endowed. . . . At one time the complexity
. . . of its assigned properties seemed to some physicists
seriously to suggest the simultaneous existence of six ethers
side by side, or interwoven throughout all space. . . ."
The difficulty here seems to be that the complexity of the
ether leads to a total loss of analogy. Having no experience
of anything like this medium we do not know what rules
of inference would be appropriate in such a theory, and
consequently we have no means of working out the implications of the theory. Indeed the theory has no implications
which lead beyond the observations which it was designed
to explain, and consequently it is sterile. Furthermore, because the complexity of the ether is far more puzzling than
the relevant observations, it is useless as an explanation.

Difficulties of the second kind are exemplified in contemporary work on fundamental particles. Not only was
Yukawa's meson discovered, but also seven or eight others.
The theory was equal to this, inasmuch as the charges and
masses of all these mesons have been worked out. But
Powell, commenting on a table which shows the characteristics of fifteen fundamental particles, writes: ". . . the
variety displayed in this table appears to us as an assembly
of empirical facts without any coherence, and this emphasizes the inadequacy of our present theoretical views."
The trouble here is that, although the translation rules,
the rules for interpreting observations in terms of the theory,
have proved satisfactory, the logical structure of the theory
has broken down. T-statements are no longer related as
they must be if they are to explain, or, to use Powell's
words, to give coherence to the observations.

So far I have been concerned to establish an analogy
between a theory and a language, and to show that such
an analysis gives a coherent account of the way in which
theories are developed, used, and found to be unsatisfactory. The analogy is not complete—the language of a theory
could not be anyone's mother tongue, no matter how often
he used it or how early he learned it—but I think that I
can carry the analogy further than I have yet done.

The vocabulary of a theory is partly that of ordinary
language, but words which are used in both often have
different senses. We might say that, from all that we had
heard, we had inferred that so-and-so was a tall man,
but that when we met him we saw that he was not.

When we saw him, our inferences were at an end. When we "see" molecules or mesons, however, the most elaborate inferences are necessary before we can be sure of what we "see." But although some of the ways in which we use "see" are changed when we move from ordinary language to the language of a theory, others are not. "Seeing is believing," and consequently some observations which are much the same as the others that support a theory are picked out as being more striking and more conclusive than the others. It is partly because it is impossible to remove, by definition and qualification, the "emotive meaning" of a word that to describe a theory as true or false is undesirable.

Both O-statements and T-statements are true or false. If a T-statement can be directly verified, then it must be possible to translate it into O-statements, but this does not mean that such a translation is actually made. A physicist who examines a photographic plate does not have to describe the lines on the plate and then translate his observations, although he may do this if he is describing his methods. In this context it would be more appropriate to describe the T-statements as observation statements in the language of the theory. Despite this, however, the distinction between O-statements and T-statements does not break down, for it is always possible to speak either of the pressure of a gas or of the change of momentum of particles per unit area, and either of a mark on a plate or of the path of a meson, although one way of speaking may sometimes be out of place or pointless. If a translation rule is questioned, it is necessary to consult an exposition of the theory, just as a dictionary might be consulted in order to see what "dog" is in German. Because theories change more rapidly than natural languages, if an exact translation is required it might be necessary to consult publications subsequent to the formulation of the theory. It is appropriate to ask whether T_1 is true, or whether O_3 is true, and translation rules may be learned or checked, but it is inappropriate to ask whether a theory is true. Just as English is widely used, Welsh only in some districts, and Anglo-Saxon not at all, so some theories have a very general application, others apply only in restricted fields, and some are of interest only to the historian of the sciences. A theory is adopted and used: observations confirm its usefulness or show it to be of limited value for explanation and discovery.

Despite the situation described by Chalmers, some physicists are still concerned with the ether, and this shows, as many other examples would show, that theories are not abandoned. They die out, leaving behind them the observations on which they were based, those which discredited them, experimental and mathematical techniques, and some technical terms.

I have already discussed the relation between a theory and an empirical law, considered as a formula together with statements about the conditions in which it holds. The law is not deduced from the theory, but is related by translation to theoretical statements which are deductively related to each other. I shall not attempt a further analysis of the relation between an observation statement and its translation in a theory at present. The application of translation rules is to be distinguished from the formulation and the modification of these rules, for the former calls for skill, and is done correctly or incorrectly, while the latter demands imagination and insight, and cannot be described as correct or incorrect.

The sentence "A gas is a collection of particles" may be used in teaching a theory or in applying it, and to use this sentence without qualification is to imply that the theory is established and unrestricted. To say that some T-statements such as "That is the path of a meson" or "A hydrogen molecule is of such and such a size" are true is to say that there are mesons and gas particles. Against the contention that a gas merely behaves as if it were a collection of particles, it may be argued that experiments show that a gas actually is a collection of particles. If it is objected that these experiments confirm only that a gas behaves as if it consisted of particles, we may ask what sort of observations would be accepted as evidence of the existence of gas particles. Since the mass of such particles, their size, their most probable velocity in any given circumstances, and the number of them present in a given volume can be calculated, it would appear that evidence of a more direct kind is required. But gases do not consist of particles which can be touched or seen, either with the naked eye or through a microscope, nor do they behave as if they consisted of such particles. In the early stages of a theory there is a point in saying, for example, that electricity behaves as if it were a fluid, for this leads to attempts to discover whether it is a fluid or not. And if it is said that in acoustics, gases behave as if they were continuous fluids, the point here is that other observations have already shown that a gas is not such a fluid. But in an established and unrestricted theory the situation is different: if it is accepted that there are no known circumstances in which a gas behaves as if it were not a collection of particles, but also contended that no possible observations would lead us to say, not that a gas behaves as if it were a collection of particles, but that it is such a collection, then the distinction becomes pointless. If we say that A behaves as if it were a B, we could then say either that B behaves as if it were a C, or that B is a C. Either the former leads to a statement of the latter kind or it follows that all statements are really of the "as if" form. If the statements that a gas behaves as if it consisted of particles, and that a gas is a collection of particles, are exactly equivalent, then the use of the expression "as if" is pointless. If, on the other hand, the two are not equivalent, then the former suggests that a gas behaves as if it were composed of things which we can describe in a way more direct than that in which we describe the behavior of gases. This is not so. A gas does not behave as if it consisted of particles of a kind with which we are familiar. Gas particles are unlike billiard balls, specks of dust, or any other particles of which we have direct experience. It is a mistake of the same kind to say that all the evidence for the existence of molecules or mesons is indirect, for in this context it is impossible to describe evidence which would be, in contrast, direct.

Experiments showing the escape of phlogiston from a substance can still be repeated, but further experiments would show that it is impossible to give a coherent account of what phlogiston is, or how it behaves. Our present theories may develop so that we can no longer consistently talk of electrons and protons, but the experimental results will remain, and they will be taken into account in subsequent theories. This does not mean that the language in which we describe our observations is, in some way, closer to reality than theoretical languages, but only that it changes more slowly. I agree with Mr. Thornton that "Sir J. J. Thomson is entitled to the claim that he discovered the things which coursed through his evacuated tubes," but I would add that we may not always describe these things as electrons, or even as things. To deny this would be to forget that science is an activity, and to suppose that it is approaching completion.

4

ON METHODS OF REPRESENTATION:
W. H. Watson ·

The physicist, like other natural scientists, employs language—both that of the ordinary man and his own special symbolic methods—to represent the world of fact. He does this for purposes which may be clearly evident and explicitly stated, as for example, when the application is an engineering one, or, it may be that these purposes are more closely related to the needs of the pure scientist. So much do we take for granted the use of ordinary language and of its technical counterparts in our professional life, that we are guilty more often than not of overlooking the conscious processes of representation. In everyday affairs a copy of a picture is asked for and supplied without its being necessary to specify in so many words that the copy is to be made by ordinary similarity and not by the rules of some possible distorting process of projection. An artist when asked to paint a portrait has not the liberty to paint the image of his subject as seen in a convex cylindrical mirror. To state in so many words the rule for copying generally appears pedantic. Nevertheless, in the ellipses of common usage is a habit which the physicist may easily take over into the business of representing nature. When he does not have clearly in mind the conventions of his methods, he is

· [This selection is extracted from Chapter III of Watson's *On Understanding Physics* (Cambridge: Cambridge University Press, 1938), pp. 38–44, 45–56, 62–4, 65–6. Reprinted by permission of W. H. Watson and Cambridge University Press.]

likely to be led into misuse of any bad notation which he may have, and ultimately into asking philosophical questions which arise therefrom. It is hardly necessary here to insist on the importance of notation as an aid to thought in science. In the past, however, emphasis has been placed on special notation as an aid to complicated thinking; in contrast, let us consider how a notation may trap us into error.

Imagine the orthogonal projection of a sphere on its equatorial plane. The entire spherical surface is represented on a part only of the plane. Points outside of this part of the plane correspond to no real point on the sphere. Some of the questions we ask ourselves about physics are rather like the question, "What is represented by the point *A*?" where *A* is on the plane but outside the projection of the sphere. The answer is, of course, that *A* represents *no* point of the sphere. The trap is presented to us because the method of representation employed allows us to mark the point *A* and, what is more, appears to allow the same grammatical expression when *A* is substituted for *B*, which does represent a point of the sphere. While we might invent another method of representation which would not present us with this linguistic temptation, it is not necessary, provided that we apply the rule of logical grammar for the correct use of the former method. The instance which we have just inspected seems trivial, for the logical point is so obvious whenever we think of the geometrical relation between the sphere and its projection; yet one does not have to go far to find a parallel in physics which is as direct and appears to cause confusion of thought.

Think of the spatial representation of time. The succession of points along a line only in one direction corresponds to the succession of instants of time. The motion of a particle along a straight line with uniform velocity can be represented by the equation $x = vt$, that is, by a straight line in *xt*-space. In the motion, this line is traversed in the direction away from the origin of time. We are tempted to say that the same line considered in opposite sense (i.e., toward the origin of time) represents the "motion of the particle backward in time" instead of saying that the line viewed in this way does not represent a process at all. The logic of "before : after" does not allow sense to the form of words "backward in time" any more than the geometry of the sphere allows its orthogonal projection on a plane to cover the whole plane. Nevertheless, literary grammar (as opposed to logic) appears to sanction the expression "backward in time." There is no backward in time, only backward in space. The analogy we consider is something like this—a history of events can be written in a book, and we may turn back in the book to the record of more distant past events. The very fact that in speaking of temporal relations we use words whose application properly belongs to space ought to warn us that, when we have these terms in mind, we use a spatial representation of time. Recognition of such a simple matter prevents the further temptation to theorize about entropy and "time's arrow."

How often do we use the figure "time like a river"! The measurement of time means that we compare with another process those processes whose temporal course is to be described. In physics, of course, the process of reference is standardized; but in ordinary language we do not necessarily refer to the clock, we leave the reference process unspecified, that is, a variable like x in algebra, and any process will serve as a particular value of the variable. The figure of the river is a misleading one because it suggests events strung together on a line like the pictures on a cinema film, which is pulled past us, and that if only we could arrest time we could see past, present, and future together, just as we can see the river or film spread out before us. The same idea is inherent in much of our thought about any process. Take, for instance, a musical tune. It is as if a gramophone record of the whole tune were in course of being played. It is all "there,"[1] but we hear only a little bit at a time. This same analogy pervades nearly all epistemological theory and it is nearly always wrongly applied.

In using analogy we must have caution. If the method of representation which we denote by A is analogous to the method B, it is necessary to avoid the temptation to employ the grammatical forms which belong to A when we are speaking of the representation by B. Roughly speaking, the word "analogy" has a bad reputation in science and particularly so among mathematicians. This is perhaps surprising to anyone who considers the growth of physics. The theory of electrostatics borrowed some of its symbolism from elasticity, and optics borrowed from elastic solid theory. More recently wave mechanics was developed from

[1] One is justified in asking, where?

classical mechanics in terms of the analogy between mechanics and optics. Whatever the newest views of quantum mechanics may be, it cannot be denied that this analogy played a useful part. To-day, it may almost be said that the mathematicians wish to suppress the analogy or at least not to emphasize its existence and historical place in the subject. Is there any explanation of this state of affairs? Let us look at two analogies in the history of physics and we shall find something to guide us. First recall to mind the model of the ether devised during last century to explain Maxwell's theory of light. This analogy usually raises the question of the existence of the mechanism which is postulated in the explanation. As a matter of fact it need not raise this question, as we can see when we think of electrical models of acoustical systems and recognize that there is no question of the existence of coils of wire or of condensers in the acoustical apparatus. It is noteworthy that we should accept easily this electrical-acoustical analogy without being tempted to ask philosophical questions, whereas with the theory of light in terms of a mechanical model, philosophical questions have always been to hand. We recognize clearly in acoustics that the analogy in question is completely expressed by mathematical equations, but we also find it convenient to use some of the electrical terms when we wish to name quantities which have the same mathematical properties in the two theories. In electromagnetic optics, however, the mechanism of the model of the ether does not help in this way at all. Once we have expressed by means of Maxwell's equations the electromagnetic connections between different places at different times, we have an adequate symbolism for representing optical phenomena. We no longer feel the need even for a medium of which to predicate undulation. The equation $x = a \sin nt$ represents the vibration of a particle or the oscillation of an electric current and so on, but the equation does not vibrate and neither does a graph of this function. (We could, on the other hand, represent the oscillating electric current by means of a vibrating particle such as a pendulum.)

The mathematician's objection to analogy arises in part from this: that the mathematical equations which express the law common to the method A and its analogue B are all that is essential to the analogy. One does not require the picturesque and in some respects misleading language appropriate to the analogy. Such forms of speech can be dispensed with, for correct application of mathematics does all that is necessary. We find therefore that although analogy may serve useful purposes in the development of theoretical ideas, in the course of time reference to the particular analogy almost inevitably drops out of the subject because one comes to recognize the immediate applicability of the mathematical theory which was in the first place used via analogy, and secondly because, generally speaking, the analogy breaks down and becomes therefore a hindrance to correct thinking about the subject to which it had been applied. The analogy itself never shows that it is misapplied; this is shown only when the logic of the analogy is compared with the logic of the possibilities it is used to describe, and such comparison is usually a tedious and difficult process.

The well-founded attitude of caution in the use of analogy has tended to become transformed in some quarters into the attitude of objecting to any use whatever of analogy. When Heaviside invented what has now become the operational calculus, mathematicians were at first unwilling to admit the validity of his methods. This calculus is based on the idea that if p denotes the sign d/dt of differentiation, then p can be treated like an ordinary number in algebra. Any analogy of this type, according to which one proposes to apply to a sign used in one calculus (C) the rules for calculation in another calculus (C'), is an interesting one, and as a rule the mathematician as a critic of innovation is liable to occupy a strong position. It is quite likely that certain combinations of signs, although permitted by the rules of C', have no meaning when applied to C, and that ambiguities arise as to the application of the rules of the calculus C to the result of a calculation by means of C'. For example, suppose that in C the signs do not obey the communicative law of multiplication, whereas in C' they do obey that law, then there will be a doubt as to how the result of a calculation by means of C' is to be read whenever it involves a product. One should observe, however, that so long as one avoids such ambiguities and meaningless combinations of signs, one may be able to use the analogy in question quite effectively in applying mathematics to physical problems. For instance, without introducing a student of physics to the operational calculus as a body of mathematical knowledge from which the last trace of ambiguity and lack of clarity has been removed, one may teach him to deal with alternating current circuits by means of a generalization of Ohm's law which is in effect to treat Kirchhoff's laws by operational methods. As a result the student learns a symbolic method which is very powerful. Until he has to apply the method to problems which refer to the subtleties of the operational calculus, however, he is not *compelled* to know more about the calculus. Now this principle applies not only to mathematical but also to physical representation in these very same problems. The so-called residuals in his resistance boxes and impurities in his condensers and mutual inductances are not taken into account until the experimental results call for such interpretations.

Under the influence, perhaps, of our mathematical mentors, we are often too ready to regard physics as a single theory (relic of philosophical monism) that should be presented like Euclid's geometry, as if it were one method of representation which, possibly owing to the intellectual laziness of experimental physicists, never appears to be presented as a logical whole, although it could be. In the writings of mathematicians on physics, however, one seems to see the subject unfold itself with a certain inevitability hardly, if ever, referring to the laboratory or to the experimental facts which support the structure. As if one could say *a priori* what the world must be like. Now physics is actually a conglomeration of methods of representation. Two methods of representing the same phenomena must agree in some way, otherwise one method necessarily gives a picture wrong in every respect when the other gives a correct one. What is common to the two pictures by the different methods of representing is like what is common to two photographs of the same scene printed from half-tone blocks with differing screen mesh. If the meshes differ greatly in size, one photograph will be a picture with cruder detail than the other, but so long as the mesh is not made so large as to prevent the possibility of one's recognizing some of the form of the picture, one is still able to agree that they are pictures of the same scene by different methods of representation.

The cheerful dismissal of Newtonian mechanics by relativists ignores just this matter. It is not a question of Newton's laws being wrong and Einstein's being right. In many cases our experiments do not yield pictures of grain fine enough to represent what the relativist asserts should be the case.

For such pictures Newton's laws are quite exact, and naturally, on account of the greater simplicity, we employ this system in calculating what is to be expected. Only when the experiments call for relativistic representation do we employ that method. The fact is that in physics we choose the particular method of representation adequate to the purpose in mind, just as a carpenter chooses on one occasion a saw and on another a plane to give a particular shape to a piece of wood. In electrical practice one sees a like multiplicity of method. In a circuit to be used with direct current, one does not take into account its inductive or capacitive properties unless one is concerned with the effects of transients on the line. Even when one is concerned with transients one does not apply the whole Maxwellian theory which requires us to know the geometrical arrangement of the conductors and insulators in space—we make a schematic diagram of the circuit, inserting resistance, inductance, and capacity, and apply Kirchhoff's laws. Only when the time scale of the process is sufficiently brief do we have to give up quasi-static conceptions of the electrical properties of the network and describe the entire electromagnetic process in space by means of Maxwell's equations—assuming that sufficient mathematical skill is available to accomplish the calculation. . . . From the philosopher's point of view, an analogy helps one to surmount the ever-recurring difficulty which one experiences in getting accustomed to any new method of representation. Once one has seen in what respects the new resembles that with which one is already familiar, one is prepared to accept on trial its novelties and let the success of the application of the new method justify it. In course of time when a method has been tried and accepted, the analogy tends to be forgotten, and it is not necessary unless one wishes to exhibit the relation of one method of representation to the other.

The important analogies of physics deal with the substitution of one calculus for another. Being mathematically expressed the substitution is usually easy to comprehend. If one were to use mathematics exclusively in this connection, there would be few possibilities of confusion, but one has also to employ words to express thoughts in the usual literary forms which can be spoken, for, generally speaking, mathematical equations are not suited for speech. And for the following reason. In speech the mathematical equation has really to be described in words, and just as a complicated picture is not presented all together by a description, whereas a drawn picture is so presented, so the listener has difficulty in "seeing" the mathematical form of the equation read out to him. This inescapable resort to ordinary linguistic signs, as opposed to mathematical signs, is one of the main sources of our philosophical problems in physics. We have to use words which play more than one rôle in language, and whose meanings therefore depend on their application; more confusing still there are some words which have not a sharp meaning in ordinary language, and some which have no regular function at all, such, for instance, as the word "meaning" itself; in applying them to science we try to endow them with a regular function. This process commonly occurs in philosophical writing about science, especially whenever a change in the method of representation is being "explained" in nonmathematical terms. The transition from the one method to the other leads us in talking of the second to take over words and forms of expression which have a clear application only with respect to the first. For instance, the "state" of a dynamical system, taken to mean a set of values of the momenta and of the coordinates corresponding to a particular time, is a clear conception which does not do violence to the logic of the use of the word "state" in ordinary language. A system cannot be in two different states at the same time. But with the advent of quantum mechanics, the word "state" was given a new meaning and it became necessary to explain the mathematical representation of one wave function as a linear combination of others by means of the so-called "principle of superposition," as if to say that an atomic system can be in different "states" at the same time (meaning the states of ordinary dynamics). There is an argument here in favor of changing our notation and of inventing a new term in place of this confusing word "state." So long as we restrict our thought to the mathematical calculation, everything appears clear and straightforward, but whenever we attempt to make physical analogies or models of the mathematical process, we are liable (but not *compelled*) to get into difficulties; and whenever one piece of the model is not joined to the rest we attempt to *force* them to fit into each other instead of carefully rearranging the parts of our analogy so that they fit properly as do the parts of a correctly completed jig-saw puzzle.

Perhaps the most striking instance of this process in modern physics is the bringing together of the particle and wave ideas with regard to the electron. Here is an excellent example of the piecemeal nature of the development of physical theories. On the one hand there is the dynamics of a particle and on the other the theory of wave optics. In the former we have as the essence of the idea of a particle, something at some place at some particular time. In the latter it is characteristic of the wave motion that we do not localize it like a particle; the essential wave properties depend on its being extended through space over a period of time long compared with the period of vibration. Of course a wave packet or group of waves has the possibility of representing the localized propagation of energy with the group velocity, and this supplies its logical connection with the particle method of representation, namely, that in a picture of coarse grain the two methods of representation give the same picture. Whenever we look on the matter in this way it appears quite clear and without logical difficulties, but if we think of the moving electron itself there is a difficulty. With one method of representation we may say "the electron is a particle," and with the other method we are tempted to use the same form of expression and say "the electron is a wave." This is a source of logical difficulty in modern physics. These two statements about the electron do not go together because one of them postulates properties of the electron which appear to contradict the properties asserted by the other. Now one way of appearing to get rid of a contradiction is to legislate that it be disguised as not a contradiction and to invent a "principle of complimentarity" which, while it seems to allow us either expression as we see fit, is concerned really with permission to choose the method of representation which is appropriate to our needs.

Is it not rather striking that in ordinary dynamics we find no need for a principle of complementarity to enable us to represent the earth on the one hand as a particle without extension and on the other as a body extended throughout a sphere of 8000 miles diameter, or that in the dynamics of a gas we find no need of a principle of complementarity to enable us at one time to represent the gas as a continuous medium for acoustical problems and on another occasion to represent it as an assembly of molecules? It ought to be clear that in the older parts of physics we do not have any difficulty when we wish to change over from one method of representation to another.

Physicists are accustomed to this process as an everyday affair. Yet in the description of the motion of electrons and other elementary particles, the change in the method of representation appears to cause a logical difficulty. It cannot be merely that the two methods have different possibilities of representation—we are ready to expect a difference between the assembly of molecules and the continuous medium. The difficulty in the present instance seems to arise from the form of words "the electron is a wave," the electron still being thought of as a particle, and correctly so because the substantive "electron" makes us treat it grammatically, as we do other *things* in physics. Compare the sentence "The electron is a wave" with "The electron is an angular velocity" or with "The electron is an aperiodic motion." Both of these statements are clearly bad grammar. It is formally correct to endow a rigid body with angular velocity or a galvanometer coil with aperiodic motion, but we do not say "The rigid body is its angular velocity" any more than we say that the galvonometer coil is its aperiodic motion. Now a wave motion is a process, not a thing, and an electron regarded as an object is not a process, but its translation is. So if we must use "is" we might try "The translation of an electron is a wave," but clearly a translation is not a wave. It would be correct, however, to say that the translation of an electron is the translation of a group of waves without implying that an electron is a group of waves. What we mean by such a statement in the cramping form of speech into using which we have been trapped, is that the laws for calculating the translation of an electron are the laws for calculating the translation of a group of waves in a particular system. The present analysis does not dispose of all the difficulties associated with the wave method of representing the motion of an electron, and, it may be said, arising from lack of a sense of conscious management of the symbolism of physics.

Whenever one is clearly aware that one is representing and is using one method of representation *as opposed to another one*, one is likely to be careful not to make the mistake of mixing up the grammar of the two systems, or if one has been trapped by misuse of grammar into difficulties which are definitely logical, one is able to analyze the situation objectively and disentangle the proper grammatical usages of the one method from those properly belonging to the other. In the growth of a subject, however, when a new method of representation is in course of being developed, confusion of the old with the new is almost inevitable. Some men find one way out of the difficulties caused by the confusion, other men find other ways. There are those who dispose of the difficulty by a literary *tour de force,* and in the process probably create for less brilliant but more critical minds new problems where none existed before. Others are content whenever they have learned to manage the methods of physical calculation in the uncritical spirit found among students of elementary physics who render explanations without understanding. Familiarity with a difficulty will in the course of time lead one into the habit of ignoring it or, in order to dispose of it, tempt one to formulate a "policy" for bridging the gap between the two opposed points of view. None of these devices will appeal to the man who wishes an elucidation of the grammatical situation which gave rise to the difficulty, and who having once become clear about the matter will strive to have accepted by other scientists a notation appropriate to the new ideas and not confused with the old.

In the foregoing pages it has been explained that in physics we choose the method of representation appropriate to our needs; that does not mean, however, that we are content to treat all methods of representation as on the same level of importance. A method which gives correctly the possibility of representing nature with greater detail than another, is thought of as the better method—and it is so when it is a question of showing detail. We think of the second method as an approximation to the first. We tend, therefore, to arrange methods in a series according to the degree of fineness of the pictures of phenomena that can be made by means of them, and of course from this point of view the last member of the series is the best. If this one has been in successful use for some years it is in danger of being looked on as the best possible. Indeed, all reference to the series of methods, if it ever was in the thought of physicists who think in the following manner, is forgotten, and the laws of the method of representation in question are thought of in the same way that the laws of nature have been regarded by mankind for hundreds of years.

Roughly speaking, the expression "laws of nature" is based on the analogy with the laws imposed by a political sovereign on his subjects, except that when in physics we find what ought to correspond to the disobedience of a subject, we invent the alibi that we really did not know the correct laws of nature or we regard the phenomenon as an exception governed by a special rule, as if the sovereign had granted an indulgence. According to this way of looking on experience, so long as we have no experimental facts which break the law we are sure that we know the law of nature and are tempted to regard an infringement of the law as impossible. There is no need to labor this point, for every physicist knows of instances where the confident theorist has proved wrong in his predictions; at the same time one would perhaps have wished some of our leading experimenters had more frequently pointed out the error whenever a theorist has asserted that a particular experimental result *must* be wrong *on theoretical grounds only*. Only experimental physicists are competent to judge whether the result is experimentally correct *after* they have investigated the matter in the laboratory. As soon as well-authenticated evidence is produced, the failure of a law of nature causes us to change the law. Something that was hidden has been discovered, and very soon the new law takes on the authority of the old. Now, if a law of nature can be altered, what is the source of its authority? We have been misled by our analogy if we think that the correct law which we are groping to find by experimental investigation is *the* law imposed on the world and that phenomena *must* be governed by it, for what is meant by "the correct law"? How are we to be sure that one hundred years from now, the laws of nature which we know and use may not have been given up and others substituted in their place? It seems that the expression "*the* correct law of nature" is not a proper grammatical expression because, not knowing how to establish the truth of a statement employing this form of speech, we have not given it a meaning. The analogy we see breaks down here, and the authority which we have been accustomed to attribute to a law of nature must be found in a place quite different from that suggested by analogy with political laws. Having been impressed by the fact that "the laws of nature" have been subject to change, some writers have gone to the other extreme and proposed to dismiss, for example, the laws of conservation of energy and momentum as "mere conventions," and apparently overlook altogether the difficult processes by which physical scientists came to these ideas.

It should be clear that the laws of mechanics are the

laws of our method of representing mechanical phenomena, and that since we actually choose a method of representation when we describe the world, it cannot be that the laws of our method say anything about the world. If they do, experimental scientists have been misguided for three hundred years. What experience teaches us is that one method of representation is more appropriate than another in the sense that a map of the earth is more appropriate on the surface of a sphere than on a plane. The authority which we formerly attributed to the laws of nature in one way has now to be attributed in another to the logic of our method of representation, namely, in this way, that if we wish to make pictures of the world according to a particular scheme, then we *must* follow the rules of that scheme. This is not to say that the scheme determines what must be the form of the actual pictures we draw, but it does decide what pictures are possible. If distances on the map were literally interpreted as proportional to distances on the earth's surface, the plane representation of the earth's surface by means of Mercator's projection would allow some queer processes to take place on the earth, whereas a spherical map read in the same way would not allow those possibilities.

Thus what we have called the laws of nature are the laws of our methods of representing it. The laws themselves do not show anything about the world, but it does show something about the world that we have found by experience how true pictures of the world of a certain degree of fineness or of a certain simplicity can be made by means of the methods which we have learned to use. We *can* describe the process seen on a cinema screen, as if it were a continuous one provided that we make the rule that observations are not to be so refined that we can show the actual succession of images of discrete pictures. We *can* describe the motion of the particles of atomic physics by classical dynamics provided that the dynamically significant fields of force in which they move are not given structure on too small a spatial and temporal scale. We *can* describe the motion of the planets round the sun over a few years without introducing relativity and so on. In every one of these cases, the structure of the facts being represented is shown in that the particular method of representation adopted in order to describe them is successful or appropriate *in a particular way.*

Our choice of a method of representation is a real choice; we are guided by our experience in finding it. Once we have adopted a method and new facts appear which do not fit at once into the scheme, we again have a choice— either to give up the former method and use a new one which does have a place for the new facts, or else to adopt a special hypothesis to enable us to retain the old method. Either alternative may have the consequence that certain possibilities are created, whose correspondence with reality can be investigated experimentally. If the facts are found to disagree with these possibilities, we are free again to invent another hypothesis or to start once more with a new method. Generally speaking, we proceed in science like the mechanic who is continually adding gadgets to deal with this or the other defect in his machine. Sooner or later the gadgets weaken the whole structure, and he is well advised to make a new engine the design of which incorporates as essential to its structure the law of functioning which removes the need for the gadgets. In science the process that corresponds to the designing of a new machine is the invention of a new method of representation. Once it is adopted the structure of the science in which it is to be used appears to have been tidied up and loses its patchwork appearance. A new method may have wide application, in which case its invention will probably be attended by philosophical discussion concerning its "fundamental" importance for human activities which certainly do not enter into the profession of physics; on the other hand, the new method may appear to clear up only a small part of the subject, and if the change is noticed at all by others than specialists closely interested in the matter, it is accepted as the customary thing. The development of any new experimental technique is of this character; experimental facts are simplified and made clear when the proper procedure is followed, as for instance in the science of the photoelectric emission from metals and of the photoconductance of insulating crystals.

It should be made clear that a hypothesis added to a method of representation is not *necessarily* an excrescence —only experiment can decide this. The discovery of the neutron is an excellent example of a successful hypothesis which easily finds a place in our theories; it was based in the first place on what at the time seemed the curious failure of other possible mechanisms to explain the properties of the radiation observed in certain atomic transformations. In contrast, the neutrino which has been invented to account for the lack of energy balance in β-ray changes has the appearance of a much less appropriate hypothesis because up to the present the properties postulated of this particle seem expressly designed to exclude the possibility of its detection in ways analogous to those used for the other particles of atomic physics. The question, however, is not to be settled on the grounds we have just mentioned. It is for the experimental scientist to discover whether or not there lies before the hypothesis a useful life or a rapid disappearance into oblivion. We have to learn physics a little at a time, and there is no good purpose served by refusing to give a hypothesis a fair trial merely because one feels that it does not fit easily into our present scheme of things; one may be right as judged from the point of view of the distant future, but wrong in one's judgment as to the way in which the goal is to be reached. Think of the introduction of the hypothesis of quanta into physics. It has brought twenty years of discomfort in physical theory and ended by developing into a full-grown method of representing atomic phenomena which derives from the systems of mathematical knowledge that have supplied its calculus an impressive appearance of logical completeness just like classical mechanics. This is not to say that all the problems of atomic physics have been solved, but to emphasize that we now have a method of representation which has the scope of certain well-defined branches of mathematics; its alliance with them gives to the physical theory the appearance of being well established in its "fundamentals." Compare the present mathematical form of quantum mechanics in the hands of Heisenberg, Dirac, Schrödinger, and Weyl, to mention only a few outstanding names, with the form given to classical mechanics by Lagrange, Hamilton, and Jacobi. The Hamiltonian method in ordinary dynamics involves the assimilation in the subject of the whole theory of systems of linear differential equations of the first order and their treatment by means of the solution of a partial differential equation. Since we have the possibility of choosing our methods of representation it is good to take advantage whenever we can of the symbolic systems with which mathematics provides us and to use them to give a logical backbone, and what is just as important, a good notation to our physical theories.

Having done this we have to remind the mathematician where the appearance of infallibility originates in his method. It is because we have chosen his method and are prepared to support it with special hypotheses to cover any facts which are not at first correctly described by the method; we are little disposed to give up using the method until, as the scope of experimental investigation widens, the patches become so numerous and disjoined that one begins to look for a new method of representation. Then the process of growth usually repeats itself, the mathematical theorist falls in love with the new method, and the experimenter gradually accumulates the knowledge which may lead sooner or later to a change in the method of representation or to the invention of a new one where none existed before.

We build the theory just as we develop experimental technique. At first there is the trial with crude temporary devices in our apparatus; how crude they may be every experimenter knows. Once such a device is made to work we incorporate it in our apparatus and technique—we trust it and depend on it. It is so with hypotheses. Tentative at first, they become the foundation of new developments in our theory; we trust them as long as they will work, or accept them for what they do and make up for their deficiencies by additional ones which in turn have to go through the same process. We can never tell when we shall have to give up a theory any more than we can tell before we have used it when an experimental technique has to be abandoned. A theory or a technique becomes infallible only when we agree to make it so by a convention. . . .

There is no clear division between the mathematical theory so-called and what the experimenter does. The mathematical theory is not a representation of the experimental laws, it is the expression of them; the experimenter employs the same mathematical connections in stating the laws he has found by induction. Consider the emission of electrons by a hot body. The dependence of the current on the temperature is given by a formula which is not simple, and the choice of the particular law used in preference to other empirical laws which might be used to fit the data of experiment is governed entirely by theory. The experimenter is guided by theory in his choice of the mathematical relationship between current and temperature, and this leaves on one side another important matter, namely, that the current depends on the electric field in the neighbourhood of the emitter, and here his treatment is again guided by theory. In such a case as this the mathematical theory is not something superposed on the experimental facts, as if we knew the laws from experiment then expressed them mathematically; as a matter of fact mathematics got into the laboratory in the nude state. To distinguish alleged nonmathematical experimental results from the so-called mathematical theory is entirely artificial and shows ignorance of how language functions. The results of Faraday's investigations of electrostatics and electromagnetism were presented in nonmathematical terminology, and were expressed by Maxwell in explicit mathematical form. Is one to say then that Maxwell created the mathematical form which represents Faraday's results? No. Maxwell translated Faraday's thoughts into different words, namely, the symbols of mathematics; the logical form of thoughts is unaltered by such translation if correct. Either the logical form of the mathematical relationships used by Maxwell was present in Faraday's thought of the phenomena or else Maxwell invented the form, in which case we should have no longer any right to speak of a mere translation of Faraday's experimental facts. Maxwell did of course make his own contributions to electrical theory. The contrast we have been considering is comparable with that between the description of a situation in space by words and its specification by mathematical equations.

One cannot expel mathematics from the laboratory, but one can refuse to deal with complicated mathematical calculations which are necessary only to present details that are beyond the reach of our most refined methods of measurement. In this connection, consider the equation of state of a gas. As the first general statement of the law we have $pv = RT$, and this is satisfactory until sufficiently precise measurements over a wide range of temperature and pressure lead us to Van der Waals' equation, for example. The application of quantum statistics has yielded a form of the equation of state with still greater detail of representation. Are we justified in asserting that this newest law is *the* correct one rather than either of the others? The only test of correctness is comparison with experiment, so the word "correct" as applied to a physical theory has to be understood as "correct relative to a certain degree of fineness of the observations." Once we learn to look on the matter in this way we shall put behind us the temptation to endow any theory with absolute correctness and shall be less willing to criticize as incorrect from the theoretical point of view a formula such as $pv = RT$, without having in mind the manner of applying the equation to experimental facts. This may seem a small thing, but insistence on it will probably make less generally held the attitude to physical theories which enthrones the most elaborate theory we know as the essentially correct one. . . .

When one is dealing with a theory which purports to show why a constant of nature has its measured value, one has a right to ask what is represented in the theory and on what grounds the chosen mathematical structure is relevant to physics, for clearly we can imagine a particular number being produced as the result of an endless variety of mathematical processes. Relevance is established logically only by the appearance in the theory of laws that can be compared with fact. Any other connection such as that by the use of physical terminology in speaking of the mathematical structure is not a substitute for this logical connection by identity of structure in some respects between theory and fact. If it is asserted that the theory can be compared with experiment in no other way than by means of the values to be assigned to the constants of nature, the theory is useless for experimental science, and its logical value is likely also to be negligible.

A constant of nature is a fixed number, not a variable number. If this number is to be fixed by a theory, the function of the theory is to show how in a calculation by means of it a variable number is not to be given on one occasion one value and on a different occasion another, but is to have the one particular value found by measurement. The theory shows the constant as a particular value of a variable, but the possibilities from which it makes a choice do not represent actual physical possibilities of nature, for the theory pretends to establish that they are not.

It is always possible to think of an explanation of a physical law by means of a more elaborate theory which picks out the law in question from other possible laws. For example, the kinetic theory of gases explains Boyle's law. But this process must come to an end just as soon as we are unwilling to consider as relevant to the description of nature the system of possibilities from which the theory has to make a selection. The only test of this relevance is that the representation we have in mind is that required to show experimental facts connected by a coherent theory.

The molecular theory of gases was at one time objected to on this very ground, but as soon as Dunoyer demonstrated the properties of a molecular ray, that attitude had to pass away. It is pertinent therefore to ask of any theorist who proposes a superstructure to physics in the form of an explanation of what we accept as fixed things of our methods of describing nature, that he show some place where his theory can be compared with experiment in addition to those respects in which he "explains" what already is accepted.

5

THEORIES AS REPRESENTATIONS:

Ludwig Boltzmann ·

All of our ideas and concepts are, after all, only inner thought-pictures or, when uttered, combinations of sounds. The task of our thinking, then, is to use and connect concepts in such a way that with their help we always and most easily perform the right actions and also guide others to right actions. Here metaphysics has been tied to the most sober, practical position: extremes meet. The conceptual signs we form thus have only a single existence in us: we cannot gauge external appearances with the measure of our ideas. Formally, therefore, we can raise questions of this kind: does only matter exist and is force one of its properties or does the latter exist independently of matter or, conversely, is matter a product of force? None of these questions, however, has any meaning, since all of these concepts are merely thought-pictures that have the purpose of correctly representing appearances.

This was expressed with special clarity by Hertz in his famous book on the principles of mechanics, only that

· [This selection is extracted from Boltzmann's *Die Grundprinzipien und Grundgleichungen der Mechanik*, I, which was delivered as a series of lectures at Clark University in 1899 and published in *Populäre Schriften* (Leipzig: J. A. Barth, 1905), pp. 253–69. It is especially translated for this volume by Rudolph Weingartner, of the Department of Philosophy, San Francisco State College.]

there Hertz lays down as his first requirement that the pictures we construct must correspond to the laws of thought.[1] About this demand I should like to raise certain doubts or at least elucidate it somewhat more closely. We must certainly bring along a rich treasure of laws of thought. Without them experience would be completely useless; we would have no way of fixing it by means of inner pictures. Although these laws of thought are almost without exception innate, they nevertheless undergo modifications at the hand of upbringing, instruction, and personal experience. They are not altogether the same in the child, the plain, uneducated man, and the man of learning. We can also see this when we compare the trend of thought of a naïve people such as the Greeks with that of the scholastics of the Middle Ages and it, in turn, with that of today. To be sure, there are laws of thought which have held good so unexceptionally that we trust them without reservations, that we consider them as *a priori*, unchangeable principles of thought. In spite of this, I believe that they have developed only slowly. Their first source was in the primitive experiences of mankind in its original state; gradually they were strengthened and became clearer by means of complicated experiences, until finally they took on their present sharp formulation. Still, I do not wish to recognize these laws of thought as the highest standards without qualification. We cannot know whether they will not, after all, undergo this or that modification. We might recall the certainty with which children or uneducated people are convinced that one ought to be able to distinguish by means of mere feeling, between the directions of up and down in all places of the universe and how thereby they believe themselves able to deduce the impossibility of antipodes. Were such people to write logic, they would surely take this to be a law of thought that is evident *a priori*. At first, various *a priori* objections were also raised against the Copernican theory. The history of science exhibits numerous cases where assertions were now supported, now refuted with reasons which were then held to be self-evident laws, while today we are convinced of their invalidity.

I should therefore like to modify Hertz's demand as follows. Insofar as we possess laws of thought which we

[1] [The section of Hertz's book referred to by Boltzmann is reprinted in Part III of this volume.]

have recognized as undoubtedly correct, on the basis of constant confirmation in experience, we can initially test the correctness of our pictures on them. However, the final and sole decision about the usefulness of the picture lies in the condition that it represent experience as simply and accurately as possible. And precisely in this we again have the test for the correctness of the laws of thought.

When we have in this way understood the task of thought in general and of science in particular, consequences will follow which at first blush are quite startling. We shall call an idea of nature false, if it represents certain facts incorrectly or if there are obviously simpler ideas which represent the facts more clearly, but especially if the idea contradicts generally confirmed laws of thought. Yet in spite of this, it is possible to have theories which represent a great number of facts correctly, but which are incorrect on other points. To them we must therefore ascribe a certain relative truth. Indeed, it may even be that we can construct a system of pictures of the appearances in different ways. Each of these systems is not equally simple and does not represent the appearances equally well. Still, it may be doubtful—a matter of taste, as it were—which one we consider to be the simpler one, with which representation of the appearances we feel more satisfied. In this way science loses its uniform character. Heretofore we held fast to the tenet that there could be only *one* truth: that errors were manifold, but truth unique. Given our present standpoint, this view must be opposed, although the difference between the new as distinguished from the old view tends to be a formal one. There was never any doubt that man would never be able to know the full compass of truth. Such knowledge is only an ideal. But for our present idea we have a similar ideal: the most perfect picture which represents all appearances in the simplest and most useful way. Thus, according to the one way of viewing things we turn our glance more to the unattainable ideal which is only a unitary one; according to the other way, we look to the multiplicity of what is attainable.

Now, if we are convinced that science is only an inner picture, a thought-construction, which is never identical with the multiplicity of appearances, but is always capable of representing perspicuously only certain of its parts, how do we attain such a picture? How do we represent it as systematically and perspicuously as possible? Formerly, a method was popular which imitates that employed in geometry by Euclid; it might therefore be called the Euclidean method. It proceeds from as few and as evident propositions as possible. In ancient times these were regarded as evident *a priori*, as given directly to the mind; hence they were called axioms. Later, however, they were considered only to be sufficiently well-founded experiential propositions. Since certain pictures were deduced from these axioms only with the help of the laws of thought, it was believed that a proof had been found to the effect that these pictures were the only possible ones and that they could not be replaced by others. As examples I may mention the inferences which served for the derivation of the parallelogram of forces or Ampère's law, or which served as proof that the force acting between two material points acts in the direction of the distance between them and must be a function of that distance.

But the evidential force of this mode of inference gradually came into ill repute. The first step in this direction (as previously recounted) was the change from a foundation that was *a priori* evident to one that was warranted merely experientially. It was further recognized that the deduction, too, from this foundation could not be carried out without numerous new hypotheses. Finally, Hertz pointed out that especially in the field of physics our conviction of the correctness of a general theory ultimately does not rest on its derivation by means of the Euclidean method, but rather on the fact that the theory leads us to correct inferences about appearances in all the cases then known. He first made use of this view in his account of Maxwell's fundamental equations of the theory of electricity and magnetism. There he proposed not to concern himself at all with their derivation from certain fundamental principles. Instead, he simply set them at the head of his account and proposed to look for their justification in the fact that one could subsequently show that they always agreed with experience. Experience, after all, remains the sole judge of the usefulness of a theory; from its judgment there can be no appeal; it is irrevocable. Indeed, when we take a closer look at those theorems that are most closely tied to objects—the law of inertia, the parallelogram of forces, and the other fundamental laws of mechanics—we shall find that none of the different proofs offered in all the textbooks of mechanics for each and every one of these propositions is by far as convincing as the fact that all the consequences drawn from the content of each of these propositions have been well confirmed in experience. Not infrequently, the paths by which we reach such pictures are very diverse and dependent upon a variety of coincidences.

Some pictures, such as the mechanical theory of heat, were only gradually constructed in the course of centuries, by the combined effort of many scientists. Others were discovered by a single, genial scientist, though again, often via many circuitous detours. Only afterward did other individuals subject these pictures (such as Maxwell's theory of electricity and magnetism, just discussed) to very different kinds of examination. Now there is one mode of representation which possesses quite special advantages, though it also has its defects. This mode of representation is characterized by the fact that at first we operate only with thought-abstractions, mindful of our task only to construct inner representation-pictures. Proceding in this way, we do not as yet take possible experiential facts into consideration, but merely make the effort to develop our thought-pictures with as much clarity as possible and to draw from them all possible consequences. Only subsequently, after the entire exposition of the picture has been completed, do we check its agreement with experiential facts. We thus justify only afterwards why the picture had to be chosen in precisely this and in no other way; at the beginning we do not give the slightest hint about this. We shall call this method deductive representation.

The advantages of this representation are obvious. In the first place, no doubt can arise that it proposes to present not things in themselves, but only an inner, mental picture, and that it seeks only to form this mental picture into a skillful designation of the appearances. Since the deductive method does not constantly mingle external pictures forced upon us by experience with inner ones that are arbitrarily chosen by us, it is far easiest for it to develop the latter clearly and free from contradictions. It is, after all, one of the most important requisites of these pictures that they be perfectly clear: we must never be perplexed as to how they should be formed in every particular case and we must be able to deduce results from them unambiguously and indubitably. Just such clarity suffers from a too-early mingling with experience and is preserved most securely by the deductive mode of representation. On the other hand, what stands out particularly in this manner of representing is the arbitrariness of the pictures: one begins with thought-constructions that are quite arbitrary without initially supporting their necessity; only afterward are they justified. Not a shred of evidence is offered against the possibility that other thought-pictures could be invented which would equally agree with experience. This appears to be a flaw, but may nevertheless be an advantage, at least for him who holds the view on the nature of any theory which was previously explained. However, that the path by which the picture in question was arrived at does not become visible is a genuine defect of the deductive method. But of course it is usually the case in the theory of science that the coherence of conclusions stands out most clearly when they are analyzed as much as possible in their natural order and without heed to the path, often crooked, by which they were discovered.

In the field of mechanics, too, Hertz (in the book already cited) has given us a model of such a purely deductive representation. I believe that I can here assume familiarity with the content of Hertz's book and may therefore confine myself to a brief characterization. Hertz starts with material points which he regards as pure thought-pictures. Mass, too, he defines entirely in independence of all experience, by means of a number which we must think of as associated with every material point, namely, the number of simple mass points it contains. From these abstract concepts he constructs a motion which, like the points themselves, is at first of course present only in thought. From all of this the concept of mass is completely missing. Taking its place are certain conditions which are formulated as equations among the differentials of the coordinates of the material points. Now, these material points are endowed with certain initial velocities and at all subsequent times they move according to a very simple law which, as soon as the conditional equations are given, unambiguously determines their motion for all times. Hertz expresses this as follows: for every temporal moment, the sum of the masses multiplied by the squares of the deviations of the material points from a straight, uniform motion must be a minimum; or more briefly still: motion must occur in the straightest line. This law has the greatest resemblance to Gauss' principle of the least constraint; indeed, it is, so to speak, that special case which occurs when Gauss' principle is applied to a system of points which, while subjected to a constraint, are not subjected to any other external forces.

In my book entitled *Lectures on the Principles of Mechanics,* I have also attempted a purely deductive representation of the fundamental principles of mechanics, but in quite a different way and much more closely tied to the usual treatment of mechanics. Like Hertz, I begin with pure thought-objects: exact material points. I relate their position to a rectangular coordinate system that is also thought and I imagine a mental picture of the motion which, at first, is constructed in the following way: Every time that two material points are at a distance, r, from each other, each of them is to experience an acceleration in the direction of r, which is a function $f(r)$ of this distance. Later, this function can be disposed of at will. Furthermore, the accelerations of both points are to have a numerical relationship that remains unchanged at all times and which defines the relation of the masses of the two material points. How we are to imagine the motion of all material points is then unambiguously determined by the indication that the actual acceleration of each point is the vector sum of all accelerations found for it by means of the previous rule. This sum is then also added, as vector quantities are added, to the velocity of the point which is already given. Where these accelerations come from and just why I give the instruction that the picture should be constructed in this way is not further discussed. It suffices that the picture is a perfectly clear one which, by means of calculations, can be worked out in detail for a sufficient number of cases. It finds its justification only in the fact that the function $f(r)$ can in all cases be determined, such that the thought motion of the imagined material point becomes a faithful copy of actual appearances.

By means of this mode of treatment which we have called the purely deductive one, we have of course not solved the question of the nature of matter, mass, and force. However, we have avoided these questions by making their initial posing completely superfluous. In our thought schema these concepts are fully determinate numbers and directions for geometric constructions. We know how we are to think and execute them, so that we may obtain a useful picture of the world of appearance. What the real cause for the fact that the world of appearance runs its course in just this way may be; what may be hidden behind the world of appearance, propelling it, as it were— such investigations we do not consider to be the task of natural science. We may here leave it completely undecided whether it is or could be the task of another science or whether, in analogy with other word concatenations, we may here have merely joined together words which in this particular combination do not express a clear thought. By means of this deductive method we have solved neither the problem of absolute space nor the problem of absolute motion; yet even this question no longer creates any pedagogical difficulties. We need no longer raise it at the beginning of the development of the laws of mechanics, but can discuss it only when we have deduced all the laws of mechanics. For, since initially we in any case introduce only thought constructions, a coordinate system that is only thought does not at all look odd among them. It is just one of the various intelligible and familiar means of construction with which we compose our thought-picture. It is no more and no less abstract than the material points whose motion we represent relative to the coordinate system and for which alone we first pronounce laws and give them mathematical formulation. By checking with experience, we then find that a coordinate system which is invariably associated with the fixed stars is in practice perfectly sufficient to secure agreement with experience. One day we may be able to express the motion of the fixed stars by means of mechanical formulae; but the question as to what kind of coordinate system we must then take as a basis stands at the very last place in our repertory.

6

PROBABILITY AND DEGREE
OF CONFIRMATION:

Ernest Nagel ⋅

It is possible to distinguish writers on probability according to the following schema: (1) Writers who interpret
"probable" in a *univocal* sense; such writers differ among
themselves according as they accept the classical view, the
view of probability as a unique logical relation, or the frequency view. (2) Writers who do not believe that the
term "probable" can be interpreted in precisely the same
manner in every one of the contexts in which it occurs.

The present state of research, therefore, leaves the issue
unsettled as to the scope of the frequency theory of probability. We shall examine the points at issue, but our conclusion will of necessity have to be highly tentative. We
shall concern ourselves explicitly with statements ascribing
a probability to a theory, because of lack of space; but
the discussion will apply without essential qualifications
to probability statements about singular statements like
"Caesar visited Britain," whenever such probability statements are not analyzable as elliptic formulations involving
relative frequencies. By "theory" will be understood any

⋅ [This selection is excerpted from Ernest Nagel's "Principles of
the Theory of Probability," Vol. I, No. 6 of *The International Encyclopedia of Unified Science* (Chicago: University of Chicago
Press, 1939), pp. 62–75. We omit the footnotes. Reprinted by permission of Ernest Nagel and the University of Chicago Press.]

statement of whatever degree of complexity which contains one or more universal quantifiers, or a set of such statements.

1. *The probability of theories.* We begin with examining the proposal to interpret probability statements about theories in terms of relative frequencies; and, since Reichenbach has expounded this proposal more fully than anyone else, we shall examine his views. Reichenbach has given two distinct but allied methods for defining "the probability of a theory." The first of these methods has received an improved formulation by C. G. Hempel, which avoids serious difficulties present in Reichenbach's own version. It should be noted that the definitions given by both methods are semantic ones.

a) Let T be some theory, for example, the Newtonian theory of gravitation. Let C_n be a class of n singular statements, each of which specifies an initial state of a system. (For from T alone, without the specification of initial conditions, no empirically controllable consequences can be obtained; thus, the mass, initial position, and velocity of a planet must be assigned before a future state of the planet can be predicted.) From every such statement with the help of T, other statements may be derived, some of which are empirically controllable by an appropriate observation. Therefore, let E_n be the class of n such singular statements derived from C_n with the help of T. We suppose that a one-to-one correspondence is established between the elements of C_n and E_n; and without loss of generality we shall suppose that every statement in C_n is true. (From a single statement in C an indefinite number of statements belonging to E may be derived; but we can simply *repeat* a statement in C for every one of the distinct consequences drawn from it.) Let nu (E_n) be the number of statements in E_n which are true. The relative frequency with which a statement in E_n is true when its corresponding statement in C_n is true is given by nu $(E_n)/n$. Suppose now that n increases indefinitely, so that C_n will include all possible true initial conditions for T, while E_n will include all the possible predictions which are made from them with the help of T. The numerical expression

$$\text{prob } (E, C) = \lim_{n \to \infty} \frac{\text{nu}(E_n)}{n},$$

will then be the probability that the consequences, obtained with the help of T from appropriate initial conditions, are true. This, in essence, is Reichenbach's first method of assigning a probability to a theory *T*.

Although the foregoing exposition requires supplementation in several ways, there seems to be little question that a precise definition for "the probability of a theory" can be given on a relative frequency basis. It is, however, by no means evident that such a definition formulates the concept people seem to be employing when they discuss the probability of theories.

(i) On the foregoing definition the probability of a theory is the limiting value of relative frequencies in an infinite ordered class *E*. This value is therefore independent of the *absolute number* of true instances in *E*, and is also independent of the absolute or relative number of instances in *E* which we know to be true *at a given time*. However, we often do say that on the basis of *definite evidence* a theory has some "degree of probability." Thus, a familiar use of this phrase permits us to say that, because of the accumulated evidence obtained since 1900, the quantum theory of energy is more probable today then it was thirty years ago. The foregoing definition is not suitable for this use of the phrase.

(ii) Because the probability of a theory is defined as the limit of relative frequencies, the probability of a theory may be 1, although the class *E* of its empirically confirmable consequences contains an infinite number of statements which are in fact false. This conclusion could follow even if some of these exceptions to the theory are ruled out as not being genuine negative instances (see the discussion of this point in § 7)[1]. But, according to the familiar usage of "probability of a theory" already referred to, if a theory did have an infinite number of exceptions, not only would not a "high degree of probability" be assigned to it: it would be simply rejected.

(iii) It is difficult to know how even the approximate value of the probability of a theory, in Reichenbach's first sense, is to be determined. The situation here is not quite the same as for the probability statements which occur *within* a natural science and which have been already discussed in § 7. In the present case it does not seem possible to obtain other than direct statistical evidence for an assigned numerical value; for it is not apparent how a statement about the probability of theories can be part of an inclusive

[1] [§ 7 of Nagel's monograph, not reprinted here.]

system, so that the statement might possibly be confirmed indirectly, perhaps even by nonstatistical evidence. Reichenbach's proposal of a hierarchy of probabilities, according to which the probability of a probability statement may be estimated, postpones this problem by referring it to a higher level of probabilities; but postponing a problem does not solve it.

b) The second method proposed by Reichenbach for assigning a probability to a theory in a frequency sense depends upon the first method. The theory *T* under consideration will now be regarded as an element in an infinite class *K* of theories. These theories are supposed to be alike in some respects and unlike in others; and the theory *T* will share with a number of others in *K* a certain definite property *P*. (The following crude illustration may help fix our ideas: Suppose *T* is the Newtonian theory, and *K* the class of possible theories dealing with the physical behavior of macroscopic bodies. *P* may then be the property that the force functions in the theory are functions of the coordinates alone.) The probability of the theory *T* is then defined as the limit of the relative frequency with which theories in *K*, possessing the property *P*, have a probability in Reichenbach's first sense which is not less than a specified number *q*.

We can comment only briefly on this proposal.

(i) Although it is easy to introduce the reference class *K* and the property *P* in the formal definition, in practice it is by no means easy to specify them. The class *K* must not be selected too widely or arbitrarily, but no way is known for unambiguously grouping together a set of allegedly "relevant" theories. The difficulty is even greater in specifying the property *P* for a concrete case. We might wish to say, for example, that the theory of relativity is more probable than the Newtonian theory. But just what is the property *P* in this case on the basis of which they are to be distinguished?

(ii) We do not at present possess a sufficiently extensive collection of theories, so that appropriate statistical inquiries cannot be made with respect to them in accordance with this proposal. This proposal therefore completely lacks practical relevance. Indeed, there is some ground for suspicion that the proposal would be feasible only if, as Peirce suggested, "universes were as plentiful as blackberries"; only in such a case could we determine the relative frequency

with which these different universes exhibit the traits formulated by a theory under consideration.

(iii) If we could assign a probability value to a theory according to the first of Reichenbach's two proposals, there would be little need for estimating its probability by the second method. It is consistent with these proposals that a theory which has a probability of 1 on the first method, has the probability of only 0 on the second method. But since we are, by hypothesis, interested in that *one* theory, of what particular significance is it to know that theories of such a type have almost all their instances in conformity with the facts with only a vanishingly small relative frequency? This second proposal, like the first, does not therefore formulate the sense of those statements which assign a "degree of probability" to a theory on the basis of *given* finite evidence. For this second proposal does not permit us to talk *literally* about the degree of probability which *one definite theory* has on the evidence at hand; and it is just this which is intended when the evidence for a theory at one time is compared with the evidence at another time.

2. *Degree of confirmation or weight of evidence.* These difficulties with the two proposals for assigning a probability to a theory, in the relative frequency sense of the term, are serious enough to have led competent students to seek a different interpretation for such statements. Guided by the actual procedure of the sciences, a long line of writers have urged that a different concept is involved in such statements from the one specified by the frequency theory of probability. This concept has been designated as "degree of confirmation" or "weight of evidence," in order to distinguish it from the various interpretations given to the term "probable." We shall briefly explain what is meant by "degree of confirmation" and discuss some of the problems which center around its use.

The initial task which must be performed before a satisfactory account of "degree of confirmation" can be given is a careful analysis of the logical structure of a theory in order to make precise the conditions under which a theory may be confirmed by suitable experiments. This has been partially done by Carnap with considerable detail and refinement. We shall, however, not reproduce the results of his analyses, and shall employ distinctions inexactly formulated but which are familiar in the literature of scientific method. In particular, we shall take for granted the following, of which use has already been made: No theory (or for that matter no singular statement) can be established completely and finally by any finite class of observations. But a theory can be tested by examining its instances, that is, the singular sentences E derived with the help of the theory from the sentences C stating the initial conditions for the application of the theory. Both C and E may increase in number; but, while theoretically there are an infinite number of instances of a theory, no more than a finite number will have been tested at any given time. Indeed, a theory is said to be capable of being confirmed or verified only incompletely, just because no more than a finite number of its instances can be actually tested. The instances may be confirmed by observation, in which case they are called the *positive instances* for the theory; or they may be in disaccord with the outcome of observations, in which case they are called the *negative instances*.

We shall assume for the sake of simplicity that there are no negative instances for a given theory T. Then as we continue the process of testing T, the number of positive instances will usually increase. Now it is generally admitted that, by increasing the positive instances, the theory becomes more securely established. What is known as "the weight of evidence" for the theory is thus taken to be a function of the number of positive instances. And we may accordingly state as a preliminary explanation of what is meant by "the degree of confirmation" for a theory that the degree of confirmation increases with the number of the positive instances for T.

This explanation is, of course, far from precise; but at present no precise definition for the term is available. As matters stand, the term is used in a more or less intuitive fashion in the actual procedures of testing theories. It would obviously be highly desirable to have carefully formulated semantical rules for employing the term; but there is no early prospect that the rules for weighing the evidence for a theory will be reduced to a formal schema. The following observations, however, indicate some of the conditions under which the weighing of evidence is carried on, and will contribute something to making more precise the meaning of "degree of confirmation."

a) It does not seem possible to assign a quantitative value to the degree of confirmation of a theory. Thus, at one stage of investigation a theory *T* may have twenty positive instances in its favor, while at a later stage it may have forty such instances. While the degree of confirmation of *T* at the second stage would in general be acknowledged as greater than at the first stage, it is nevertheless not appropriate to say one degree of confirmation is twice the other. The reason for this inappropriateness is that, if degrees of confirmation could be quantized, all degrees of confirmation would be comparable and be capable therefore of a linear ordering. That this does not seem to be the case is suggested by the following hypothetical situation.

Suppose that the positive instances for *T* can be analyzed into two nonoverlapping classes K_1 and K_2, such that the instances in K_1 come from one field of inquiry and those in K_2 from another field. For example, if *T* is the Newtonian theory, K_1 may be the confirmatory instances for it from the study of planetary motions, while K_2 may be those coming from the study of capillarity phenomena; each set of instances is in an obvious sense qualitatively dissimilar from the other. Now imagine the following possibilities as to the number of instances of K_1 and K_2:

	P_1	P_2	P_3	P_4	P_5	P_6	P_7	P_8	P_9
K_1.....	50	50	100	101	99	100	200	100	198
K_2.....	0	50	0	49	52	90	0	100	2
E	50	100	100	150	151	190	200	200	200

The last row of figures gives the total number of positive instances for *T*. These nine possibilities are arranged in order of increasing number of positive instances. Would we say, however, that this order also represents the order of increasing degrees of confirmation?

It would generally be granted that for both P_2 and P_3 the degree of confirmation is greater than for P_1, simply because of the total number of positive instances. On the other hand, many scientists would be inclined to assign a greater degree of confirmation to P_2 than to P_3, even though the total number of positive instances is the same in these cases. And the reason they would give is that in P_2 there are *different kinds* of instances, while in P_3 there is only one kind. For this reason also P_6 would be assigned a higher degree of confirmation than P_7, even though the total number of positive instances in the former case is less than in the latter case. Again, P_4 and P_5 would often be assigned the *same* degree of confirmation, even though the total number of instances is different in these cases, because the relative number of instances of each kind is approximately the same. Finally, P_8 and P_9 would often be regarded as *incomparable* with respect to their degrees of confirmation, because of the disparity in the relative number of different kinds of instances.

Variety in the kinds of positive instances for a theory is a generally acknowledged factor in estimating the weight of the evidence. The reason for this is that experiments which are conducted in qualitatively different domains make it easier to control features of the theory whose relevance in *any* of the domains may be in question. Hence, by increasing the possibility of eliminating what may be simply accidental successes of a theory under special or unanalyzed circumstances, the possibility of finding negative instances for the theory is increased. In this way of conducting experiments, the theory is subjected to a more searching examination than if all the positive instances were drawn from just one domain. A large increase in the number of positive instances of one kind may therefore count for less, in the judgment of skilled experimenters, than a small increase in the number of positive instances of another kind. It follows, however, that the degree of confirmation for a theory seems to be a function not only of the absolute number of positive instances but also of the kinds of instances and of the relative number in each kind. It is not in general possible, therefore, to order degrees of confirmation in a linear order, because the evidence for theories may not be comparable in accordance with a simple linear schema; and a fortiori degrees of confirmation cannot, in general, be quantized.

Indeed, the foregoing hypothetical situation is only a highly simplified outline of the considerations which are usually taken to be relevant in estimating the weight of the evidence for a theory. Among other factors usually considered is the precision with which the confirmable consequences of a theory are in agreement with experimental findings. Although, as has been repeatedly explained, a theory is not rejected simply because perfect agreement between predicted and experimentally determined magnitudes does not occur, the more closely the observed values center around the theoretically expected magnitudes, the greater weight is usually attached to the supporting observations for a theory. Furthermore, evidence for a theory often consists not only of its own positive instances but also of the positive instances for *another* theory, related to the first within a more inclusive theoretical system. The number of direct positive instances may in such cases be regarded as of small importance, in comparison with the fact that support is given to the theory by the accumulated positive instances for the inclusive system.

b) How large must the number and kinds of positive instances be in order that a theory can be taken as adequately established? No general answer can be given to such a question, since the answer involves practical decisions on the part of those who conduct a scientific inquiry. There is an ineradicable conventional element among the factors which lead to the acceptance of a theory on the basis of actual evidence at hand. It is always theoretically possible to demand further evidence before agreement is reached that a theory has been sufficiently well tested. However, the practical decision is in part a function of the contemporary scientific situation. The estimation of the evidence for one theory is usually conducted in terms of the bearing of that evidence upon alternative theories for the same subject matter. When there are several competing theories, a decision between them may be postponed indefinitely, if the evidence supports them all with approximately the same precision. Furthermore, the general line of research pursued at a given time may also determine how the decision for a theory will turn out. For example, at a time when a conception of discontinuous matter is the common background for physical research, a theory for a special domain of research formulated in accordance with the dominant leading idea may require little direct evidence for it; on the other hand, a theory based on a continuous notion of matter for that domain may receive little consideration even if direct empirical evidence supports it as well as, or even better than, it does the alternative theory.

In particular, the acceptance of definite numerical values for probabilities also involves practical decision, for which no general rules can be given. As already explained, such numerical values are often computed on the basis of more or less comprehensive theoretical systems, and the confidence which we have in the correctness of those values depends on the confidence we have in those systems. It

may happen that we can determine the value of a probability with only small accuracy by a theory which has a
relatively high degree of confirmation, while a different
value may be computed with great precision by an alternative theory with an inferior degree of confirmation. The
supposition that in such a case the dilemma can be resolved
by a clear-cut method neglects the human and accidental
factors which determine the history of science. Certainly
no mathematical or logical formula can be given which
would mechanically supply a coefficient of weight for
the correctness of the decisions which are made in many
analogous cases.

c) Assuming that these desultory observations are based
on the study of actual scientific procedure, it may be asked
why it is that we seem to feel that theories with a greater
degree of confirmation deserve our confidence on logical
grounds more than those with less—whenever such comparisons can be made. Why, in other words, should a theory
be regarded as "better established" if we increase the number and kinds of its positive instances?

Perhaps a simple example will help suggest an answer.
Suppose a cargo of coffee is to be examined for the quality
of the beans. We cannot practically examine every coffee
bean, and so we obtain some sample beans. We do not,
however, sample the cargo by taking a very large number
of beans from just one part of the hold; we take many
relatively small samples from very many different parts of
the ship. Why do we proceed in this way? The answer
seems to be that our general experience is such that, when
we conduct our samplings in this manner, we approximate to the distribution of qualities in the entire hold; and,
in general, the larger our individual samples and the more
diversified our choice of the parts of the ship from which
they are taken, the more reliable (as judged by subsequent
experience) are the estimates we form. It is at least a
plausible view that in testing a theory we are making a
series of samplings from the class of its possible instances.
A theory is "better established" when we increase the number and kinds of its positive instances, because the *method*
we thereby employ is one which our general experience
confirms as leading to conclusions which are stable or which
provide satisfactory solutions to the specific problems of
inquiry. At any rate, this was the answer which Charles
Peirce proposed to the so-called "problem of induction," and

which has been independently advanced in various forms by many contemporary students of scientific method (e.g., M. R. Cohen, J. Dewey, H. Feigl, O. Neurath, and many others). As Peirce succinctly put the matter, "Synthetic inferences are founded upon the classification of facts, not according to their characters, but *according to the manner of obtaining them.* Its rule is that a number of facts obtained in a given way will in general more or less resemble other facts obtained in the same way; or, *experiences whose conditions are the same will have the same general characters.*" A degree of confirmation is thus a rough indication of the extent to which our general *method of procedure* has been put into operation. While no probability in a frequency sense can be significantly assigned to any formulation of our method (because it is that very method which is involved in estimating and testing such probabilities), scientific inquiry is based upon the assumption, which is supported by our general experience, that the method of science leads to a proportionately greater number of successful terminations of inquiry than any alternative method yet proposed.

Attempts to find a systematic answer to "the problem of induction" within the framework of a theory of probability, though often made, have not in general been regarded as successful. The *process* of induction has been usually conceived as the search for more or less stable and pervasive relations between properties of objects; and the *problem* of induction has been taken to be the discovery of a principle (the principle of induction) which would "justify" the various conclusions of that process. Stated in this way, it is rather difficult to know just how the "problem" is to be conceived in empirical terms. On the face of it, the "problem" seems to involve a futile infinite regress; and indeed the Achilles heel of attempted solutions of it has usually been the status of the proposed principle of induction: how is the principle itself to be "justified"? The number of different types of answers which have been given to this last question is relatively small; among them are the following: the inductive principle is a synthetic a priori proposition concerning the nature of things in general, it is an a priori proposition concerning the fundamental constitution of the human mind, it is a generalization from experience, and it is a "presupposition" or "postulate" of scientific procedure. It would take too long to examine these answers in detail. It is perhaps sufficient to note that the first two involve positions incompatible with the conclusions of modern logical research; that the third commits a *petitio principii;* and the the fourth, assuming it to have a clear meaning, cannot make of the proposed inductive principle a "justification" of the procedure of science or of its conclusions, since according to this answer the principle is simply an *instrument* of scientific procedure. The position taken in the present monograph is that no antecedent principle is required to justify the procedure of science, that the sole justification of that procedure lies in the specific solutions it offers to the problems which set it into motion, and that a *general* problem of induction in its usual formulation does not exist. Since the notion of the probability of theories (in the specific senses discussed above) has been found to involve serious difficulties, and since the degree of confirmation for a theory has been argued to indicate the extent to which the theory has been tested by the procedure of science, the problem of induction which the present writer recognizes as genuine is the formulation of the general features of scientific method—of the method which, in short, leads to a proportionately greater number of successful terminations of inquiry than the number which other methods may have to their credit.

One brief final remark: It has been customary in the traditional discussions of scientific theories to seek grounds for our knowledge of their *truth* or at least of their *probability* (in some one of the many senses previously discussed). Omitting more than mention of those students (e.g., Wittgenstein and Schlick) who have dismissed such discussions as meaningless because, according to them, theories are not "genuine" propositions since they are not completely verifiable, reference must be made to another group of writers. According to this group, the traditional discussions have not fruitfully illuminated the character of scientific inquiry because those who take part in them neglect the *function* which theories have in inquiry. When this function is examined, it has been urged, it turns out that questions of the *truth* of theories (in the sense in which theories of truth have been traditionally discussed) are of little concern to those who actually use theories. Reflective inquiry is instituted for the sake of settling a *specific* problem, whether it be practical or theoretical, and inquiry terminates when a resolution of the problem is obtained. The various procedures distinguishable in inquiry (such as observation, operation upon subject matter including the manipulation of instruments, symbolic representation of properties of subject matter, symbolic transformation and calculation, etc.) are to be viewed as instrumental to its end product. The use of theories is one patent factor in reflective inquiry. They function primarily as means for effecting transitions from one set of statements to other sets, with the intent of controlling natural changes and of supplying predictions capable of being checked through manipulating directly experienceable subject matter. Accordingly, in their actual use in science, theories serve as *instruments* in specific contexts, and in this capacity are to be characterized as good or bad, effective or ineffective, rather than as true or false or probable. Those who stress the instrumental function of theories are not necessarily committed to identifying truth with effectiveness and falsity with uselessness. Their major insight does not consist in denying the meaningfulness of certain types of inquiries into the truth of theories but in calling attention to the way theories function and to the safeguards and conditions of their effectiveness. A theory is confirmed to the degree that it performs its specific instrumental function. From this point of view, which has been developed with much detail by Dewey, the degree of confirmation for a theory may be interpreted as a mark of its proved effectiveness as an intellectual tool for the purposes for which it has been instituted.

7

THE SIGNIFICANCE AND PURPOSE
OF NATURAL LAWS:
Ernst Mach ·

One often refers to natural laws. But precisely what *are* natural laws? Generally we will be told that they are rules in accordance with which natural occurrences must regulate themselves, very much in the way that people are obliged to regulate their behavior in accordance with civil laws. The two kinds of laws are indeed not thought to be indistinguishable; a frequently noted difference between them being that civil laws can be broken while exceptions to natural laws are allegedly impossible. Far more damaging to this analogy is the fact that we obtain our natural laws by studying what actually occurs, by abstracting from nature, and that we are consequently never secure from error. Every violation of natural laws can readily be accounted for in terms of an erroneous interpretation of our observations, and the inviolability of these laws thus loses all meaning and importance. The danger here is that, once the subjective aspect of our conception of nature is introduced, little seems to prevent us from taking the extreme position that our mode of perception and our concepts alone *prescribe* laws to nature. But if we con-

· [This selection is reprinted, with the omission of some passages and footnotes, from the last chapter of Mach's *Erkenntnis und Irrtum* (Leipzig: 1908). It was specially translated for this volume by Frederic Schick. Included by permission of Johann Ambrosius Barth and Anna Mach.]

sider the development of science with a truly open mind, we will come to associate its origin with the fact that our earliest observations are always of those aspects of events which are of immediate biological importance to us, the extension of our interest to those aspects which are of derivative biological significance being recognized as a later development. In the light of this consideration, it will perhaps be agreed that *laws of nature are delimitations which, on the basis of our experience, we set our expectations.*

K. Pearson, whose views closely resemble mine, expresses himself on these issues as follows:[1] "The civil law involves a command and a duty; the scientific law is a description, not a prescription. The civil law is valid only for a *special* community at a *special* time; the scientific law is valid for *all* normal human beings, and is unchangable so long as their perceptive faculties remain at the same stage of development. For Austin,[2] however, and for many other philosophers too, the law of nature was not the mental formula, but the repeated sequence of perceptions. This repeated sequence of perceptions they projected out of themselves, and considered as a part of an external world unconditioned by and independent of man." Although the word "description" already occurred in the exchanges between Mill and Whewell and has been familiar since Kirchhoff's time, I would like to use the expression "delimitation of expectation" in its stead, thus alluding to the biological significance of natural laws.

A law always consists of a delimitation of possibilities, whether this be conceived as a restriction on our behavior, as an unalterable channel for the course of events, or as a guide for our anticipation of them. Galileo and Kepler considered the various possibilities of free fall and of planetary motion. Seeking to discover those which corresponded to observation, they reshaped their ideas to fit in with their observations, reformulating them with greater precision. The law of inertia, which attributes a uniform, rectilinear motion to a body not acted upon by any external forces, identifies one of an infinity of possible ways of conceiving the situation as authoritative. Even Lange's interpretation of the inertial movement of a system of freely moving masses treats it as one of an innumerable set of kinematic possibilities. The very fact that a natural domain is subject to classifica-

[1] *The Grammar of Science* (2d ed.; London; 1900), p. 87.
[2] The English authority on jurisprudence.

tory analysis, that we can construct concepts to correspond to the various classes, indicates a delimitation of possibilities. For a law need not express itself in the form of a sentence. The applicability of the concept of mass thus introduces the following delimitations: if one of the bodies of a closed system is taken as the unit of measurement, the sum of the masses of the system must be constant. Further, two bodies each of which is equal in mass to a third must themselves be equal in mass.

All organisms equipped with memory are obliged to govern their expectations in the light of what is attainable in the circumstances in which they find themselves. The organism's psychic make-up satisfies its simplest requirements instinctively, in that in the overwhelming preponderance of cases its faculty of association awakens the appropriate disposition. The more complicated requirements, depending for their satisfaction on more circuitous approaches, demand a richer psychic equipment. The several stages of these detours, along with the circumstances which prompt their being taken, thus acquire a derivative significance. Indeed we can interpret all scientific interests as biologically derivative concerns with some step in such a detour. However close or distant a particular concern may be to those of immediate biological significance, only *correct* expectations, only expectations adapted to the circumstances, will gratify them. It must be acknowledged that in different circumstances we adopt quite unequal standards of the *correctness* of expectations. Should we be hungry and find ever so little nourishment where under the circumstances we had expected to find it, we would rest content that our expectation was indeed correct. Should we however expect a projectile of a given weight, fired from a barrel of a given elevation with a given powder charge, to travel a specific distance, and discover that the actual distance traveled diverged even slightly from that which we had expected, we might well suspect that we had made a serious error. If some goal is to be attained at the end of several or many separate steps, a slight error in the measurement of the size or direction of the various steps is enough to lead us astray. Small errors in several of the numbers of a computation may thus significantly falsify the conclusion.[3] Since

[3] As a result of only moderately imprecise measurements, J. R. Mayer thought 365 (instead of 425) to be the mechanical equivalent of the thermal unit.

science is concerned with precisely such intermediary steps as are customarily taken in the indirect gratification of our biological needs, the *precise* specification of our expectations is here of particular importance.

With the progress of natural science comes a progressive delimitation of our expectations, a noticeably more precise organization of them. The earliest delimitations are of a qualitative sort. Whether science can designate the factors $A, B, C \ldots$ prompting some expectation M in a single sentence, or whether it instructs us on how to produce them serially in the way, for instance, that a botanical or chemical analysis does this, is unimportant. A further delimitation is achieved if, in qualitatively indistinguishable cases, it turns out to be possible to draw quantitative distinctions between the various properties being manifested, and thus to correlate a quantitatively specified expectation M to any quantitatively specified complex of properties $A, B, C. \ldots$ The extent of this delimitation depends upon the precision of the available means of measurement and observations. It too may take place all at one time or in successive stages. The latter occurs when a supplementary stipulation restricts our already delimited attention to a still narrower area. The sum of the interior angles of a plane, convex-rectilinear polygon in Euclidean space is $(n-2).2R$. In the case of a triangle $(n = 3)$, this reduces to $2R$, a formula by means of which each of the three angles is determined by the sizes of the other two. This most precise delimitation is thus based on an extended series of mutually supplementary conditions, or of conditions some of which, being the more fundamental, assign a more precise meaning to the others. The same situation holds in physics. The equation "$PV/T = $ const." holds for a gaseous body of constant mass, in all of whose parts P, V, and T have the same value, and which is sufficiently removed from the conditions of condensation. The delimitation affected by the law of refraction, "Sin α/Sin $\beta = n$" is further narrowed by being restricted to a definite pair of homogeneous substances, to a definite temperature, to a definite density or a certain pressure, and to the absence of any difference in magnetic or electrical potential in the two substances. When we apply a physical law to a specific substance we stipulate that the law is to hold in a domain in which the familiar properties of the substance in question are discoverable. These additional stipulations are generally covertly introduced, being implicit in the *name* of the substance in question. Those physical laws which hold in empty space (in a vacuum or the ether), likewise hold only for specific values of electrical and magnetic constants, etc. In applying a law to a specific substance we introduce new stipulations of precisely the sort we introduce when we say (or only implicitly acknowledge) of a theorem of geometry that it holds for triangles or for parallellograms or for rhombuses. Should we discover that a law no longer holds in circumstances in which it had hitherto always held—we would be led to look for an as yet undiscovered condition of applicability. The identification of such a condition always constitutes a significant discovery. Electricity and magnetism were, for instance, discovered in precisely such a manner, as a result of the mutual attraction and repulsion displayed by bodies hitherto assumed to be indifferent to one another. A geometrical or a physical thesis is grounded not only on various explicitly stated hypotheses but also on conditions of applicability which are implicitly stated. It would be well always to keep in mind that conditions as yet unidentified, whose visible modifications we had hitherto ignored, might also be involved.

In our view of the matter, natural laws are the consequence of our psychological need to find our way in nature, and to avoid having to confront it as a confused stranger would. This is clearly demonstrated by the standards which these laws are expected to meet, though such standards express the current cultural situation as well as the above-mentioned psychological need. The earliest attempts at self-orientation are mythological, demonological, and poetic. The period of the rebirth of natural science, the period of Copernicus and Galileo, strove for a primarily qualitative, preliminary orientation, and ease of comprehension, simplicity, and aesthetic satisfaction were accordingly the principles governing the search for those laws which might contribute to the mental reconstruction of the observed facts. Research of a more precise, quantitative sort aims at as complete a specificity as possible, at *unambiguous specificity*—an objective already apparent in the early history of mechanics. With the accumulation of information, the demand for laws diminishing the effort required for assimilating it, the demand for intellectual economy, continuity, permanence, and as general an applicability and practicality as possible becomes particularly pressing. The later history of mechanics or of any advanced part of physics amply illustrates this development.

It is only natural that in periods lacking in epistemological sophistication the psychological motive for scientific research is projected into nature itself. It is God or nature which strives toward simplicity and aesthetic satisfaction—at a later period toward a firm regularity and specificity—finally, toward frugality and economy in all respects, toward the attainment of every end with the least possible expense. Contrasting the *general* applicability of the wave theory with the limited applicability of the older corpuscular theory, Fresnel [4]—writing in quite recent times—attributes to nature the inclination to achieve a great deal with the simplest of means. "The earlier hypothesis has the advantage of having simpler consequences, since they are readily subject to analysis by the principles of mechanics. The second, on the other hand, presents serious difficulties in this connection. In the choice of a theory, however, one may consider nothing but the simplicity of hypotheses; their computational advantages may carry no weight in the assessment of their probability. Nature is not embarrassed by computational difficulties. She *does* avoid cumbersome means. She seems to have decided to do much with little, a principle in support of which the progress of the physical sciences provides constant evidence."

The progressive tightening of natural laws, the gradually increasing delimitation of our expectations, corresponds to an ever more precise adjustment of our ideas to actuality. A complete adjustment in every particular, to every future, unpredictable fact, is of course impossible. The multifarious, extremely general applicability of natural laws is indeed only made possible by abstraction, by the simplification, schematization, and idealization of actuality, by our intellectual dissection of facts into simple elements of such a sort that the same facts can be reconstructed of them again to an appropriate degree of accuracy. Uniform motion and uniform acceleration, stationary (constant) thermal and electrical current, current of a uniformly increasing and uniformly decreasing intensity, etc., are examples of such idealized factual constituents. Though nothing precisely resembling these elements is ever actually encountered in experience, every actual motion and current is reconstructi-

[4] Fresnel, "Mémoire couronnée sur la diffraction," *Oeuvres* (Paris: 1866), Vol. 1, p. 248.

ble with their aid to whatever degree of precision may be required, and the application of natural laws is thus facilitated. The differential equations of physics serve this very purpose. Our natural laws thus consist of a series of readily utilizable propositions, indeed of propositions adopted because of their ease of practical utilization. And science itself may be considered an accumulation of instruments for the sounding out of our picture of some only practically manifest domain of facts, or for the precise delimitation of our expectation of the future.

Facts are not obliged to govern themselves in accordance with our ideas. But our expectations *are* governed by our ideas, in particular by our conceptions of the facts which comprise our evidence. Our expectations of the future are always considerably vague. Should the facts however correspond precisely to our idealized conception of them, the expectations we base on them would likewise be precisely specified. A scientific proposition is never more than conditional; it asserts that *if* fact A precisely corresponds to conception M, consequence B corresponds precisely to conception N, B corresponding to N to exactly the degree to which A corresponds to M. Absolute precision, an altogether accurate specification of the consequences of an hypothesis, can only be found in physical theory; it cannot be expected in applied physics (any more than in applied geometry.) Progress is directed at an ever closer adaptation of theory to reality. But even after numerous quantitative observations of refraction through a pair of media, our anticipation of the angle of refraction of some specific impinging ray of light retains a vagueness proportioned to the imprecision of our observation and measurement. Only the establishment of the law of refraction and the choice of a specific value for the index of refraction enables us to predict the unique angle of refraction of any particular impinging ray. . . .

Only a theory which describes the invariably complicated and variously distorted facts of observation in a manner more simple and precise than is strictly speaking authenticable by experience satisfies the ideal of unequivocal specificity. Such a degree of clarity in the theory enables us to trace out lengthy series of deductive consequences and thus to arrive at far-reaching inferences, whose conformity with the theory is of course guaranteed. The conformity or lack of conformity of these inferences with experience is generally however (because of the possibility of accumulating discrepancies) a far more precise measure of the accuracy or inaccuracy of the theory than can be provided by the comparison of the principles of the theory with experience. Consider, for instance, the Newtonian principles of mechanics and the inferences drawn from them in astronomy....

Are then natural laws, being nothing but subjective rules for the guidance of an observer's expectations, without any value? Certainly not! For even though actuality meet with our expectations only to a limited extent, it has often proved our laws to be correct and proves them progressively more so daily. We are thus guilty of no error in adopting the principle of the uniformity of nature, though the inexhaustibility of experience rules out any possibility of verifying its temporal and spatial universality and the exactness of its applicability, even though it must remain, as must all the instruments of science, an ideal to be approximated. Besides, the postulate deals only with uniformity; it says nothing about its particular character. Should our expectations be disappointed, we are always free to look for uniformities of a form different from those we had anticipated.

8

EXPLANATION, PREDICTION, AND ABSTRACTION: [1]

Israel Scheffler *

Introduction

In recent philosophy of science, three basic views concerning explanation and prediction have received wide support, attaining almost canonical status. They are (1) the view that explanation and prediction share a *common structure,* with but the pragmatic difference that an explained event antedates the statement of its explanation while a predicted event can only follow its prediction, (2) the view that explanation and prediction represent the *central purpose* of science and are epistemologically basic, and (3) the view that explanation and prediction are abstract in reference, their objects being not concrete things but *idealistic or intensional entities* like phenomena, facts, or states-of-affairs. I shall argue, in what follows, that these three views are untenable, and I shall affirm instead that explanation and prediction are structurally distinct, that,

[1] The writer wishes to thank Professors C. G. Hempel, N. Goodman, W. V. Quine, and N. Chomsky for critical comments.
* [This selection is reprinted, with the omission of Part III, from *The British Journal for the Philosophy of Science,* Vol. VII, No. 28, 1957, by permission of Israel Scheffler and the editor of the *British Journal of the Philosophy of Science.*]

associated with control, they are subsidiary to the primary concern of science with comprehensive relationships among events, and that they require no abstract, idealistic entities as objects.

1. THE STRUCTURAL IDENTITY CLAIM

The notion of explanation has a variety of uses both in ordinary speech and in scientific contexts. In both spheres we speak alternatively of explaining concepts or terms, laws or generalizations, and concrete occurrences or events. It is interesting to observe, at the outset, how this very variety of uses contrasts with those of the notion "prediction." For while we speak of predicting occurrences or events, we surely do not speak of predicting concepts or terms, nor, in any obvious sense, laws or generalizations. The claim of structural identity is made, however, not with reference to all patterns of scientific explanation, but specifically regarding explanation of events, usually described somewhat as follows.[2]

Let a and b be distinct events, described by the sentences A and B respectively, and let L be a law or conjunction of laws. Suppose, also, that B is a logical consequence of A and L, but not of A alone. If A and L are true, while b has already occurred, we may say that b has been accounted for or explained by the conjunction of A and L, or that this conjunction satisfies the requirements for an explanans of the explanandum B.

This sketch incorporates the four conditions listed by Hempel and Oppenheim in their discussion of the logic of explanation,[3] which we take here as a model:

(R1) The explanandum must be a logical consequence of the explanans.

[2] The description here discussed (as well as the structural identity claim) is given in various forms by a number of authors. Among recent empiricist writings, the following should be especially mentioned: K. R. Popper, *Logik der Forschung* (Wien: 1935), pp. 26 ff., and *The Open Society and its Enemies* (London: [first published 1945] 1947), Vol. II, p. 249 and pp. 342–3, C. G. Hempel, "The Function of General Laws in History," *Journal of Philosophy*, Vol. 39, 1942, pp. 35–48, and C. G. Hempel and P. Oppenheim, "Studies in the Logic of Explanation," *Philosophy of Science*, Vol. 15, 1948, pp. 135–75.

[3] Hempel & Oppenheim, *op. cit.*, pp. 137–8.

(R2) The explanans must contain general laws required for the derivation of the explanandum.[4]

(R3) The explanans must have empirical content.

(R4) The sentences constituting the explanans must be true.

Justifying (R4) as contrasted with an alternative requirement of high confirmation for the explanans, Hempel and Oppenheim cite the case of a purported explanans highly confirmed at time t_1 but later highly disconfirmed at time t_2, in which event we should not wish to say that what was an explanans at t_1 ceased to be one at t_2 but should rather prefer to assert that, while its truth had been probable relative to available evidence at t_1, its falsity was probable at t_2, and correlatively, its inadequacy as an explanation at any time.

It is this pattern which is alleged to identical with that of scientific prediction. As Hempel and Oppenheim put it, "the same formal analysis, including the four necessary conditions, applies to scientific prediction as well as to explanation." The pragmatic difference as they, in agreement with several other authors, formulate it consists in the fact that for explanation, B is given, b having occurred, and the conjunction of A and L is provided afterward, while for prediction, this conjunction is given and B is derived prior to the occurrence of b. Explanation, as they put it, "is directed towards past occurrences," prediction "towards future ones."

Now this account implies that every explanation, if stated prior to the event described by its explanandum, would be predictive, while every prediction, stated after the event in question, would be explanatory. The first of these consequences is indeed explicitly drawn in the study of Hempel and Oppenheim, "It may be said, therefore, that an explanation is not fully adequate unless its explanans, if taken account of in time, could have served as a basis for pre-

---

[4] Hempel and Oppenheim do not also require the explanans to include one statement which is not a law, for "to mention one reason," they wish to consider an explanation of generalizations a bona fide explanation. In the light of what was observed above, regarding the restriction of the notion of "prediction" to events, it would seem unlikely that they wish to extend their statement of the explanatory pattern to the *prediction* of generalizations, though they do not make this point explicit.

dicting the phenomenon under consideration." The second consequence, though equally necessary for the structural identity in question, is not further elaborated.[5] In view of the following considerations, it seems to me that it is untenable.

(a) First, note that "is a prediction" is not properly applicable to abstract sentences or propositions, since the same sentence "It rains on May 8, 1952" is or is not a prediction depending on the temporal circumstances of its utterance. Or, more accurately, since what predicts must have an appropriate time relative to what is predicted, and since abstract sentences or propositions are nontemporal altogether, they cannot be properly denoted by "is a prediction." We may distinguish the abstract sentence from the uses made of it at various times and denote uses as predictions, if we like. Alternatively, we shall here construe "is a prediction" as predicable of concrete utterances or inscriptions (i.e., tokens) with temporal boundaries, but the point to be made can be readily put in terms of the other usual analyses.

Consider now any utterance or inscription of declarative, noncompound form. In accordance with the dominant ordinary notion of prediction, any such utterance or inscription is a prediction if it explicitly asserts something about some time later than any of its own. But it is clearly false that restating each such prediction following the time of its predicted occurrence, explains this occurrence even when both prediction and restatement are true. Thus, no inscription like "Eisenhower is elected President on November 4, 1952" *explains* Eisenhower's election, though every such inscription prior to November 4, 1952, is a prediction in the ordinary sense, and true at that. The point then is that, in the usual sense of "prediction," not every restatement of a prediction after the event is explanatory, even though every statement of an explanation prior to the event is predictive.

Nor will it do to invoke epistemology at this point by

[5] This sentence does, however, appear (p. 138) though it does not figure importantly in the later treatment of the authors: "only to the extent that we are able to explain empirical facts can we attain the major objective of scientific research, namely not merely to record the phenomena of our experience, but to learn from them, by basing upon them theoretical generalisations which enable us to anticipate new occurrences and to control, at least to some extent, the changes in our environment."

asking how a prediction of Eisenhower's election could have been made without the use of general laws and statements of relevant antecedent conditions. That the methodological genesis of a prediction does not meet rational or scientific requirements may involve irrational behavior by its producer, but is no bar to its predictiveness in the ordinary sense, nor even to its truth. Clairvoyants, prophets, and news commentators all predict in the sense under consideration, just as do scientists. For pragmatists and positivists in particular, who justify scientific method by success in prediction, a restriction of the latter to *scientific* prediction would reduce their justification to triviality.

(*b*) Suppose, however, that structural identity is interpreted as holding between explanation and *rational* prediction *as practiced in the sciences,* involving reference to general statements and specific condition statements.[6] Even so, it will appear that not all predictive restatements after the event are explanatory, since predictive success involves the possibility of predictive failure, i.e., false predictions. But no explanation is false, since it consists of an explanans, which by (*R*4) must be true, and an explanandum which, being a logical consequence of the latter, cannot be false

[6] One might, incidentally, raise the question whether scientific prediction always takes the form mentioned, in view of predictions only inductively well-grounded, but not implied by any relevant conjunction of universal generalizations and condition statements. For example, suppose we predict that the 5,000th ball drawn at random from an urn will be red, since all have heretofore been red with, say, the exception of the first drawn. If such prediction is acknowledged as rational, surely its full restatement after the event is non-explanatory even if true. Thus, suppose our prediction is fulfilled and we are told that the explanation why the 5,000th ball was red is because the previous 4998 were. This seems unacceptable as an explanation though it restates the rational grounds for having made the prediction previously. Indeed, were there not a single exception, the fact that, e.g., 4,999 balls were red does not explain why the 5,000th is red though it does rationally ground the prediction that it will be. This example serves to illustrate a distinction, of some general importance, between asking "Why *P*?" in the sense, "What is the explanans for *P*?" and in the often divergent sense, "What are rational grounds for asserting *P*?" The distinction is sufficient to invalidate a widespread identification of the *explanation of A* with *showing that A was to be expected,* as suggested, e.g., by Toulmin, *The Place of Reason in Ethics* (Cambridge: Cambridge University Press, 1950), pp. 122 ff., and many others.

either. This divergence is related to the use of scientific predictions in testing the body of assumptions at a given time; for such testing to occur, it must make sense to judge a derived prediction false, thereby forcing a revision in its ground-premises. Indeed, to the extent that predictive test is involved in confirming the truth of general laws, themselves required for explanation by ($R2$), to that extent the possibility of falsifying predictions is presupposed by the confirmation of explanations.

If this divergence between scientific explanation and prediction is granted, one might still attempt to reinterpret the structural identity claim as holding between rational prediction (by deduction from general statements and condition statements) and *proffered* explanation, which, of course, may be false. Without artificial restriction of the latter notion, however, such reinterpretation fails. For in its ordinary sense, "proffered explanation" refers not only to certain explanations which are false, i.e., violate ($R4$), but also to some which fail to exhibit the required logical character as specified by ($R1$), fail to contain general laws as required by ($R2$), or lack the empirical content demanded by ($R3$). Artificial expansion of this notion would moreover, also be necessary since we would not, ordinarily, consider any account to be even a proffered explanation unless it purported to explain some *fact*, i.e., unless at least its explanandum were true; derived *predictions*, on the other hand, may clearly be false. To specify then explicitly that we are to require fulfillment of ($R1$), ($R2$), and ($R3$), but neither ($R4$), nor the truth of the explanandum (while certainly legitimate and often convenient for other purposes), renders trivial the claim of structural identity between prediction and explanation. For, if true, this claim appears no longer a surprising description of two antecedently known patterns which happen to correspond, but rather a consequence of our deliberate theoretical tampering. What is finally correlated to the term "prediction" is a technical artifact independently related neither to the ordinary sense of "explanation" nor to that of "proffered explanation."[7]

[7] Furthermore, it is doubtful if even this explicit delimitation of just what is supposed to correspond to prediction is sufficient. For on one widely held view (shared by Hempel), abstract, partially interpreted theories are an integral part of advanced sciences and, as such, are essential to rational prediction in those sciences. It is

We conclude, then, that the **structural** identity claim should be rejected; far from differing only in pragmatic relationships, explanation and prediction have different logical characteristics: explanations are true, predictions need not be; making predictions is part of one way of confirming the existence of explanations; predictions may be made with or without rational grounds, and some rational grounds adequate for prediction fail to *explain* the predicted occurrences. If, then, the structural identity claim is to be approved for implying that every explanation must have been capable of prediction, it is no less censurable for glossing over these important differences in structure and role.

2. THE CENTRALITY CLAIM

If explanation and prediction are structurally distinct, the usual claim of centrality in scientific procedure is at least ambiguous: Are they both central, or is one more important than the other? The following considerations will specify some distinctive temporal asymmetries peculiar to each, arguing for their irrelevance to general scientific inference, and hence the inadvisability of incorporating them into typical or central models of such inference.

(*a*) Consider first prediction. A necessary condition for the predictive character of an utterance or inscription is its asserting something about some time later than its own. This is the force of future-tense indicators often taken as a sign of predictive character in ordinary usage, though, of course, not essential to such character. If, now, we examine the four requirements of Hempel and Oppenheim, we find no temporal conditions among them.[8] To be sure, this pattern of requirements is intended to reflect the inferential process of making (scientific) predictions, but the inferences admitted by the pattern include other types as well, which

---

unclear, however, in what sense we may speak of the truth or falsity of *partially* interpreted formal systems. If we cannot, then such theories, though predictive, are not even proffered explanantia in our explicit sense. For though this sense does not *require* truth, it does require that the explanans be, in point of fact, either true or false.

[8] Often, indeed, terms like "consequence," "derivation," "antecedent condition," "presuppose," etc., are ambiguously employed with occasional temporal reference. It does not appear, however, that such interpretation is here intended.

cannot be classed as explanations either. Thus, even if this pattern is not exhaustive, but represents one scheme of scientific inference, it is much wider and more general than inferences of predictive or explanatory nature.

Thus, as the distinction between explanation and prediction is drawn by Hempel, Oppenheim, and others, it would be said, with reference to our earlier example, that if B is given, i.e., if we know that the phenomenon described by B has occurred, and a suitable set of statements A and L is provided afterwards, we have an explanation, while if the latter statements are given, and B is derived prior to the occurrence of the phenomenon it describes, we speak of a prediction. Note, however, one way in which this description fails to exhaust the inferences allowable by the pattern: If A and L are given rather than B, thus precluding explanation, their logical consequence B may be derived not prior to, but simultaneous with or after the occurrence of b. For example, b may have occurred prior to B's derivation but later than a, or it may have occurred prior to a.[9]

For an illustration of the first case (i), consider an astronomer who, from statements describing the *beginning of an ancient eclipse a*, plus the appropriate laws, deduces a statement describing *its end b*. For an example of the second case, (ii) imagine the same astronomer who, from appropriate laws plus statements describing *some relevant configuration of heavenly bodies at some time during his own personal experience a*, deduces statements describing *some eclipse in former times b*. In neither case do we have a prediction, yet both inferences fulfill the pattern in question.[10] What is common to both and to the predictive inference in question is not any temporal relation between statements and described events, but rather the givenness of A and L and the later derivation of B. The latter sequence, however, bears no simple relation to the sequence of described occurrences. It seems reasonable, then, to avoid the partial notion of prediction altogether in this connec-

[9] b may, it goes without saying, have occurred at any time relative to the givenness of A and L as well.

[10] We might call one or both of these inferences "postdictive," following Reichenbach in *Philosophic Foundations of Quantum Mechanics* (California: University of California Press, 1944), but, contrary to Hempel and Oppenheim, *op. cit.*, p. 138, "postdiction" is not applicable to explanation.

tion and suggest the full potentialities of the pattern when A and L are given, by assigning a temporally neutral term to the derivation of B, say "positing."[11] From assumed laws and information about some spatiotemporal regions, we posit phenomena at other such regions, in any spatial or temporal relations to our assumed phenomena or our own utterance. Some positing is also predicting, but prediction has no more primacy for the pattern in question than positing events to the left of us in space has. Whether, aside from the pattern, there is independent reason to consider prediction scientifically or epistemologically primary is a question which we shall discuss at a later point.

(b) Now consider explanation, i.e., with B given, and a suitable set of statements A and L provided afterward, fulfilling Hempel and Oppenheim's four requirements. Once again we find that, since no temporal criteria are to be found among these requirements, they define a wider class of inferences than simply explanatory ones. A nonexplanatory instance which fits the pattern is afforded by any case where b precedes a. A concrete illustration is at hand in any situation analogous to our previous example (ii). Thus, given a description of *some eclipse in former times b*, an astronomer who provides appropriate laws L and statements describing *some relevant configuration of celestial bodies during his own lifetime a* from which B is deducible, is fitting the pattern, but is surely not *explaining* or *accounting for b*. For explanation, we require, in addition to our four desiderata, that a must not temporally follow b.[12]

[11] Our use of this term should be clearly distinguished from other uses in the literature, especially that of Reichenbach in his many discussions of probability and confirmation, e.g., in *Experience and Prediction* (Chicago: University of Chicago Press, 1938).

[12] This does not imply that all these requirements are sufficient even if necessary. For example, suppose symptom S precedes and is a lawfully sufficient condition for contraction of cancer, enabling prediction. Yet we do not, it might plausibly be said, *explain* contraction of cancer by the presence of S. It may be noted that, while we require that a not follow b, we have not also required that b precede the explanation-utterance accounting for it. Since Hempel and Oppenheim interpret the givenness of B as implying that b precedes its explanation-utterance, it may be worth while to justify here our departure from this view: The givenness of B, it seems to us, means in practice, merely that we are fairly confident in its truth, but such confidence is surely not limited to statements about the past. If common use is any guide here, then if asked "Why will

What is common to our above instance and explanation is not the temporal order of *a* and *b*, but rather the givenness of *B* and the later provision of *A* and *L*. To suggest the full potentialities of the pattern in such a case, we ought to drop the partial notion "explanation" here and again assign a temporally neutral term to the provision of *A* and *L*, e.g., "substantiating."[13]

---

the sun rise tomorrow?" I may reasonably be said both to be predicting and explaining the sun's rising when I offer the appropriate astronomical information. Of course, I cannot here be certain of the *truth* of *B*, which truth is necessary if I am truly to explain. But the same uncertainty holds for a *B* which refers to the past, though I am confident in its truth. It seems then that there is here no sharp temporal difference crucial to explanation, though it is required that *b* must not precede *a*, whenever *b* occurs.

[13] The distinction between explanation and our case cannot be easily discerned by attending to the ordinary use of "Why . . . ?" as a clue. For while explanations often answer the question "Why *B*?" in the sense, "In accordance with what laws and following what conditions does *b* occur?" our case answers the question "Why *B*?" often asked in the sense, "What rational grounds are there for asserting '*B*'?" Perhaps the confusion of these two senses is at least partially responsible for the notion that "functional" or "teleological" explanations are explanatory in the ordinary sense, whereas they actually share the logical form of our nonexplanatory instance. For Nagel, in "Teleological Explanation and Teleological Systems" in *Vision and Action*, ed. by S. Ratner, 1953, for example, the statement, "The function of chlorophyll in plants is to enable plants to perform photo-synthesis" is equivalent to "A necessary condition for the occurrence of photosynthesis in plants is the presence of chlorophyll." In his words, "A teleological explanation states the *consequences* for a given biological system of one of the latter's constituent parts or processes; the equivalent non-teleological explanation states some of the *conditions* under which the system persists in its characteristic organization and activities."

Now it is clear that in Nagel's use here, "necessary condition" means "necessary nonsubsequent condition" and "consequence" is temporal in reference. Otherwise, knowing that all breathing organisms die, we might say that since death is a necessary condition for breathing in organisms, the function of death is to enable organisms to breathe. Hence, for his view presumably, to explain *b* functionally or teleologically is to refer to a suitable *later a* such that *A* and *L* imply *B*. Actually, his equivalent nonteleological statement is simply *L* and does not alone provide deductive grounds for asserting the presence of chlorophyll, and hence explaining it. But assuming that we add the appropriate *A*, i.e., "Photosynthesis occurs at *t* in plant *P*," this does not *explain* why

(c) If both explanation and prediction are characterized by temporal asymmetries which are irrelevant to the generality of scientific inference, is there any independent epistemological ground for considering explanaton or prediction as central to scientific procedure?

(i) It may be noted that the interpretation of explanation in question is generally taken as a reflection of causal notions, and that the peculiar temporal asymmetry of explanation is identical with the temporal asymmetry of cause and effect. To consider the latter notions central to science is to justify treating explanation as scientifically primary.

A number of authors have however remarked the fact that causal notions come to be used less and less by an advancing science, while they remain of relatively constant importance is practical affairs. The point often made in this connection is to stress the relation of causal notions to interest in control by voluntary action. As Braithwaite has recently expressed it,[14]

If an earlier event's occurring is a nomically sufficient condition for a later event to occur, we can (in suitable cases) ensure that the later event should occur by taking steps to see that the earlier event does occur. For this purpose it is irrelevant whether or not the later event's occurring is a nomically sufficient condition for the earlier event to occur. . . . But, if a later event's occurring is a nomically sufficient condition for the earlier event to occur, we cannot indirectly produce the earlier event by producing the later event, since by the time that we should be producing the later event the earlier event would irrevocably either have occurred or not have occurred. This difference between the case of regular sequence and that of regular precedence is, I think, the reason why we are prepared to call a nomically sufficient

---

chlorophyll occurs at some earlier time in *P*, though it *substantiates* such occurrence. We ought therefore not to speak, as Nagel does here, of "equivalent non-teleological *explanations*." Given a case of photosynthesis at *t* however, we may ask "Why must chlorophyll have been present?" though we do not intend to ask, "Following what antecedent conditions and in accordance with what laws did cholorophyll occur?" Confusion of the two questions may partly account for the misleading idea of functional *explanation* as an answer to some "Why . . . ?"

[14] R. B. Braithwaite, *Scientific Explanation*, (Cambridge: Cambridge University Press, 1953), p. 313.

condition for an event a cause of that event if it precedes the event but are not prepared to call it a cause if it succeeds the event.

If this general account is true of causal notions, it would seem to apply equally to so-called causal explanation, which is characterized by the same temporal asymmetry. If scientific inference, however, unlike voluntary control of the future, may be based on temporally backward as well as forward nomic regularities,[15] it is misleading and partial to view science from the vantage point of such control, and of its cognate notions, "cause" and "explanation." It would seem a better reflection of the full generality of scientific reasoning if we view it as concerned with comprehensive nomological relations among events and abstract from causal explanation entirely. Science may then be compared, in Toulmin's apt analogy,[16] to a route-neutral map, quite general as regards direction, but capable of guiding variant itineraries for those with practical purposes.[17]

(ii) Much of what has been said of the relation of explanation to voluntary control holds in an obvious way for prediction. In addition, however, the scientific primacy of prediction is often supported by reference to the acceptance or confirmation of statements.

It may, for instance, be granted that we posit events both past and future to our posit-utterances, but it is pointed out, for any present posit-utterance, it is peculiarly contingent on the future since there is a possibility that it is reasonably rejected then, owing to future rejection of some confirmatory sentence asserting a future occurrence. But, in the first place, such future rejection may be due to future rejection of some confirmatory sentence asserting an occurrence prior to the present posit-utterance. And, in the second

[15] History, geology, archaeology, astronomy are only some striking instances of scientific use of backward regularities. Backward inference, whether postdictive positing or the substantiation (by use of information about the present) of past events, is a partial goal of all sciences, it seems to me, including physics.

[16] S. Toulmin, *The Philosophy of Science,* (London: University Library, Hutchinson, 1953), p. 121.

[17] In addition, the connection of explanation with control may indicate why, as pointed out above, temporal requirements alone may not be sufficient to explicate it.

place, it is equally true for any present posit-utterance that there is a possibility of its reasonable rejection in the past. That something is a posit-utterance at t implies neither its acceptance at all times following t nor its acceptance at all times preceding t.

It may then occasionally be suggested that the predictiveness of any given posit-utterance is not a matter of its own future acceptance but involves rather the fact that it is false if any confirmatory sentence asserting a future occurrence is false. Obviously, however, it is also false if any confirmatory sentence asserting a prior occurrence is false. It may, of course, be held that a posit-utterance, all of whose confirmatory sentences asserting prior occurrences are true, is false only if some confirmatory sentence asserting a future occurrence is false. But the obvious converse is equally the case.[18]

It may, however, finally be countered that we cannot now voluntarily choose to carry through a past test, while we can now decide to institute a test of a specified posit-utterance in the future. This claim, true enough, is as trivial as the general truth that voluntary control at a given time is of later phenomena, never of earlier; we cannot now choose to institute any past event, *a fortiori* we cannot now choose to institute a past test. There is no special relevance to science in this truism. Furthermore, we have seen that a given posit-utterance is false if a confirmatory sentence asserting a prior occurrence is false, even if all confirmatory sentences asserting future events are true. Hence, even if all its tests which are voluntarily choosable (hence in the future) at t are positive, i.e., yield true confirmatory sentences asserting later events, the posit-utterance at t may still be false.

Pragmatists and positivists have championed the further doctrine that the meaning or content of a physical-object statement *is* its future verifiability. Hence, e.g., even an apparently retrodictive posit-utterance of historian H in 1950, "Caesar crosses the Rubicon" is really *about* future possible confirmations or disconfirmations in experience. This doctrine of meaning is however, ambiguous, since "future" is

---

[18] I am throughout this passage following the usual type of argument in talking of confirmatory sentences, etc., but this does not commit me to such an epistemology.

unclear.[19] In our example above, are the future confirmations future to 1950 or future to Caesar's crossing the Rubicon? Only if they are future to 1950 is it plausible to construe the content of *H*'s assertion as its testing future to the assertion, but this interpretation leads to quite undesirable results, e.g., a replica of *H*'s utterance in 1954 has a quite different content. If, on the other hand, "future" here means "future to Caesar's crossing the Rubicon," then it refers also to confirmations prior to *H*'s utterance, and the ground for considering its predictive content primary disappears. It goes almost without saying that once we are prepared to admit confirmations prior to *H*'s utterance, there is no longer any advantage in excluding those which precede the historical event itself.

But the general difficulties of this dictum on meaning far outweigh in importance the ambiguity mentioned.[20] Abandoning it in favor of some other criterion of meaning, we remove a reason for considering prediction as primary which has been dominant in recent philosophy.

[19] For a discussion of this point, in relation to C. I. Lewis's analysis of historical statements, see the writer's "Verifiability in History: A Reply to Miss Masi," *Journal of Philosophy*, Vol. 47, 1950, pp. 164 ff.

[20] For a critical review of these difficulties leading to an alternative proposal in terms of translatability into some empirical language, see C. G. Hempel, "Problems and Changes in the Empiricist Criterion of Meaning," *Revue internationale de philosophie*, Vol. II, 1950, pp. 41–63.

9

THE MEANING OF REDUCTION
IN THE NATURAL SCIENCES:
Ernest Nagel ·

The science of mechanics was the first branch of mathematical physics to assume the form of a comprehensive theory. The success of that theory in explaining and bringing into systematic relation a large variety of phenomena was for a long time unprecedented; and the belief entertained by many eminent scientists and philosophers, sometimes supported by *a priori* arguments, that all the processes of nature would eventually fall within the scope of its principles was repeatedly confirmed by the absorption of several sectors of physics into mechanics. However, it is now common knowledge that classical mechanics no longer occupies the position of the "universal" physical science once claimed for it; for since the latter part of the nineteenth century the difficulties facing the extension of mechanics to various further domains of physical inquiry have come to be acknowledged as insuperable, and rival candidates for the office of a universal physical science have been proposed. Moreover, with some exceptions, no serious students today believe that some particular physical theory can be established on *a priori* grounds as the universal or

· [This selection is reprinted in its entirety from Robert C. Stauffer, Ed., *Science and Civilization* (Madison: University of Wisconsin Press, 1949), pp. 99–145, by permission of Ernest Nagel and the copyright owners, the Regents of the University of Wisconsin.]

fundamental theory of natural processes; and to many thinkers it is even an open question whether the ideal of a comprehensive theory which would thoroughly integrate all domains of natural science is realizable. Nevertheless, the phenomenon of a relatively autonomous branch of science becoming absorbed by, or "reduced" to, some other discipline is an undeniable and recurrent feature of the history of modern science and there is no reason to suppose that such reduction will not continue to take place in the future.

It is with this phenomenon that the present paper is concerned. The successful reduction of one science to another, as well as the failures in effecting such a reduction in a number of notable cases, have been occasions, exploited by both practicing scientists and professional as well as lay philosophers, for far-reaching reinterpretations of the nature and limits of knowledge, science, and the allegedly ultimate constitution of things in general. These interpretations take various forms. Discoveries concerning the physics and physiology of perception have been frequently used to support the conclusion that the findings of physics are incompatible with so-called common sense or naïve realism (the belief that things encountered in normal experience do possess the traits which are manifest to controlled observation); and elaborate epistemologies have been proposed for resolving the paradox that, in spite of this presumed incompatibility, science takes its point of departure from, and finds its evidence in, such common-sense knowledge. The successful reduction of thermodynamics to statistical mechanics in the nineteenth century, and the more recent expansion of electrical theories of matter, have been taken to show that spatial displacements are the only form of intelligible and genuine change; that the qualitative and behavioral diversities noted in ordinary experience are "unreal" and illusory; or, conversely, that the "mysterious world" discovered by microscopic physics is but an insubstantial symbol which expresses a pervasive spiritual reality not alien to human values. On the other hand, the failure to explain electrodynamical phenomena in terms of the principles of mechanics, and the general decline of mechanics as the universal science of nature in contemporary physics has been hailed as evidence for the bankruptcy of classical science, for the necessity of instituting an "organismic" point of view and "organismic" categories of explanation in the study of all natural phenomena, and for a variety of metaphysical doctrines concerning levels of being, emergence, and creative novelty.

I do not believe that these speculative interpretations of the assumed facts of science are warranted by the evidence. On the contrary, I believe that the problems to which they are addressed are generated by misconstruing the statements of the natural sciences and reading them in senses not in accordance with the meanings that actual usage in scientific contexts establishes for those statements. However, it is not my present aim to examine the detailed arguments which lead to the adoption of views such as those just briefly indicated. I wish instead to consider what is done when one science is reduced to another, and to suggest that an important source of much dubious commentary on the nature and the interrelations of the sciences lies in the failure to recognize the conditions which must be fulfilled when such a reduction is effected. It is a commonplace that linguistic expressions, associated with established habits or rules of usage in one set of homogeneous contexts, frequently come to be used in other contexts on the assumption of definite analogies or continuities between the several domains. But judging from the practice of many philosophers and scientists, it is still not a commonplace that when the range of application of expressions is thus extended, these expressions may undergo critical changes in meaning, and that unless care is exercised in interpreting them so that specific contexts of relevant usage are noted, serious misunderstandings and spurious problems are bound to arise. In any event, misconceptions having their basis in just such careless handling of language seem to me to accompany much traditional and current discussion of the significance of scientific reduction. The present essay is an attempt to indicate some quite familiar and yet frequently neglected distinctions that are pertinent to the analysis of this recurrent phenomenon in the development of the natural sciences.

Before turning to my actual theme, it will be useful to distinguish a type of reduction in the history of science which generally, though certainly not always, is unaccompanied by serious misapprehensions. I have in mind the normal expansion of some body of theory, initially proposed for a certain extensive domain of phenomena, so that laws which previously may have been found to hold in a narrow sector of that domain, or in some other domain homogenous in a readily identifiable sense with the first, are shown to be derivable from that theory when suitably specialized. For example, Galileo's *Two New Sciences* was a contribution to the physics of freely falling terrestrial bodies; but when Newton showed that his own general theory of mechanics and gravitation, when supplemented by appropriate boundary conditions, entailed Galileo's laws, the latter were incorporated into the Newtonian theory as a special case. Were we to regard this branch of inquiry cultivated by Galileo as a distinctive science, the subsequent facts could be described by saying that Galileo's special discipline was reduced to the science of Newton. However, although it is possible to distinguish the subject matters of the Newtonian and the (initially distinct) Galilean sciences (for example, the latter was concerned solely with terrestrial phenomena, while the former included celestial ones), these subject matters are in an obvious sense homogenous and continuous; for it is the motions of bodies and the determinants of such motions that are under investigation in each case, and in each case inquiry is directed toward discovering relations between physical traits that are the common concern of both disciplines. Stated more formally, the point is that no descriptive terms appear in the formulations of the Galilean science which do not occur essentially and with approximately the same meanings in the statements of Newtonian mechanics. The history of science is replete with illustrations of reductions of this type, but I shall ignore them in what follows, because the logical issues involved in them do not appear to generate typical forms of philosophic puzzlement or to stimulate fundamental reinterpretations of the nature of knowledge.

The situation seems to be quite different, however, in those cases of reduction in which a subject matter possessing certain distinctive properties is apparently assimilated with another that supposedly does not manifest those traits; and acute intellectual discomfort is often experienced in those instances of reduction in which the science that suffers reduction is concerned with so-called "macroscopic" or "molar" phenomena, while the science to which the reduction is effected employs a theory that postulates some "microscopic" structure for molar physical systems. Thus, consider the following example. Most adults, if provided with ordinary mercury thermometers, are able to determine with reasonable accuracy the temperatures of various bodies, and understand what is meant by such statements as that the temperature of a glass of milk is 10° C. Accordingly, such individuals know how to use the word "temperature," at any rate within a broad context, though doubtless a large fraction of them would be incapable of stating adequately the tacit rules governing such usage, or of explicating the meaning of the word to the satisfaction of someone schooled in thermodynamics. However, if such an individual were to use the word so that its application was always associated with the behavior of a mercury column in a glass tube when the latter was placed in proximity to the body whose temperature was in question, he might be at a loss to construe the sense of such a statement as that the temperature of a certain substance at its melting point is several thousand degrees high; and he might protest that since at such alleged "high temperatures" ordinary thermometers would be vaporized, the statement had no definite meaning for him. But a slight study of physics would readily remove this source of puzzlement. The puzzled individual would discover that the word "temperature" is associated with a more inclusive set of rules of usage than he had originally supposed, and that in its extended usage it refers to a physical state of a body, which may be manifested in other ways than in the volume expansion of a mercury column—for example, in changes in electrical resistance, or in the generation of electric currents. Accordingly, once the laws are understood which connect the behavior of ordinary thermometers with the behavior of bolometers, pyrometers, and other overtly identifiable recording instruments, the grounds for the more inclusive usage of the term "temperature" become intelligible. This wider use of the word, then, rarely appears to cover a mystery, any more than does the extension of the word from its uses in contexts of direct experience of hot and cold to contexts in which the mercury thermometer replaces the human organism as a test body.

Suppose, however, that the layman for whom the word "temperature" thus acquires a more generalized meaning than he originally associated with it now pursues his study of physics into the kinetic theory of matter. Here he discovers that the temperature of a body is simply the mean kinetic energy of the molecules constituting the body. But this bit of information usually produces renewed perplexity, and, indeed, in an especially acute form. For the layman is assured by the best authorities that while on the one hand individual molecules possess no temperatures, nevertheless the meaning of the word "temperature" must by definition be taken as identical with the meaning of such expressions as "energy of molecular motions." And questions that are typical of a familiar philosophical tradition now seem both relevant and inescapable. If the meaning of "temperature" is the same as that of "kinetic energy of molecular motion," what are we talking about when milk is said to have a temperature of 10° C? Surely not the kinetic energies of the molecular constituents of the liquid, for the uninstructed layman is able to understand what is thus said without possessing any notions about the molecular composition of milk. Perhaps, then, the familiar distinctions between hot and cold, between various temperatures as specified in terms of the behavior of identifiable instruments, are distinctions which refer to a domain of illusion. Perhaps, also, the temperatures that are measured in ordinary experience as well as in laboratories are merely indications of some fundamental underlying reality which is inherently incapable of being characterized by such expressions as "temperature" understood in its customary sense. Or should we perhaps regard temperature as an emergent trait, not present on lower levels of physical reality? But if this is the correct way of viewing the matter, does a theory that is about such lower levels ever really explain emergent traits such as temperature? It would be easy to enlarge the list of such queries, but those cited suffice to suggest the general character of the instances of reduction which provoke them. To avoid repeated circumlocution, and for lack of better labels, let me refer to a science to which another is reduced as the "primary science," and to the science which suffers such reduction as the "secondary science." Philosophical problems of the sort indicated, then, seem to be generated when the subject matter of the primary science is "qualitatively discontinuous" or "in-homogenous" with the subject matter of the secondary science—or, to put the matter perhaps more clearly, when the statements of the secondary science contain descriptive terms that do not occur in the theories of the primary science.

It is reductions of this type that I wish to consider. And since the reduction of thermodynamics to mechanics, more exactly, to statistical mechanics and the kinetic theory of matter, is both a typical and a relatively familiar and simple example of this type, I propose to center my discussion around this illustration.

I will first briefly recall some well-known historical facts. The study of thermal phenomena goes back in modern times to Galileo and his circle, and during the subsequent three centuries a large number of laws were established dealing with special phases of the thermal behavior of bodies—laws which were eventually exhibited as systematically interrelated on the basis of a small number of general principles. Thermodynamics, as this science came to be called, employed concepts, distinctions, and general laws which were also used in mechanics—for example, the notions of volume, weight, mass, and pressure, and laws such as the principle of the lever and Hooke's Law. Nevertheless, it was regarded as a science relatively autonomous with respect to mechanics, because it made use of such distinctive notions as temperature, heat, and entropy, and because it assumed laws and principles which were not corollaries of the fundamental assumptions of mechanics. Accordingly, though many propositions of mechanics were constantly employed in the exploration of thermal phenomena, thermodynamics was generally assumed for a long time to be a special discipline, plainly distinguishable from mechanics and not simply a chapter of it. In this respect, the relation of thermodynamics to mechanics was considered analogous to the relation between mechanics and physical geometry: mechanics was held to be distinguishable from physical geometry, even though geometrical propositions were employed in the formulation of mechanical laws and in the construction of instruments used to test these laws. Indeed, thermodynamics is still frequently expounded as a physical theory that is autonomous in the indicated sense with respect to mechanics; and in such expositions the findings of the science are presented in such a manner that the propositions asserted can be understood and verified in terms of explanations and procedures which do not assume the reducibility of thermodynamics to some other theory. However, experimental work early in the nineteenth century on the mechanical equivalent of heat stimulated theoretical inquiry to find a more intimate connection between thermal and mechanical phenomena than the bare facts seemed to assert. And when Maxwell and Boltzmann were finally able to "derive" the Boyle-Charles law from assumptions apparently statable in terms of mechanics concerning the molecular constitution of ideal gases, and especially when the entropy principle was shown to be capable of interpretation as a statistical law concerning the aggregate mechanical behavior of molecules, thermodynamics was widely believed to have lost its autonomy and to have been reduced to mechanics.

Just how is this reduction effected, and what is the argument which apparently makes possible the derivation of statements containing such terms as "temperature," "heat," and "entropy" from a set of theoretical assumptions that do not use or mention them? It is not possible, without producing a treatise on the subject, to exhibit the complete argument. I shall therefore fix my attention on a small fragment of the complicated analysis, the derivation of the Boyle-Charles law for ideal gases from the assumptions of the kinetic theory of matter.

Suppressing most of the details that do not contribute directly to the clarification of the main issues, a simplified form of the derivation is in outline as follows. Assume an ideal gas to occupy a volume V. The gas is taken to be composed of a large number of molecules possessing equal mass and size, each perfectly elastic and with dimensions that are negligible when compared with the average distance between them. The molecules are further supposed to be in constant relative motion, and subject only to forces of impact between themselves and the walls of the containing volume, also taken to be perfectly elastic. Accordingly, the motions of the molecules are assumed to be analyzable in terms of the principles of Newtonian mechanics. The problem now is to determine the relation of the pressure which the molecules exert on the walls of their container to other aspects of their motion.

However, since the instantaneous coordinates of state of the individual molecules are not actually ascertainable, the usual mathematical procedure of classical mechanics cannot be applied; and in order to make headway with the problem, a further assumption must be introduced—an assumption which is a statistical one concerning the positions and momenta of the molecules. This statistical assumption takes the following form. Suppose that the volume V of the gas is subdivided into a very large number of smaller volumes whose dimensions are equal but nevertheless are large compared with the diameters of the molecules; suppose also that the maximum range of velocity of the molecules is divided into a large number of equal intervals of velocity; and associate with each small volume all possible velocity intervals, calling each complex obtained by associating a volume with a velocity interval a "phase-cell." The statistical assumption then is that the probability of a molecule's occupying an assigned phase-cell is the same for all molecules and phase-cells, and that (subject to certain qualifications which need not be mentioned here) the probabilities that any pair of molecules will occupy the same phase-cell are independent. From this set of assumptions it is now possible to deduce that the pressure p which the molecules exert on the walls of the container is related in a definite way to the mean kinetic energy E of the molecules of the gas, and that in fact $p = 2E/3V$, or $pV = 2E/3$. But a comparison of this equation with the Boyle-Charles law (according to which $pV = kT$, where k is constant for a given mass of gas and T its absolute temperature), suggests that the latter could be deduced from the assumptions mentioned, if temperature were "identified" with the mean kinetic energy of molecular motions. Accordingly, let us adopt this "identification" in the form of the hypothesis that $2E/3 = kT$ (i.e., that the absolute temperature of an ideal gas is proportional to the mean kinetic energy of the molecules which are assumed to constitute it). The Boyle-Charles law is then a logical consequence of the general principles of mechanics, when these are supplemented by a statistical postulate on the motions of molecules constituting a gas, a hypothesis on the connection between temperature and kinetic energy, and various further assumptions that have been indicated.

If the derivation of the Boyle-Charles law is used as a basis for generalization, what are the essential requirements for reducing one science to another? The following comments fall into two groups, the first dealing with matters that are primarily of a formal nature, the second with questions of an empirical character.

1. In the first place, the derivation requires that all the assertions, postulates, or hypotheses of each of the sciences involved in the reduction are available in the form of explicit statements, whose meanings are assumed to be fixed

in terms of procedures and rules of usage appropriate to each discipline. Moreover, the statements within each science fall into a number of fairly distinct groups when a classification is introduced on the basis of the logical functions the statements possess in the discipline. The following schematic list, though not exhaustive, indicates what I believe to be the more important groupings.

a. In a highly developed science such as mechanics there usually is a class *T* of statements which constitute the fundamental theory of the discipline and thus serve as principles of explanation and as partial premises in most deductions undertaken in the science, e.g., the principles of Newtonian mechanics. In a given exposition of the science, these statements are logically primitive, in the sense that they are not derived from any other class of statements in the science. Whether this class of statements is best conceived as a set of leading principles, empirical rules of inference, or methodological rules of analysis, rather than as premises in the usual sense of the word, is a question that can be ignored here.

b. A science which contains a fundamental theory will also contain a class of statements or theorems which are logically derivable from *T*. These theorems in all but trivial cases are usually of a conditional form, and their consequents are derivable from *T* only if the latter is supplemented by various special assumptions which appear as the antecedents in the theorems. Two subdivisions of this class of special assumptions may be distinguished. (i) There is the group of assumptions which serve as general hypotheses concerning a variety of conditions to which the fundamental theory may be applied. Thus, one such assumption in the application of Newtonian principles to the study of gases is that of a physical system composed of a large number of point-masses, with forces of impact as the only forces present. An alternative assumption might be that of a physical system consisting of bodies with non-negligible diameters subject to gravitational forces. (ii) And there is also the group of assumptions which specify the detailed boundary or initial conditions for the application of the theory. Thus, in the above example the initial conditions are stated as a statistical assumption concerning the position and velocities of gas molecules.

c. Finally, every positive science will contain a large class of singular statements which formulate procedures and the outcome of observations relevant for the conduct of inquiry in the science; and it will usually also make use of general laws which its fundamental theory does not pretend to explain but which are simply borrowed from some other special discipline. Call the first group of these statements "observation statements," and the second group "borrowed statements." Observation statements may on occasion serve as specifications of the initial conditions for the application of the theory, or they may state the predicted consequences of the theory when other such statements are used to supplement the latter as initial conditions. Accordingly, observation statements will normally have members in common with the class of statements of boundary and initial conditions, though in general these two classes will not coincide. Indeed, many observation statements will describe instruments required for testing general assumptions of the science, and in doing so may make use of general laws and hence of expressions referring to distinctions that fall within the province of some other specialized discipline. For example, if Newtonian assumptions are employed in the study of celestial phenomena, telescopes may be required to test these assumptions; but the description of telescopes, and the interpretation of the observations that are obtained through their use, generally involves the use of expressions that refer to distinctions studied primarily in theoretical optics rather than in Newtonian mechanics.

2. This brings me to my second formal observation. The statements of a science, to whichever of the above classes they may belong, can be analyzed as linguistic structures compounded out of more elementary expressions in accordance with tacit or explicit rules of construction. These elementary expressions E are of various sorts, but they may be assumed to have fairly definite meanings fixed by habit or explicit rules of usage. Some of them are the familiar expressions of logic, arithmetic, and perhaps higher mathematics; but most of them will usually be so-called "descriptive" terms or combinations of terms which signify allegedly empirical objects, traits, and processes.

Though there may be serious difficulties both theoretical and practical in distinguishing descriptive expressions from others, let us suppose that the distinction can be carried through in some fashion, and let us consider the class of descriptive expressions in E. Many of the descriptive expressions of a science are taken over from the language of ordinary affairs and retain their customary, everyday meanings; others, however, may be specific to the science, and may, moreover, have meanings which preclude their application to matters of familiar experience. Thus the statements constituting the fundamental theory of a science, as well as many of the special assumptions which are used to supplement the theory in various ways, normally contain several descriptive expressions of this latter sort.

Now it is generally possible to explicate the meanings of many descriptive expressions in E with the help of other such expressions, though of course logical expressions will play a role in the explication. Let us refer to those descriptive expressions with the help of which the meanings of all other such expressions may be explicated—whether the explication is given in the form of conventional explicit definition or through the use of different and more complicated logical techniques—as the "primitive expressions" of the science. (Expressions that are primitive in this sense may be primitive only in some specific context of analysis and not in another. But this point, though not without importance for a general theory of definition, does not affect the present discussion.)

However, the explication of the meaning of an expression may have either of two objectives, and accordingly it is useful to distinguish between two classes of primitive expression. (a) The explication may aim at specifying the meaning of an expression in terms familiar from everyday usage; and in consequence, the primitives employed may be restricted to those expressions which refer to matters of common observation, laboratory procedure, and other forms of overt behavior. Call such primitives "experiential primitives," even if no sharp line may be drawn between expressions that are experiential and those that are not. For example, the meaning of the word "temperature" is often specified by means of statements describing the volume expansion of liquids and gases, or the behavior of other readily observable bodies; and in this instance the primitives employed in the explication are experiential ones.

(b) On the other hand, an explication may aim at specifying the meaning of an expression by exhibiting its relation to the meanings of expressions used in formulating the fundamental theory or the various supplementary assumptions of the science. And in consequence, the primitives employed may in fact contain no expression which refers to matters accessible to direct observation. Call such primitives the "theoretical primitives" of the science. For example, the meaning of the word "temperature" is sometimes specified with the help of statements describing the Carnot cycle of heat transformations, statements which contain expressions like "perfect nonconductor," "infinite heat-reservoir," and "infinitely slow volume expansion," that have no manifest reference to anything that is observable. Again, the explication of the expression "center of mass," as customarily given in treatises on mechanics, involves the use of other expressions that are basic in formulating the principles of mechanics, though they do not all refer to directly observable characteristics of bodies.

It is not necessary to decide, for the purpose of the present discussion, whether the meanings of all theoretical primitives of a science are explicable with the help of its experiential primitives. And though the class of theoretical primitives of a discipline and the class of its experiential primitives may have expressions in common, the two do not in general coincide.

3. I come to my third comment of a formal nature. A comparison of the statements belonging to the primary science involved in a reduction with those belonging to the secondary science shows that in general the two sciences share a number of common statements and expressions, the fixed meanings of these expressions being the same for both sciences. Statements certifiable in logic and demonstrative mathematics are obvious examples of such common expressions, but, in addition to them, the two sciences will frequently share statements and other expressions which have a descriptive or empirical content. For example, many propositions that fall within the field of mechanics, such as the law of the lever, also enjoy important uses in thermodynamics, as one of the borrowed statements of the latter science; and thermodynamics also employs such expressions as "volume," "weight," and "pressure" in senses which coincide with the meanings of these words in mechanics. On the other hand, the secondary science prior to its reduction generally contains statements and expressions not occuring in the primary science, except possibly as members of the class of observation and borrowed statements. For example, theoretical mechanics in its classical form contains neither the Boyle-Charles law nor the word "temperature," though both of these occur in thermodynamics, and though the word may on occasion be employed in statements which

describe the conditions of application of the first principles of mechanics.

Now it is of the utmost importance to observe that expressions peculiar to a science will possess meanings that are fixed by its *own* procedures, and that are therefore intelligible in terms of its own rules of usage, whether or not the science has been or will be reduced to some other discipline. In many cases, to be sure, the meanings of some expressions in a science can be explicated with the help of those occurring in another, and, indeed, even with the help of the theoretical primitives of the latter. For example, it is usually assumed that an analytical equivalence can be exhibited between the word "pressure" as employed in thermodynamics and other expressions belonging to the class of theoretical primitives in the science of mechanics. But it obviously does *not* follow that every expression used in a sense that is specified in a given science must or need be explicable in terms of the primitives, whether theoretical or experiential, of another discipline.

Let us finally consider what is formally required for the reduction of one science to another. The objective of the reduction is to show that the laws or general principles of the secondary science are simply logical consequences of the assumptions of the primary science. However, if these laws contain expressions that do not occur in the assumptions of the primary science, a logical derivation is clearly impossible. Accordingly, a necessary condition for the derivation is the explicit formulation of suitable relations between such expressions in the secondary science and expressions occurring in the premises of the primary discipline.

Now it may be possible to explicate the meaning of an expression occurring in a law of the secondary science in terms of the experiential primitives of the primary one, especially if, as is perhaps normally the case, the experiential predicates of the two sciences are the same. But this possibility is not in general sufficient for the purposes of reduction, since the problem here is to establish a certain kind of connection between expressions that occur in the secondary science but not in the premises of the primary discipline and expressions that do appear in these premises, especially those expressions of the latter class in terms of which the fundamental theory of the primary science is formulated. For though the uses of each of two expressions may be specifiable with the help of a common set of experiential primitives, it by no means follows that one of the expressions must be definable in terms of the other. The words "uncle" and "grandfather," for instance, are each definable in terms of "male" and "parent," but "uncle" is not definable in terms of "grandfather." Accordingly, a crucial step in reduction consists in establishing a proper kind of relation—that is, one which will make possible the indicated logical derivation—between expressions occurring in the laws of the secondary science and the theoretical primitives of the primary science.

There appear to be just two general ways of doing this. One is to show that an expression in question is logically related, either by synonymity or entailment, to some expression in the premises of the primary science. In consequence, the meaning of the expression in the secondary science, as fixed by the usage established in this discipline, must be explicable in terms of the theoretical primitives of the primary science. The other way is to adopt a material or physical hypothesis according to which the occurrence of the properties designated by some expression in the premises of the primary science is a sufficient, or a necessary and sufficient, condition for the occurrence of the properties designated by the expression of the secondary discipline. But in this case the meaning of the expression in the secondary science, as fixed by the established usages of the latter, is not declared to be analytically related to the established meaning of the corresponding expression in the primary science. In consequence, the indicated hypothesis cannot be asserted on the strength of purely logical considerations, but is at best a contingent truth requiring support from empirical data.

Let us now assume that the word "temperature" is the only expression that occurs in the Boyle-Charles law which does not also occur in the various premises of mechanics and the kinetic theory of gases from which the law is to be derived. Accordingly, if the deduction is to be possible, an additional assumption must be introduced—the assumption that temperature is proportional to the mean kinetic energy of the gas molecules. How is this assumption to be understood, and in particular what sort of considerations support the indicated connection between the word "temperature" and the expression "mean kinetic energy"? But it is clear that in the sense in which "temperature" is used in thermodynamics, the word is neither synonymous with "mean kinetic energy" nor is its meaning entailed by the meaning of the latter expression. For it is surely not by analyzing the meaning of "temperature," in its thermodynamical sense, that the additional assumption required for deducing the Boyle-Charles law from the premises of mechanics can be established. This additional assumption is evidently an empirical hypothesis, which postulates a determinate factual connection between two properties of physical systems that are in principle independently identifiable—between temperature as specified in thermodynamics on the one hand and the state of having a certain mean kinetic energy on the other; and if the hypothesis is true, it is at best only contingently true.

One objection to this last claim must be briefly considered. It is well known that though an expression may possess a certain fixed meaning at one stage in the development of inquiry, the redefinition of expressions is a recurrent feature in the history of the sciences. Accordingly, so the objection runs, while in an earlier usage the word "temperature" possessed a meaning which was specified by the procedures of thermometry and classical thermodynamics, it is now so used that temperature is "identical by definition" with molecular motion. The deduction of the Boyle-Charles law does not therefore require that the premises of mechanics be supplemented with a contingent physical hypothesis but simply makes use of this definitional identity. This objection seems to me to illustrate the curious double talk of which highly competent scientists are sometimes guilty, to the detriment of essential clarity. It is obviously possible to so redefine the word "temperature" that it becomes synonymous with "mean kinetic energy of molecules." But it should be no less obvious that on this redefined usage, the word has a different meaning from the one associated with it on the basis of the usage customary in thermometry and thermodynamics, and in consequence a different meaning from the one associated with it in the Boyle-Charles law. If, then, thermodynamics is to be reduced to mechanics, it is temperature in the sense specified in the former science which must be shown to be connected with mean kinetic energy. Accordingly, if the word "temperature" is redefined as proposed, the hypothesis must be adopted that the state of bodies described by the word "temperature" in its thermodynamical meaning is also correctly characterized by the word "temperature" in its redefined and different sense.

But then this hypothesis is one which does not hold simply by definition. And unless it is adopted, it is not the Boyle-Charles law which is derived from the premises of mechanics; what is derived is a sentence with a physical and syntactical structure similar to the law, but with a sense that is entirely different from what the law asserts.

I now turn to my second set of comments, those concerned with matters that are not primarily formal.

1. Thus far, I have been arguing the doubtless obvious point that the reduction of one science to another is not possible unless the various expressions occurring in the laws of the former also appear in the premises of the latter. But it is perhaps equally evident that these premises must satisfy further conditions if a proposed reduction is to count as an important scientific achievement. For if the premises of an alleged primary science could be selected quite arbitrarily, subject only to the formal requirements that have been mentioned thus far, the logical deduction of the laws of a secondary science from such premises selected *ad hoc* would in most cases represent only a trivial scientific accomplishment. And in point of fact, an essential condition that is normally imposed upon the assumptions of the primary science is that they be supported by empirical evidence possessing some measure of adequacy. The issues raised by this requirement, and especially the problems connected with the notion of adequate evidence, cannot be discussed in the present paper, and in any case are not pertinent exclusively to the analysis of reduction. However, a few brief reminders bearing on this requirement that are especially relevant to the reduction of thermodynamics to mechanics may contribute something to the present analysis.

It is well known that the general assumption according to which physical bodies in different states of aggregation are systems of molecules is confirmed by a large number of well-established experimental facts of chemistry and of molar physics, facts which are not primarily about thermal properties of bodies. Accordingly, the adoption of this hypothesis for the special task of accounting for the thermal behavior of gases is in line with the normal strategy of the natural sciences to extend the use of ideas fruitful in one set of inquiries into related domains. Similarly, the fundamental principles of mechanics, which serve as partial premises in the reduction of thermodynamics to mechanics, are supported by evidence drawn from many fields of study distinct from the study of gases. The assumption that these principles characterize the behavior of the hypothetical molecular constituents of a gas thus involves what is essentially the extrapolation of a theory from domains in which the theory has been well confirmed to another domain whose relevant features are postulated to be homogenous with those of the former domains. But in addition to all this, it is especially noteworthy that the combined set of assumptions employed in the reduction of thermodynamics to mechanics, including the special hypothesis on the connection of temperature and kinetic energy, make it possible to bring into systematic relations a large number of propositions on the behavior of gases as well as of other bodies, propositions whose factual dependence on one another might otherwise not have become evident. Many of these propositions were known to be in approximate agreement with experimental facts long before the reduction was effected, but some of them, certainly, were discovered only subsequently to the reduction, and partly as a consequence of the stimulus to inquiry which the reduction supplied.

This last point needs to be stressed. It is fairly safe to maintain that the mere deduction of the Boyle-Charles law from the assumptions of mechanics does not provide critical evidence for those assumptions, and especially for the assumption on the connection between temperature and kinetic energy, for prior to the reduction this law was already known to hold, at least approximately, for most gases far removed from their points of liquefaction. And though the adoption of those assumptions does effect, in consequence of the mere deduction of the law, a unification of physical knowledge, the unification is obtained on the basis of what to many practicing scientists seems an *ad hoc* postulation. The crucial evidence for those assumptions, and therefore for the scientific importance of the reduction, appears to come from two related lines of inquiry: the deduction from these assumptions of hitherto unknown connections between observable phenomena, or of propositions which are in better agreement with experimental findings than any that had been previously accepted; and secondly, the evaluation, from data of observation, of various constants or parameters that appear in the assumptions, with the proviso that there is good agreement between the values of a constant calculated from data obtained from independent lines of inquiry. For example, though the Boyle-Charles law holds approximately for ideal gases, most gases under all but exceptional circumstances do not behave in accordance with it. On the other hand, if some of the assumptions used in the deduction of the law from mechanics are modified in a manner not radically altering their main features—specifically, if molecules are assumed to have diameters that are not negligible in comparison with the mean distances separating them, and if cohesive forces between molecules are also postulated—the proposition known as Van der Waal's equation can be derived, which is in much closer approximation to the actual behavior of most gases than is the Boyle-Charles law. Again, to illustrate the second type of evidence generally accepted as critical for the importance of the reduction of thermodynamics to mechanics, one of the assumptions involved in that reduction is that under conditions of standard pressure and temperature equal volumes of a gas contain an equal number of molecules, quite irrespective of the chemical nature of the gas. Now the number of molecules contained in a liter of a gas (Avogadro's number) can be calculated on the basis of data obtained from observations, though to be sure only if these data are interpreted in a specified manner; and it turns out that alternative ways of calculating this number yield estimates that are in good agreement with one another, even when the measurements which serve as the basis of the calculations are obtained from the study of quite different materials—e.g., Brownian movements and crystal structure, as well as thermal phenomena.

2. These admittedly sketchy remarks on the character of the empirical evidence which supports the assumptions of a primary science merely hint at the complex considerations that are actually involved in judging whether a proposed reduction of one science to another is a significant advance in the organization of knowledge or whether it is simply a formal logical exercise. However, these remarks will perhaps help make plain that even though a science continues to be distinguished from other branches of inquiry on the basis of the general character of its fundamental theory, it may with the progress of inquiry modify or supplement the details of many of its subordinate and yet still quite general assumptions.

And this brings me to my next comment. For if this last point is well taken, it is clear that the question whether a given science is reducible to another needs to be made more explicit by the introduction of a definite date. No practicing physicist will take seriously the claim that, say, electrodynamics is reducible to mechanics—even if the claim were accompanied by a formal deduction of the equations of electrodynamics from a set of assumptions that by common consent are taken to fall within mechanics—unless these assumptions are warranted by independent evidence available at the time the claim is made. It is thus one thing to say that thermodynamics is reducible to mechanics when the latter includes among its assumptions certain hypotheses on the behavior of molecules, and quite a different thing to claim that the reduction is possible to a science of mechanics that does not countenance such hypotheses. More specifically, thermodynamics can be reduced to a mechanics that postdates 1866, but it is not reducible to a mechanics as this science was conceived in 1700. Similarly, a certain part of chemistry is reducible to a post-1925 physical theory, though not to the physical theory of a hundred years ago.

In consequence, much traditional and recent controversy over the interrelations of the various special sciences and concerning the supposed limits of the explanatory power of physical theory can be regarded as a debate over what at a given time is the most promising line of research and scientific advance. Thus, biologists who insist upon the importance of an "organismic" theory of biological behavior and who reject "machine-theories" of living structures may be construed as maintaining, though by no means always clearly, that in the present state of physical and biological theory it is advantageous to conduct their inquiries without abandoning distinctions peculiar to biology in favor of modes of analysis typical of modern physics. On the other hand, the mechanists in biology can be understood as recommending, though often in the language of a dogmatically held ultimate philosophy, a general line of attack on biological problems which in their opinion would advance the solution of these problems and at the same time hasten the assimilation of biology to physics—even if the physics to which biology may eventually be reduced may differ from the present science of physics in important though unspecified respects. However this may be, if the controversy over the scope of physics is conceived in this manner, no major philosophical or logical issue appears to be raised by it, though subsidiary questions involved in the controversy may require logical clarification. If one takes sides in the debate, one is primarily venturing a prediction, on what are often only highly conjectural grounds, as to what will be the most fertile avenue of exploration in a given subject matter at a given stage of the development of several sciences. On the other hand, when such controversies overlook the fact that the reduction of one science to another involves a tacit reference to a date, they assume the character of typically irresoluble debates over what are alleged to be metaphysical ultimates; and differences and similarities between departments of inquiry that may possess only a temporary autonomy with respect to one another come to be cited as evidence for some immutably final account of the inherent nature of things.

3. These last remarks have prepared the way for my final comment. Unlike the present discussion, which views the reduction of one science to another in terms of the logical connections between certain empirically confirmed statements of the two sciences, analyses of reduction and of the relations between sciences in general frequently approach these questions in terms of the possibility or impossibility of deducing the properties of one subject matter from the properties of another. Thus, a contemporary writer argues that because "a headache is not an arrangement or rearrangement of particles in one's cranium" and our sensation of violet is not a change in the optic nerve, psychology is demonstrably an autonomous discipline; and accordingly, though the mind is said to be connected with physical processes, "it cannot be reduced to those processes, nor can it be explained by the laws of those processes." Another recent writer, in presenting the case for the occurrence of "genuine novelties" in the inorganic realm, warns that "it is an error to assume that *all* the properties of a compound can be deduced solely from the nature of its elements." And a third influential contemporary author asserts that the characteristic behavior of a chemical whole or compound, such as water, "*could* not, even in theory, be deduced from the most complete knowledge of the behavior of its components, taken separately or in other combinations, and of their properties and arrangements in this whole."

Such an approach to the question almost invariably transforms what is eminently a logical and empirical problem, capable in principle of being resolved with the help of familiar scientific methods and techniques, into a specu-

lative issue that becomes the concern of an obscure and inconclusive dialectic. And in any case, formulations such as
those just cited are highly misleading, in so far as they
imply that the reduction of one science to another deprives
any properties known to occur of a status in existence, or
in so far as they suggest that the reducibility of one science
to another can be asserted or denied without reference
to the specific theories actually employed in a primary science for specifying the so-called "natures" of its ostensible
elements.

It is clearly a slipshod formulation, and at best an elliptic
one, which talks about the "deduction" of properties from
one another—as if in the reduction of one science to another
one were engaged in the black magic of extracting one set
of phenomena from others incommensurably different from
the first. Once such an image is associated with the facts
of scientific reduction, the temptation is perhaps irresistible
to read these facts as if in consequence some characters of
things were "unreal" and the number of "genuine" properties in existence were being diminished. And it is simply
naïveté to suppose that the natures of the various hypothetical objects assumed in physics and chemistry can be ascertained once and for all and by way of a direct inspection
of those objects, so that in consequence it is possible to
establish for all time what can or cannot be deduced from
those natures. To the extent that one bases one's account of
these matters on the study of scientific procedure, rather
than on the frequently loose talk of scientists, it is plain
that just as the fundamental nature of electricity is stated
by Maxwell's equation, so the natures of molecules and
atoms and of the properties of these postulated objects are
always specified by a more or less explicitly articulated
theory or set of general statements.

It follows that whether a given set of properties or behavioral traits of macroscopic objects can be explained by
or reduced to the properties and behavioral traits of atoms
and molecules is in part a function of the theory that is
adopted for specifying the natures of the latter. Accordingly,
while the deduction of the properties studied by one science from those of another may not be possible if the latter
discipline postulates certain properties for its elements in
terms of one theory, the reduction may be quite feasible when
a different theory is adopted for specifying the natures of the
elements of the primary science. Thus, to repeat in the

present context a point already made, if the nature of molecules is stipulated in terms of the theoretical primitives and assumptions of classical mechanics, the reduction of thermodynamics to mechanics is possible only if an additional hypothesis is introduced connecting temperature and kinetic energy. But as has been seen, the impossibility of the reduction without some such special hypothesis follows from purely formal considerations, and not from some alleged ontological hiatus between the microscopic and the macroscopic, the mechanical and the thermodynamical. Laplace was thus demonstrably in error when he imagined a divine intelligence that could foretell the future in every detail on the basis of knowing simply the instantaneous positions and momenta of all material particles as well as the magnitudes and directions of the forces acting between them. At any rate, Laplace was in error if his divine intelligence is assumed to draw inferences in accordance with the canons of logic, and is therefore assumed to be incapable of the blunder of asserting a statement as a conclusion if it contains expressions not occurring in the premises.

The question whether genuine novelties occur in nature when elements combine to form complex structures is clearly ambiguous. It can be construed as asking whether properties may not occur from time to time which have never before appeared anywhere in the cosmos. And it can also be understood as asking whether properties exhibited by various bodies assumed to be complex are in some cases at least different from and irreducible to the properties of their constituents. The question in the first sense clearly raises a problem in history which requires to be resolved with the help of the normal methods of historical inquiry; and the considerations raised in the present paper are not directly relevant to it. But the question in the second sense does call for a brief comment at this place. For the issue whether the properties of complexes are novel, in the nontemporal sense of the word, in relation to the properties of their elements, appears to be identical with the issue whether statements about the former are reducible to a primary science which deals with the latter. And if this is so, then the question whether the reduction is possible—and whether the properties alleged to be novel are indeed as thus described—cannot be discussed without reference to the specific theory which formulates the nature of the elements and of their properties. Failure to observe that novelty is a relational characteristic of properties with respect to a definite theory, and the supposition that on the contrary certain properties of compounds are inherently novel relative to the properties of the elements, irrespective of any theory which may be used to specify these elements and their properties, are among the chief sources for the widespread tendency to convert the analytic truths of logic into the dogmas of a footless ontology.

The chief burden of this paper, accordingly, is that the reducibility or irreducibility of a science is not an absolute characteristic of it. If the laws of chemistry—e.g., the law that under certain specified conditions, hydrogen and oxygen combine to form a stable compound, which in turn exhibits certain modes of behavior in the presence of other chemical substances—cannot be systematically deduced from one theory of atomic structure, they may be deducible from an alternate set of assumptions concerning the natures of chemical elements. Indeed, although not so long ago such a deduction was regarded as impossible—as it indeed was impossible from the then accepted physical theories of the atom—the reduction of various parts of chemistry to the quantum theory of atomic structure now appears to be making steady, if slow, headway, and only the stupendous mathematical difficulties involved in making the relevant deductions from the quantum-theoretical assumptions seem to stand in the way of carrying the task through to completion. At the same time, the reduction of chemical law to contemporary physical theory does not wipe out, or transform into a mere appearance, the distinctions and the types of behavior which chemistry recognizes. Similarly, if and when the detailed physical, chemical, and physiological conditions for the occurrence of headaches are ascertained, headaches will not thereby be shown to be nonexistent or illusory. On the contrary, if in consequence of such discoveries a portion of psychology will have been reduced to another science or to a combination of other sciences, all that will have happened is that the occurrence of headaches will have been explained. But the explanation will be of essentially the same sort as those obtainable in other domains of positive science. It will not consist in establishing a logically necessary connection between the occurrence of headaches and the occurrence of traits specified by physics, chemistry, or physiology; nor will it consist in establishing the synonymity of the term "headache" with expressions defined with the help of the theoretical primitives of these disciplines. It will consist, so the history and the procedures of the sciences seem to indicate, in stating the conditions, specified in terms of these primitives, which as a matter of contingent fact do occur when a determinate psychological phenomenon takes place.

PART THREE

SPACE, TIME, AND CAUSALITY

INTRODUCTION

The problems and concepts considered so far in this book relate to scientific thought in a general way, and are independent of any specific branch of science. But it is good practice in philosophy of science to try one's analyses against the detailed structure of some particular scientific theory or other. It is partly for this reason that we concentrate in this section on one such branch of science, in this case *mechanics*. A further reason for the choice of mechanics is that this branch of science has played a critical conceptual and historical role in the development of scientific thought: it was the first branch of knowledge in modern times to achieve the status of a scientific theory of wide application; the elaboration of its structure was the work of some of the greatest scientific minds of all time; and mechanical explanation was, until very recently, largely esteemed as the standard for scientific explanation in general. Within mechanics we have singled out as concepts for special analysis Space, Time, and Causality. This triad of concepts has exercised a prominent function within mechanical theories, has been subject to particular reinterpretation in the light of recent scientific theories (namely relativity and quantum mechanics), and, moreover, has always been of independent philosophical interest.

We characterize mechanics as the science which studies the motion of bodies under force. To be sure, "body" means something different in different kinds of mechanics. In some formulations of Newton's theory, "body" is frequently taken to mean "particle" or "point-mass." But in addition to particle mechanics there is the mechanics of extended rigid bodies and fluid mechanics—the mechanics of continuous deformable media. And each of these conceives of bodies as different from Newton's point-masses. Furthermore, there are formulations of mechanics alternative to Newton's in which the concept of *force* is not central. Hertz's system is a case in point. In Newton's system, force may be measured by the momentum produced by force. But Newton's famous contemporary, Leibniz, insisted that a different quantity—*vis viva* (the "living force") —is a better measure of the dynamical action of force. It has been argued persuasively that the controversy between Newton and Leibniz regarding the "real" measure of force was spurious, and that alternative definitions are possible. But it must not be overlooked that Leibniz was sketching a distinct approach to mechanics, one in which the entire study of the motion or equilibrium of a system is based on two fundamental scalar quantities—the kinetic energy and the work function (the latter replaceable by potential energy). And systems of mechanics based upon energy as a fundamental concept was developed by Euler, Lagrange, and Hamilton. But since, with special restrictions, Hamilton's principle can be deduced from Newton's three laws of motion, and vice versa, these systems are not alternative to Newton's mechanics in any ultimate sense. So we allow our initial characterization of mechanics to stand.

Part of the historical (and philosophical) importance of Newton's mechanics, so characterized, is that it solidified the conceptual revolution against Aristotelian physics in which Galileo was perhaps the most important figure before Newton. The gist of Galileo's revolution is that he transferred the problem of explaining motion from motion *simpliciter* to accelerated motion: not motion itself, but *changes* in motion require explanation. On the Aristotelian view, especially as developed in the late medieval period, the motion of a body is due, at every moment, to some moving force acting upon it. When the force desists, motion stops; and when force intensifies, motion increases. This fits well enough with cases in which, say, a horse is pulling a wagon, but it falls down badly in cases of trajectory motion, e.g., the flight of an arrow through the air: on the

ABSOLUTE AND RELATIVE SPACE, TIME, AND MOTION:

Isaac Newton •

Hitherto I have laid down the definitions of such words as are less known and explained the sense in which I would have them to be understood in the following discourse. I do not define time, space, place, and motion, as being well known to all. Only I must observe that the common people conceive those quantities under no other notions but from the relation they bear to sensible objects. And thence arise certain prejudices, for the removing of which it will be convenient to distinguish them into absolute and relative, true and apparent, mathematical and common.

1. Absolute, true, and mathematical time, of itself and from its own nature, flows equably without relation to anything external, and by another name is called "duration"; relative, apparent, and common time is some sensible and external (whether accurate or unequable) measure of duration by the means of motion, which is commonly used instead of true time, such as an hour, a day, a month, a year.

2. Absolute space, in its own nature, without relation to

• [This is the *Scholium* to the definitions in *Philosophiae Naturalis Principia Mathematica*, Bk. 1 (1689). The translation is by Andrew Motte (1729) as revised by Florian Cajori (Berkeley: University of California Press, 1934). Reprinted by permission of the University of California Press.]

Aristotelian account, the arrow should drop to the ground instantly upon quitting the bowstring. There were further difficulties in accounting for the known downward acceleration of projectiles. A number of ingenious *ad hoc* devices were introduced in order to accommodate these anomalies, but Galileo is sometimes credited with having made a wholly fresh start by *assuming* that a body will remain at rest or continue moving with uniform velocity in a straight line until some force induces a change. This of course is what is known as Newton's *First Law of Motion;* and there is an historical question whether Galileo actually had the First Law or not. Whatever the case, force figured in Newton's formulation as a way of accounting for changes in motion, either in direction or in rate. And this brings us to the concept of acceleration in connection with which part of the further philosophical importance of Newton's mechanics may be seen.

"Acceleration" may be defined as the time rate of change of instantaneous velocity. Now "instaneous velocity" and kindred terms can scarcely be made precise without appeal to concepts of the calculus, e.g., derivatives, differentials, and the like. Newton independantly invented the calculus, and though for various reasons he employed *geometrical* devices in the *Principia,* certain concepts of the calculus are implicit in his geometrical proofs. So in an important sense the calculus is intimately connected with those laws of mechanics which appealed to instantaneous rates of change and which are most naturally expressed through differential equations. Newton's contribution is accordingly twofold: he not only laid the foundations of mechanics but furnished models for the expression of scientific laws.

Differential equations, when employed as scientific laws, can only be used for purposes of explanation and prediction when supplemented with information about the systems they may be taken to describe. In most formulations of mechanics this information concerns the initial positions and momenta of the bodies composing the systems, referred to frequently as the *mechanical state* of the system. Once we know the values of the state variables of the initial state of the system, the differential equations allow us to deduce every other state of the system.

The initial state is sometimes spoken of as *determining* every other state of a physical system (it being arbitrary which state we chose as initial)—assuming the system to be isolated. The concept of "isolated system" is difficult to explicate, and many argue that the only instance of an isolated system is the universe itself. Generalizing on the above notion of "determine," one might then say that the initial state of the universe as a whole determines every other state or, in Laplace's formulation, given the required information concerning the position and momentum of every particle in the universe one could, by solving the equations, know exactly the position and momentum of each particle at any given instant. Whether Laplace's thesis entails the view that the universe is deterministic in any save the mechanical sense depends upon whether all phenomena can be accounted for in mechanical terms. And even if Laplace's thesis holds up, the connection between it and philosophical determinism is not wholly unequivocal. But our concern is only to indicate the sense in which scientific laws are said to be deterministic (or "causal").

Insofar as physics employs concepts like position and motion, it must concern itself with questions relating to the nature of space and time, these being foundational concepts. Newton is plausibly interpreted as having subscribed to a double theory of space, time, and motion. Space is, on the one hand, a special complex entity made up of points, each of which enjoys an independent existence. A body may be said to have position in an absolute sense in virtue of being located in some fixed region of space at a given instant, and to move in an absolute sense by occupying different regions of space in successive instants. But there is a sense in which bodies have relative position and relative motion as well: we select some reference body, say the fixed stars, and then calculate the position and motion of other material bodies relative to these. Relative space, motion, and time will serve well enough for many practical purposes, and for most scientific ones, but Newton also saw good reason for believing in an absolute, substantival concept of space. Historians of science (and biographers of Newton) often suggest that Newton was motivated by essentially theological concerns in this respect, but it cannot be overlooked that Newton offered scientific arguments, and pointed out phenomena—particularly rotary motion—which he felt could not be accounted for except by presupposing the absolute and substantival theory of space. This is what the famous Pail Experiment is meant to demonstrate.

Newton's theories of space (time and motion) came in for

considerable criticism, from about forty years after publication of the *Principia* until the present day. Berkeley criticized
them on essentially epistemological grounds, and Leibniz
argued, in a well-known controversy with Newton's disciple,
Samuel Clarke, that nothing in Newton's *Scholium* in fact
entails the independent existence of points. But Leibniz
himself must have held to at least an absolute theory of
space in the sense in which spatial predicates are not relational predicates, but apply to material bodies, each of which
has its own spatial properties independently of its relations
to other bodies. Mach offered important criticisms in his
Principles of Mechanics, some of them reminiscent of Berkeley's; and he moreover contended that the presence of
material bodies is a necessary and sufficient condition for
the existence of space. This suggestion was adopted by
Einstein and later, apparently, abandoned by him. At any
rate his references to the structure of the space-time field
have led many to suppose that Einstein after all maintained a
theory which admitted absolute space. But there are attempted formulations of general relativity, alternative to
Einstein's, which are in accordance with Mach's principle.

The question whether the substantival or adjectival, the
qualitative or relational theories of space (to use Johnson's
distinctions) are right is an ontological question. But there
is a related epistemological question concerning the status
of those general laws which describe spatial properties. During the nineteenth century, discussion of this was dominated
by Kant's views, in accordance with which the laws of
space—taken as identical with the laws of Euclidean geometry—were synthetic *a priori* sentences. Such laws were thus
interpreted as both necessary *and* descriptive of experience:
all spatial perception must in the nature of the case conform to them and so they could not conceivably be open
to empirical disconfirmation or to modification in the light
of empirical data. The invention of non-Euclidean geometries and the later proof that these were "equivalent" to
Euclidean geometry was a serious challenge to Kant's account. It at least opened the question whether the structure
of space might not be non-Euclidean, and at any rate strongly
suggested that it would only be a contingent fact that we
should intuit spatially in conformity with Euclidean structures. But some philosophers, notably Clifford, predicted that
science would one day employ non-Euclidean geometries, and
this indeed turned out to be the case in the general theory of

relativity. Poincaré introduced a novel, and in some respects a revised Kantian, thesis when he argued that the question of alternative geometries could not be settled independently of physical theories, that we could adopt any geometry we chose so long as we were prepared to make suitable changes in our physics, and that in the end we would employ whatever geometry should prove most convenient in the sense of requiring the least modification in the remainder of our theories. But he thought Euclidean geometry, for this reason, would prevail. And here of course he failed to anticipate the later developments in Relativity— although these developments can certainly be accounted for along the lines Poincaré suggested.

Spatial concepts were not the only ones revolutionized in the light of recent scientific advances. Many principles, held to be necessary by a number of nineteenth-century scientists and scientific theorists, had to be abandoned as a consequence of the newer theories. The principle that all physical processes are reversible (held by some to be a necessary presupposition of science) was challenged by the second law of thermodynamics. The assumption that all physical processes are continuous was challenged by Planck's work in Quantum Theory. But the most dramatic challenge came with the Uncertainty Principle of Heisenberg, which many took (and still take) to be in essential conflict with the causal character of science. On this a few words must be said.

We must distinguish between the questions (a) whether there is a general law of causality and (b) whether all ultimate scientific laws are causal laws. The first question does not particularly interest us: the challenge of Quantum Mechanics is to the belief that all ultimate scientific laws are causal (or deterministic, in the sense discussed above). It is true that quantum mechanics make use of statistical, and not causal, laws in that sense; but the sheer fact of statistical laws does not entail a negative answer to (b) unless the statistical laws are ultimate. Attempts were made in the nineteenth century to reduce statistical laws to causal laws. Whatever we think of these attempts, whether we regard them as truly successful or not, it is at least correct to say that Quantum Mechanics has put a halt to any such program —providing we accept a well-known proof of Von Neumann's which (*very* roughly) shows that Quantum Theory cannot consistently be given a deterministic formulation. But some scientists have argued that there may be phenomena *not* governed by quantum laws and that quantum mechanical laws may be reduced to the laws governing these phenomena. Such is the claim of David Bohm. But many physicists are unpersuaded by Bohm's arguments. And some physicists predict that future developments of science will yield theories stranger and more conceptually challenging than even Planck's hypothesis and the uncertainty principle.

1

ABSOLUTE AND RELATIVE SPACE, TIME, AND MOTION:

Isaac Newton •

Hitherto I have laid down the definitions of such words as are less known and explained the sense in which I would have them to be understood in the following discourse. I do not define time, space, place, and motion, as being well known to all. Only I must observe that the common people conceive those quantities under no other notions but from the relation they bear to sensible objects. And thence arise certain prejudices, for the removing of which it will be convenient to distinguish them into absolute and relative, true and apparent, mathematical and common.

1. Absolute, true, and mathematical time, of itself and from its own nature, flows equably without relation to anything external, and by another name is called "duration"; relative, apparent, and common time is some sensible and external (whether accurate or unequable) measure of duration by the means of motion, which is commonly used instead of true time, such as an hour, a day, a month, a year.

2. Absolute space, in its own nature, without relation to

• [This is the *Scholium* to the definitions in *Philosophiae Naturalis Principia Mathematica*, Bk. 1 (1689). The translation is by Andrew Motte (1729) as revised by Florian Cajori (Berkeley: University of California Press, 1934). Reprinted by permission of the University of California Press.]

anything external, remains always similar and immovable. Relative space is some movable dimension or measure of the absolute spaces, which our senses determine by its position to bodies and which is commonly taken for immovable space; such is the dimension of a subterraneous, an aerial, or celestial space, determined by its position in respect of the earth. Absolute and relative space are the same in figure and magnitude, but they do not remain always numerically the same. For if the earth, for instance, moves, a space of our air, which relatively and in respect of the earth remains always the same, will at one time be one part of the absolute space into which the air passes; at another time it will be another part of the same, and so, absolutely understood, it will be continually changed.

3. Place is a part of space which a body takes up and is, according to the space, either absolute or relative. I say, a part of space; not the situation nor the external surface of the body. For the places of equal solids are always equal; but their surfaces, by reason of their dissimilar figures, are often unequal. Positions properly have no quantity; nor are they so much the places themselves as the properties of places. The motion of the whole is the same with the sum of the motions of the parts; that is, the translation of the whole, out of its place, is the same thing with the sum of the translations of the parts out of their places; and therefore the place of the whole is the same as the sum of the places of the parts, and for that reason it is internal and in the whole body.

4. Absolute motion is the translation of a body from one absolute place into another, and relative motion the translation from one relative place into another. Thus in a ship under sail the relative place of a body is that part of the ship which the body possesses, or that part of the cavity which the body fills and which therefore moves together with the ship, and relative rest is the continuance of the body in the same part of the ship or of its cavity. But real, absolute rest is the continuance of the body in the same part of that immovable space in which the ship itself, its cavity, and all that it contains is moved. Wherefore, if the earth is really at rest, the body, which relatively rests in the ship, will really and absolutely move with the same velocity which the ship has on the earth. But if the earth also moves, the true and absolute motion of the body will arise, partly from the true motion of the earth in immovable space, partly from the

relative motion of the ship on the earth; and if the body moves also relatively in the ship, its true motion will arise, partly from the true motion of the earth in immovable space and partly from the relative motions as well of the ship on the earth as of the body in the ship; and from these relative motions will arise the relative motion of the body on the earth. As if that part of the earth where the ship is was truly moved toward the east with a velocity of 10,010 parts, while the ship itself, with a fresh gale and full sails, is carried toward the west with a velocity expressed by 10 of those parts, but a sailor walks in the ship toward the east with 1 part of the said velocity; then the sailor will be moved truly in immovable space toward the east, with a velocity of 10,001 parts, and relatively on the earth toward the west, with a velocity of 9 of those parts.

Absolute time, in astronomy, is distinguished from relative by the equation or correction of the apparent time. For the natural days are truly unequal, though they are commonly considered as equal and used for a measure of time; astronomers correct this inequality that they may measure the celestial motions by a more accurate time. It may be that there is no such thing as an equable motion whereby time may be accurately measured. All motions may be accelerated and retarded, but the flowing of absolute time is not liable to any change. The duration or perseverance of the existence of things remains the same, whether the motions are swift or slow, or none at all; and therefore this duration ought to be distinguished from what are only sensible measures thereof and from which we deduce it, by means of the astronomical equation. The necessity of this equation, for determining the times of a phenomenon, is evinced as well from the experiments of the pendulum clock as by eclipses of the satellites of Jupiter.

As the order of the parts of time is immutable, so also is the order of the parts of space. Suppose those parts to be moved out of their places, and they will be moved (if the expression may be allowed) out of themselves. For times and spaces are, as it were, the places as well of themselves as of all other things. All things are placed in time as to order of succession and in space as to order of situation. It is from their essence or nature that they are places, and that the primary places of things should be movable is absurd. These are therefore the absolute places, and translations out of those places are the only absolute motions.

But because the parts of space cannot be seen or distinguished from one another by our senses, therefore in their stead we use sensible measures of them. For from the positions and distances of things from any body considered as immovable we define all places; and then, with respect to such places, we estimate all motions, considering bodies as transferred from some of those places into others. And so, instead of absolute places and motions, we use relative ones, and that without any inconvenience in common affairs; but in philosophical disquisitions, we ought to abstract from our senses and consider things themselves, distinct from what are only sensible measures of them. For it may be that there is no body really at rest to which the places and motions of others may be referred.

But we may distinguish rest and motion, absolute and relative, one from the other by their properties, causes, and effects. It is a property of rest that bodies really at rest do rest in respect to one another. And therefore, as it is possible that in the remote regions of the fixed stars, or perhaps far beyond them, there may be some body absolutely at rest, but impossible to know from the position of bodies to one another in our regions whether any of these do keep the same position to that remote body, it follows that absolute rest cannot be determined from the position of bodies in our regions.

It is a property of motion that the parts which retain given positions to their wholes do partake of the motions of those wholes. For all the parts of revolving bodies endeavor to recede from the axis of motion, and the impetus of bodies moving forward arises from the joint impetus of all the parts. Therefore, if surrounding bodies are moved, those that are relatively at rest within them will partake of their motion. Upon which account the true and absolute motion of a body cannot be determined by the translation of it from those which only seem to rest; for the external bodies ought not only to appear at rest, but to be really at rest. For otherwise all included bodies, besides their translation from near the surrounding ones, partake likewise of their true motions; and though that translation were not made, they would not be really at rest, but only seem to be so. For the surrounding bodies stand in the like relation to the surrounded as the exterior part of a whole does to the interior, or as the shell does to the kernel; but if the shell moves, the kernel will also move, as being part of the whole, without any removal from near the shell.

A property near akin to the preceding is this, that if a place is moved, whatever is placed therein moves along with it; and therefore a body which is moved from a place in motion partakes also of the motion of its place. Upon which account all motions, from places in motion, are no other than parts of entire and absolute motions; and every entire motion is composed of the motion of the body out of its first place and the motion of this place out of its place; and so on, until we come to some immovable place, as in the before-mentioned example of the sailor. Wherefore entire and absolute motions cannot be otherwise determined than by immovable places; and for that reason I did before refer those absolute motions to immovable places, but relative ones to movable places. Now no other places are immovable but those that, from infinity to infinity, do all retain the same given position one to another, and upon this account must ever remain unmoved and do thereby constitute immovable space.

The causes by which true and relative motions are distinguished, one from the other, are the forces impressed upon bodies to generate motion. True motion is neither generated nor altered but by some force impressed upon the body moved, but relative motion may be generated or altered without any force impressed upon the body. For it is sufficient only to impress some force on other bodies with which the former is compared that, by their giving way, that relation may be changed in which the relative rest or motion of this other body did consist. Again, true motion suffers always some change from any force impressed upon the moving body, but relative motion does not necessarily undergo any change by such forces. For if the same forces are likewise impressed on those other bodies with which the comparison is made, that the relative position may be preserved, then that condition will be preserved in which the relative motion consists. And therefore any relative motion may be changed when the true motion remains unaltered, and the relative may be preserved when the true suffers some change. Thus, true motion by no means consists in such relations.

The effects which distinguish absolute from relative motion are the forces of receding from the axis of circular motion. For there are no such forces in a circular motion purely relative, but in a true and absolute circular motion they are greater or less, according to the quantity of the motion. If a vessel, hung by a long cord, is so often turned about that the cord is strongly twisted, then filled with water and held at rest together with the water, thereupon by the sudden action of another force it is whirled about the contrary way, and while the cord is untwisting itself the vessel continues for some time in this motion, the surface of the water will at first be plain, as before the vessel began to move; but after that the vessel, by gradually communicating its motion to the water, will make it begin sensibly to revolve and recede by little and little from the middle, and ascend to the sides of the vessel, forming itself into a concave figure (as I have experienced); and the swifter the motion becomes, the higher will the water rise, till at last, performing its revolutions in the same times with the vessel, it becomes relatively at rest in it. This ascent of the water shows its endeavor to recede from the axis of its motion; and the true and absolute circular motion of the water, which is here directly contrary to the relative, becomes known and may be measured by this endeavor. At first, when the relative motion of the water in the vessel was greatest, it produced no endeavor to recede from the axis; the water showed no tendency to the circumference, nor any ascent toward the sides of the vessel, but remained of a plain surface, and therefore its true circular motion had not yet begun. But afterward, when the relative motion of the water had decreased, the ascent thereof toward the sides of the vessel proved its endeavor to recede from the axis; and this endeavor showed the real circular motion of the water continually increasing, till it had acquired its greatest quantity, when the water rested relatively in the vessel. And therefore this endeavor does not depend upon any translation of the water in respect of the ambient bodies; nor can true circular motion be defined by such translation. There is only one real circular motion of any one revolving body, corresponding to only one power of endeavoring to recede from its axis of motion, as its proper and adequate effect; but relative motions, in one and the same body, are innumerable, according to the various relations it bears to external bodies, and, like other relations, are altogether destitute of any real effect, any otherwise than they may perhaps partake of that one only true motion. And therefore in their system who suppose that our heavens, revolving below the sphere of the fixed stars, carry the planets along with them, the several parts of those heavens and the planets, which are indeed relatively at rest in their heavens, do yet really move. For they change their position one to another (which never happens to bodies truly at rest) and, being carried together with their heavens, partake of their motions and, as parts of revolving wholes, endeavor to recede from the axis of their motions.

Wherefore relative quantities are not the quantities themselves whose names they bear, but those sensible measures of them (either accurate or inaccurate) which are commonly used instead of the measured quantities themselves. And if the meaning of words is to be determined by their use, then by the names "time," "space," "place," and "motion" their [sensible] measures are properly to be understood; and the expression will be unusual, and purely mathematical, if the measured quantities themselves are meant. On this account, those violate the accuracy of language, which ought to be kept precise, who interpret these words for the measured quantities. Nor do those less defile the purity of mathematical and philosophical truths who confound real quantities with their relations and sensible measures.

It is indeed a matter of great difficulty to discover and effectually to distinguish the true motions of particular bodies from the apparent, because the parts of that immovable space in which those motions are performed do by no means come under the observation of our senses. Yet the thing is not altogether desperate; for we have some arguments to guide us, partly from the apparent motions, which are the differences of the true motions; partly from the forces, which are the causes and effects of the true motions. For instance, if two globes, kept at a given distance one from the other by means of a cord that connects them, were revolved about their common center of gravity, we might, from the tension of the cord, discover the endeavor of the globes to recede from the axis of their motion, and from thence we might compute the quantity of their circular motions. And then if any equal forces should be impressed at once on the alternate faces of the globes to augment or diminish their circular motions, from the increase or decrease of the tension of the cord we might infer the increment or decrement of their motions, and thence would be found on what faces those forces ought to be impressed that the motions of the globes might be most augmented; that is, we might discover their hindmost faces, or those which, in the circular motion, do follow. But the faces which follow being known, and consequently the opposite ones that precede, we should likewise know the determination of their motions. And thus we might find both the quantity and the determination of this circular motion, even in an immense vacuum, where there was nothing external or sensible with which the globes could be compared. But now, if in that space some remote bodies were placed that kept always a given position one to another, as the fixed stars do in our regions, we could not indeed determine from the relative translation of the globes among those bodies whether the motion did belong to the globes or to the bodies. But if we observed the cord and found that its tension was that very tension which the motions of the globes required, we might conclude the motion to be in the globes and the bodies to be at rest; and then, lastly, from the translation of the globes among the bodies, we should find the determination of their motions.

2

CRITICISM OF NEWTON'S DOCTRINES ON SPACE:

George Berkeley •

109. As, in reading other books, a wise man will choose to fix his thoughts on the sense and apply it to use, rather than lay them out in grammatical remarks on the language, so, in perusing the volume of nature, it seems beneath the dignity of the mind to affect an exactness in reducing each particular phenomenon to general rules, or showing how it follows from them. We should propose to ourselves nobler views, such as to recreate and exalt the mind with a prospect of the beauty, order, extent, and variety of natural things: hence, by proper inferences, to enlarge our notions of the grandeur, wisdom, and beneficence of the Creator; and lastly, to make the several parts of the Creation, so far as in us lies, subservient to the ends they were designed for—God's glory and the sustentation and comfort of ourselves and fellow creatures.

110. The best key for the aforesaid analogy or natural science will be easily acknowledged to be a certain celebrated treatise of *mechanics*.[1] In the entrance of which justly admired treatise, time, space, and motion are distinguished into *absolute* and *relative*, *true* and *apparent*, *mathematical* and *vulgar*; which distinction, as it is at large

• [This selection is from Berkeley's *The Principles of Human Knowledge*, sections 109–16. This book first appeared in 1710.]

[1] [Newton's *Principia*, which came out in 1689.]

explained by the author, does suppose these quantities to have an existence without the mind; and that they are ordinarily conceived with relation to sensible things, to which nevertheless in their own nature they bear no relation at all.

111. As for *time*, as it is there taken in an absolute or abstracted sense, for the duration or perseverance of the existence of things, I have nothing more to add concerning it after what has been already said on that subject. Sects. 97 and 98. For the rest, this celebrated author holds there is an *absolute space*, which, being unperceivable to sense, remains in itself similar and immovable; and relative space to be the measure thereof, which, being movable and defined by its situation in respect of sensible bodies, is vulgarly taken for immovable space. *Place* he defines to be that part of space which is occupied by any body; and according as the space is absolute or relative, so also is the place. *Absolute motion* is said to be the translation of a body from absolute place to absolute place, as relative motion is from one relative place to another. And, because the parts of absolute space do not fall under our senses, instead of them we are obliged to use their sensible measures, and so define both place and motion with respect to bodies which we regard as immovable. But it is said in philosophical matters we must abstract from our senses, since it may be that none of those bodies which seem to be quiescent are truly so, and the same thing which is moved relatively may be really at rest; as likewise one and the same body may be in relative rest and motion, or even moved with contrary relative motions at the same time, according as its place is variously defined. All which ambiguity is to be found in the apparent motions, but not at all in the true or absolute, which should therefore be alone regarded in philosophy. And the true we are told are distinguished from apparent or relative motions by the following properties.—First, in true or absolute motion all parts which preserve the same position with respect to the whole partake of the motions of the whole. Secondly, the place being moved, that which is placed therein is also moved; so that a body moving in a place which is in motion does participate the motion of its place. Thirdly, true motion is never generated or changed otherwise than by force impressed on the body itself. Fourthly, true motion is always changed by force impressed on the body moved. Fifthly, in circular motion,

barely relative, there is no centrifugal force which, nevertheless, in that which is true or absolute, is proportional to the quantity of motion.

112. But, notwithstanding what has been said, it does not appear to me that there can be any motion other than *relative;* so that to conceive motion there must be at least conceived two bodies, whereof the distance or position in regard to each other is varied. Hence, if there was one only body in being it could not possibly be moved. This seems evident, in that the idea I have of motion does necessarily include relation.

113. But, though in every motion it be necessary to conceive more bodies than one, yet it may be that one only is moved, namely, that on which the force causing the change of distance is impressed, or, in other words, that to which the action is applied. For, however some may define relative motion, so as to term that body *moved* which changes its distance from some other body, whether the force or action causing that change were applied to it or no, yet as relative motion is that which is perceived by sense, and regarded in the ordinary affairs of life, it should seem that every man of common sense knows what it is as well as the best philosopher. Now I ask anyone whether, in his sense of motion as he walks along the streets, the stones he passes over may be said to *move,* because they change distance with his feet? To me it seems that though motion includes a relation of one thing to another, yet it is not necessary that each term of the relation be denominated from it. As a man may think of somewhat which does not think, so a body may be moved to or from another body which is not therefore itself in motion.

114. As the place happens to be variously defined, the motion which is related to it varies. A man in a ship may be said to be quiescent with relation to the sides of the vessel, and yet move with relation to the land. Or he may move eastward in respect of the one, and westward in respect of the other. In the common affairs of life, men never go beyond the earth to define the place of any body; and what is quiescent in respect of that is accounted *absolutely* to be so. But philosophers, who have a greater extent of thought, and juster notions of the system of things, discover even the earth itself to be moved. In order therefore to fix their notions, they seem to conceive the corporeal world as finite, and the utmost unmoved walls or shell

thereof to be the place whereby they estimate true motions. If we sound our own conceptions, I believe we may find all the absolute motion we can frame an idea of to be at bottom no other than relative motion thus defined. For, as has been already observed, absolute motion, exclusive of all external relation, is incomprehensible; and to this kind of relative motion all the above-mentioned properties, causes, and effects ascribed to absolute motion will, if I mistake not, be found to agree. As to what is said of the centrifugal force, that it does not at all belong to circular relative motion, I do not see how this follows from the experiment which is brought to prove it. See *Philosophiae Naturalis Principia Mathematica, in Schol. Def. VIII.*[2] For the water in the vessel at that time wherein it is said to have the greatest relative circular motion, has, I think, no motion at all; as is plain from the foregoing section.

115. For, to denominate a body *moved* it is requisite, first, that it change its distance or situation with regard to some other body; and secondly, that the force or action occasioning that change be applied to it. If either of these be wanting, I do not think that, agreeably to the sense of mankind, or the propriety of language, a body can be said to be in motion. I grant indeed that it is possible for us to think a body which we see change its distance from some other to be moved, though it have no force applied to it (in which sense there may be apparent motion), but then it is because the force causing the change of distance is imagined by us to be applied or impressed on that body thought to move; which indeed shows we are capable of mistaking a thing to be in motion which is not, and that is all.

116. From what has been said, it follows that the philosophic consideration of motion does not imply the being of an *absolute space*, distinct from that which is perceived by sense and related to bodies; which that it cannot exist without the mind is clear upon the same principles that demonstrate the like of all other objects of sense. And perhaps, if we inquire narrowly, we shall find we cannot even frame an idea of *pure space* exclusive of all body. This I must confess seems impossible, as being a most abstract idea. When I excite a motion in some part of my body, if it be free or without resistance, I say there is *space*; but if I

2 [Berkeley is referring to the "pail experiment." See Introduction to Part Three.]

find a resistance, then I say there is *body;* and in proportion as the resistance to motion is lesser or greater, I say the space is more or less *pure.* So that when I speak of pure or empty space, it is not to be supposed that the word "space" stands for an idea distinct from or conceivable without body and motion—though indeed we are apt to think every noun substantive stands for a distinct idea that may be separated from all others; which has occasioned infinite mistakes. When, therefore, supposing all the world to be annihilated besides my own body, I say there still remains *pure space,* thereby nothing else is meant but only that I conceive it possible for the limbs of my body to be moved on all sides without the least resistance; but if that, too, were annihilated, then there could be no motion, and consequently no space. Some, perhaps, may think the sense of seeing does furnish them with the idea of pure space; but it is plain from what we have elsewhere shown, that the ideas of space and distance are not obtained by that sense. See the *Essay Concerning Vision.*[3]

117. What is here laid down seems to put an end to all those disputes and difficulties that have sprung up amongst the learned concerning the nature of *pure space.* But the chief advantage arising from it is that we are freed from that dangerous dilemma to which several who have employed their thoughts on this subject imagine themselves reduced, to wit, of thinking either that real space is God, or else that there is something beside God which is eternal, uncreated, infinite, indivisible, immutable. Both which may justly be thought pernicious and absurd notions. It is certain that not a few divines, as well as philosophers of great note, have, from the difficulty they found in conceiving either limits or annihilation of space, concluded it must be divine. And some of late have set themselves particularly to show that the incommunicable attributes of God agree to it. Which doctrine, how unworthy soever it may seem of the Divine Nature, yet I do not see how we can get clear of it so long as we adhere to the received opinions.

[3] [Berkeley's *An Essay Towards a New Theory of Vision* (1709) came out a year earlier than the *Principles of Human Knowledge.*]

3

NEWTON'S VIEWS ON TIME, SPACE, AND MOTION:

Ernst Mach [*]

1. In a scholium which he appends immediately to his definitions, Newton presents his views regarding time and space which we must examine more in detail. We shall literally cite, to this end, only the passages that are absolutely necessary to the characterization of Newton's views.

"So far, my object has been to explain the senses in which certain words little known are to be used in the sequel. Time, space, place, and motion, being words well known to everybody, I do not define. Yet it is to be remarked, that the vulgar conceive these quantities only in their relation to sensible objects. And hence certain prejudices with respect to them have arisen, to remove which it will be convenient to distinguish them into absolute and relative, true and apparent, mathematical and common, respectively.

"I. Absolute, true and mathematical time, of itself, and by its own nature, flows uniformly on, without regard to anything external. It is also called *duration*.

"Relative, apparent, and common time, is some sensible and external measure of absolute time (duration), estimated

[*] [This selection is reprinted from *The Science of Mechanics* (Chicago: Open Court Publishing Co., 1902), trans., E. J. McCormack. The book was originally entitled *Die Mechanik in ihre Entwicklung* (Leipzig: 1883).]

by the motions of bodies, whether accurate or inequable, and is commonly employed in place of true time; as an hour, a day, a month, a year . . . .

"The natural days, which, commonly, for the purpose of the measurement of time, are held as equal, are in reality unequal. Astronomers correct this inequality, in order that they may measure by a truer time the celestial motions. It may be that there is no equable motion, by which time can accurately be measured. All motions can be accelerated and retarded. But the flow of *absolute* time cannot be changed. Duration, or the persistent existence of things, is always the same, whether motions be swift or slow or null."

2. It would appear as though Newton in the remarks here cited still stood under the influence of the medieval philosophy, as though he had grown unfaithful to his resolves to investigate only actual facts. When we say a thing A changes with the time, we mean simply that the conditions that determine a thing A depend on the conditions that determine another thing B. The vibrations of a pendulum take place *in time* when its excursion *depends* on the position of the earth. Since, however, in the observation of the pendulum, we are not under the necessity of taking into account its dependence on the position of the earth, but may compare it with any other thing (the conditions of which of course also depend on the position of the earth), the illusory notion easily arises that *all* the things with which we compare it are unessential. Nay, we may, in attending to the motion of a pendulum, neglect entirely other external things, and find that for every position of it our thoughts and sensations are different. Time, accordingly, appears to be some particular and independent thing, on the progress of which the position of the pendulum depends, while the things that we resort to for comparison and choose at random appear to play a wholly collateral part. But we must not forget that all things in the world are connected with one another and depend on one another, and that we ourselves and all our thoughts are also a part of nature. It is utterly beyond our power to *measure* the changes of things by *time*. Quite the contrary, time is an abstraction, at which we arrive by means of the changes of things; made because we are not restricted to any one *definite* measure, all being interconnected. A motion is termed uniform in which equal increments of space described correspond to equal increments of space

described by some motion with which we form a comparison, as the rotation of the earth. A motion may, with respect to another motion, be uniform. But the question whether a motion is *in itself* uniform, is senseless. With just as little justice, also, may we speak of an "absolute time"—*of a time independent of* change. This absolute time can be measured by comparison with no motion; it has therefore neither a practical nor a scientific value; and no one is justified in saying that he knows aught about it. It is an idle metaphysical conception.

It would not be difficult to show from the points of view of psychology, history, and the science of language (by the names of the chronological divisions), that we reach our ideas of time in and through the interdependence of things on one another. In these ideas the profoundest and most universal connection of things is expressed. When a motion takes place in time, it depends on the motion of the earth. This is not refuted by the fact that mechanical motions can be reversed. A number of variable quantities may be so related that one set can suffer a change without the others being affected by it. Nature behaves like a machine. The individual parts reciprocally determine one another. But while in a machine the position of one part determines the position of *all* the other parts, in nature more complicated relations obtain. These relations are best represented under the conception of a number, n, of quantities that satisfy a lesser number, n', of equation. Were $n = n'$, nature would be invariable. Were $n' = n - 1$, then with one quantity all the rest would be controlled. If this latter relation obtained in nature, time could be reversed the moment this had been accomplished with any one single motion. But the true state of things is represented by a different relation between n and n'. The quantities in question are partially determined by one another; but they retain a greater indeterminateness, or freedom, than in the case last cited. We ourselves feel that we are such a partially determined, partially undetermined element of nature. In so far as a portion only of the changes of nature depends on us and can be reversed by us, does time appear to us irreversible, and the time that is past as irrevocably gone.

We arrive at the idea of time—to express it briefly and popularly—by the connection of that which is contained in the province of our memory with that which is contained in the province of our sense-perception. When we say that time flows on in a definite direction or sense, we mean that physical events generally (and therefore also physiological events) take place only in a definite sense. Differences of temperature, electrical differences, differences of level generally, if left to themselves, all grow less and not greater. If we contemplate two bodies of different temperatures, put in contact and left wholly to themselves, we shall find that it is possible only for greater differences of temperature in the field of memory to exist with lesser ones in the field of sense-perception, and not the reverse. In all this there is simply expressed a peculiar and profound connection of things. To demand at the present time a full elucidation of this matter, is to anticipate, in the manner of speculative philosophy, the results of all future special investigation, that is, a perfected physical science.

As in the study of thermal phenomena we take as our measure of temperature an *arbitrarily chosen indicator of volume*, which varies in almost parallel correspondence with our sensation of heat, and which is not liable to the uncontrollable disturbances of our organs of sensation, so, for similar reasons, we select as our measure of time an *arbitrarily chosen motion* (the angle of the earth's rotation, or path of a free body), which proceeds in almost parallel correspondence with our sensation of time. If we have once made clear to ourselves that we are concerned only with the ascertainment of the *interdependence* of phenomena . . . all metaphysical obscurities disappear. . . .

3. Views similar to those concerning time, are developed by Newton with respect to space and motion. We extract here a few passages which characterize his position.

"II. Absolute space, in its own nature and without regard to anything external, always remains similar and immovable.

"Relative space is some movable dimension or measure of absolute space, which our senses determine by its position with respect to other bodies, and which is commonly taken for immovable [absolute] space. . . .

"IV. Absolute motion is the translation of a body from one absolute place[1] to another absolute place; and

[1] [The place, or *locus* of a body, according to Newton, is not its position, but the *part of space* which it occupies. It is either absolute or relative.—*Trans.*]

relative motion, the translation from one relative place to another relative place. . . .

". . . And thus we use, in common affairs, instead of *absolute* places and motions, *relative* ones; and that without any inconvenience. But in physical disquisitions, we should abstract from the senses. For it may be that there is no body really at rest, to which the places and motions of others can be referred. . . .

"The effects by which absolute and relative motions are distinguished from one another, are centrifugal forces, or those forces in circular motion which produces a tendency of recession from the axis. For in a circular motion which is purely relative no such forces exist; but in a true and absolute circular motion they do exist, and are greater or less according to the quantity of the [absolute] motion.

"For instance: If a bucket, suspended by a long cord, is so often turned about that finally the cord is strongly twisted, then is filled with water, and held at rest together with the water; and afterwards by the action of a second force, it is suddenly set whirling about the contrary way, and continues, while the cord is untwisting itself, for some time in this motion; the surface of the water will at first be level, just as it was before the vessel began to move; but, subsequently, the vessel, by gradually communicating its motion to the water, will make it begin sensibly to rotate, and the water will recede little by little from the middle and rise up at the sides of the vessel, its surface assuming a concave form. (This experiment I have made myself.)

". . . At first, when the *relative* motion of the water in the vessel was *greatest,* that motion produced no tendency whatever of recession from the axis; the water made no endeavor to move towards the circumference, by rising at the sides of the vessel, but remained level, and for that reason its *true* circular motion had not yet begun. But afterwards, when the relative motion of the water had decreased, the rising of the water at the sides of the vessel indicated an endeavor to recede from the axis; and this endeavor revealed the real motion of the water, continually increasing, till it had reached its greatest point, when *relatively* the water was at rest in the vessel. . . .

"It is indeed a matter of great difficulty to discover, and effectually to distinguish, the *true* from the apparent motions of particular bodies; for the parts of that immovable space in which bodies actually move, do not come under the observation of our senses.

"Yet the case is not altogether desperate; for there exist to guide us certain marks, abstracted partly from the apparent motions, which are the differences of the true motions and partly from the forces that are the causes and effects of the true motions. If, for instance, two globes, kept at a fixed distance from one another by means of a cord that connects them, be revolved about their common center of gravity, one might, from the simple tension of the cord, discover the tendency of the globes to recede from the axis of their motion, and on this basis the quantity of their circular motion might be computed. And if any equal forces should be simultaneously impressed on alternate faces of the globes to augment or diminish their circular motion, we might, from the increase or decrease of the tension of the cord, deduce the increment or decrement of their motion; and it might also be found thence on what faces forces would have to be impressed, in order that the motion of the globes should be most augmented; that is, their real faces, or those which, in the circular motion, follow. But as soon as we knew which faces followed, and consequently which preceded, we should likewise know the direction of the motion. In this way we might find both the quantity and the direction of the circular motion, considered even in an immense vacuum, where there was nothing external or sensible with which the globes could be compared. . . ."

If, in a material spatial system, there are masses with different velocities, which can enter into mutual relations with one another, these masses present to us forces. We can only decide how great these forces are when we know the velocities to which those masses are to be brought. *Resting* masses too are forces if *all* the masses do not rest. Think, for example, of Newton's rotating bucket in which the water is not yet rotating. If the mass m has the velocity v_1 and it is to be brought to the velocity v_2, the force which is to be spent on it is $p = m(v_1 - v_2)/t$, or the work which is to be expended is $ps = (v_1{}^2 - v_2{}^2)$. *All masses and all* velocities, and consequently *all* forces, are relative. There is no decision about relative and absolute which we can possibly meet, to which we are forced, or from which we can obtain any intellectual or other advantage. When quite modern authors let themselves be led astray by the Newtonian arguments which are derived from the bucket of water, to distinguish between relative and absolute motion, they do not reflect that the system of the world is only given *once* to us, and the Ptolemaic or Copernician view is *our* interpretation, but both are equally actual. Try to fix Newton's bucket and rotate the heaven of fixed stars and then prove the absence of centrifugal forces.

4. It is scarcely necessary to remark that in the reflections here presented Newton has again acted contrary to his expressed intention only to investigate *actual facts*. No one is competent to predicate things about absolute space and absolute motion; they are pure things of thought, pure mental constructs, that cannot be produced in experience. All our principles of mechanics are, as we have shown in detail, experimental knowledge concerning the relative positions and motions of bodies. Even in the provinces in which they are now recognized as valid, they could not, and were not, admitted without previously being subjected to experimental tests. No one is warranted in extending these principles beyond the boundaries of experience. In fact, such an extension is meaningless, as no one possesses the requisite knowledge to make use of it.

We must suppose that the change in the point of view from which the system of the world is regarded which was initiated by Copernicus, left deep traces in the thought of Galileo and Newton. But while Galileo, in his theory of the tides, quite naïvely chose the sphere of the fixed stars as the basis of a new system of coordinates, we see doubts expressed by Newton as to whether a given fixed star is at rest only apparently or really. This appeared to him to cause the difficulty of distinguishing between true (absolute) and apparent (relative) motion. By this he was also impelled to set up the conception of *absolute space*. By further investigations in this direction—the discussion of the experiment of the rotating spheres which are connected together by a cord and that of the rotating water bucket he believed that he could prove an absolute rotation, though he could not prove any absolute translation. By absolute rotation he understood a rotation relative to the fixed stars, and here centrifugal forces can always be found. "But how we are to collect," says Newton in the Scholium at the end of the Definitions, "the true motions from their causes, effects, and apparent differences, and *vice versa;* how from the motions, either true or apparent, we may come to the knowledge of their causes and effects, shall be explained more at large in the following Tract." The resting sphere of fixed stars seems to have made a certain impression on Newton as well. The natural system of reference is for him that which has any uniform motion or translation without rotation (relatively to the sphere of fixed stars).[2] But do not the words quoted in inverted commas give the impression that Newton was glad to be able now to pass over to less precarious questions that could be tested by experience?

Let us look at the matter in detail. When we say that a body K alters its direction and velocity solely through the influence of another body K', we have asserted a conception that it is impossible to come at unless other bodies A, B, C . . . are present with reference to which the motion of the body K has been estimated. In reality, therefore, we are simply cognizant of a relation of the body K to A, B, C. . . . If now we suddenly neglect A, B, C . . . and attempt to speak of the deportment of the body K in absolute space, we implicate ourselves in a twofold error. In the first place, we cannot know how K would act in the absence of A, B, C...; and in the second place, every means would be wanting of forming a judgment of the behavior of K and of putting to the test what we had predicated—which latter therefore would be bereft of all scientific significance.

Two bodies K and K', which gravitate toward each other, impart to each other in the direction of their line of junction accelerations inversely proportional to their masses m, m'. In this proposition is contained, not only a relation of the bodies K and K' to one another, but also a relation of them to other bodies. For the proposition asserts, not only that K and K' suffer with respect to one another the acceleration designated by $\kappa(m + m'/r^2)$, but also that K experiences the acceleration $- \kappa m'/r^2$ and K' the acceleration $+ \kappa m/r^2$ in the direction of the line of junction; facts which can be ascertained only by the presence of other bodies.

The motion of a body K can only be estimated by reference to other bodies A, B, C. . . . But since we always have at our disposal a sufficient number of bodies, that are as respects each other relatively fixed, or only slowly change their positions, we are, in such reference, restricted to no

[2] *Principia*, Coroll. V: "The motions of bodies included in a given space are the same among themselves, whether that space is at rest or moves uniformly forwards in a right line without any circular motion."

one *definite* body and can alternately leave out of account now this one and now that one. In this way the conviction arose that these bodies are indifferent generally.

It might be, indeed, that isolated bodies A, B, C ... play merely a collateral rôle in the determination of the motion of the body K, and that this motion is determined by a *medium* in which K exists. In such a case we should have to substitute this medium for Newton's absolute space. Newton certainly did not entertain this idea. Moreover, it is easily demonstrable that the atmosphere is not this motion-determinative medium. We should, therefore, have to picture to ourselves some other medium, filling, say, all space, with respect to the constitution of which and its kinetic relations to the bodies placed in it we have at present no adequate knowledge. In itself such a state of things would not belong to the impossibilities. It is known, from recent hydrodynamical investigations, that a rigid body experiences resistance in a frictionless fluid only when its velocity *changes*. True, this result is derived theoretically from the notion of inertia; but it might, conversely, also be regarded as the primitive fact from which we have to start. Although, practically, and at present, nothing is to be accomplished with this conception, we might still hope to learn more in the future concerning this hypothetical medium; and from the point of view of science it would be in every respect a more valuable acquisition than the forlorn idea of absolute space. When we reflect that we cannot abolish the isolated bodies A, B, C ..., that is, cannot determine by experiment whether the part they play is fundamental or collateral, that hitherto they have been the sole and only competent means of the orientation of motions and of the description of mechanical facts, it will be found expedient provisionally to regard all motions as determined by these bodies.

5. Let us now examine the point on which Newton, apparently with sound reasons, rests his distinction of absolute and relative motion. If the earth is affected with an *absolute* rotation about its axis, centrifugal forces are set up in the earth: it assumes an oblate form, the acceleration of gravity is diminished at the equator, the plane of Foucault's pendulum rotates, and so on. All these phenomena disappear if the earth is at rest and the other heavenly bodies are affected with absolute motion round it, such that the same *relative* rotation is produced. This is, indeed, the case, if we start *ab initio* from the idea of absolute space. But if we

take our stand on the basis of facts, we shall find we have knowledge only of *relative* spaces and motions. *Relatively,* not considering the unknown and neglected medium of space, the motions of the universe are the same whether we adopt the Ptolemaic or the Copernican mode of view. Both views are, indeed, equally *correct*; only the latter is more simple and more *practical*. The universe is not *twice* given, with an earth at rest and an earth in motion; but only *once*, with its *relative* motions, alone determinable. It is, accordingly, not permitted us to say how things would be if the earth did not rotate. We may interpret the one case that is given us, in different ways. If, however, we so interpret it that we come into conflict with experience, our interpretation is simply wrong. The principles of mechanics can, indeed, be so conceived, that even for relative rotations centrifugal forces arise.

Newton's experiment with the rotating vessel of water simply informs us that the relative rotation of the water with respect to the sides of the vessel produces *no* noticeable centrifugal forces, but that such forces *are* produced by its relative rotation with respect to the mass of the earth and the other celestial bodies. No one is competent to say how the experiment would turn out if the sides of the vessel increased in thickness and mass till they were ultimately several leagues thick. The one experiment only lies before us, and our business is to bring it into accord with the other facts known to us, and not with the arbitrary fictions of our imagination.

6. When Newton examined the principles of mechanics discovered by Galileo, the great value of the simple and precise law of inertia for deductive derivations could not possibly escape him. He could not think of renouncing its help. But the law of inertia, referred in such a naïve way to the earth supposed to be at rest, could not be accepted by him. For, in Newton's case, the rotation of the earth was not a debatable point; it rotated without the least doubt. Galileo's happy discovery could only hold approximately for small times and spaces, during which the rotation did not come into question. Instead of that, Newton's conclusions about planetary motion, referred as they were to the fixed stars, appeared to conform to the law of inertia. Now, in order to have a generally valid system of reference, Newton ventured the fifth corollary of the *Principia*. He imagined a momentary terrestrial system of coordinates, for which

the law of inertia is valid, held fast in space without any rotation relatively to the fixed stars. Indeed he could, without interfering with its usability, impart to this system any initial position and any uniform translation relatively to the above momentary terrestrial system. The Newtonian laws of force are not altered thereby; only the initial positions and initial velocities—the constants of integration—may alter. By this view Newton gave the *exact* meaning of his hypothetical extension of Galileo's law of inertia. We see that the reduction to absolute space was by no means necessary, for the system of reference is just as relatively determined as in every other case. In spite of his metaphysical liking for the absolute, Newton was correctly led by the *tact of the natural investigator*. . . .

The comportment of terrestrial bodies with respect to the earth is reducible to the comportment of the earth with respect to the remote heavenly bodies. If we were to assert that we knew more of moving objects than this their last-mentioned, experimentally given comportment with respect to the celestial bodies, we should render ourselves culpable of a falsity. When, accordingly, we say that a body preserves unchanged its direction and velocity *in space,* our assertion is nothing more or less than an abbreviated reference to *the entire universe.* The use of such an abbreviated expression is permitted the original author of the principle, because he knows that as things are, no difficulties stand in the way of carrying out its implied directions. But no remedy lies in his power, if difficulties of the kind mentioned present themselves; if, for example, the requisite, relatively fixed bodies are wanting.

7. Instead, now, of referring a moving body *K* to space, that is to say to a system of coordinates, let us view directly its relation to the bodies of the universe, by which alone such a system of coordinates can be determined. Bodies very remote from each other, moving with constant direction and velocity with respect to other distant fixed bodies, change their mutual distances proportionately to the time. We may also say, all very remote bodies—all mutual or other forces neglected—alter their mutual distances proportionately to those distances. Two bodies, which, situated at a short distance from one another, move with constant direction and velocity with respect to other fixed bodies, exhibit more complicated relations. If we should regard the two bodies as dependent on one another, and call *r* the

distance, t the time, and a a constant dependent on the directions and velocities, the formula would be obtained: $d^2r/dt^2 = (1/r) \ [a^2 - (dr/dt)^2]$. It is manifestly much *simpler* and *clearer* to regard the two bodies as independent of each other and to consider the constancy of their direction and velocity with respect to other bodies.

Instead of saying, the direction and velocity of a mass μ in space remain constant, we may also employ the expression, the mean acceleration of the mass μ with respect to the masses m, m', m'' . . . at the distances r, r', r'') . . . is $= 0$, or $d^2(\Sigma \, m \, r/\Sigma \, m)/dt^2 = 0$. The latter expression is equivalent to the former, as soon as we take into consideration a sufficient number of sufficiently distant and sufficiently large masses. The mutual influence of more proximate small masses, which are apparently not concerned about each other, is eliminated of itself. That the constancy of direction and velocity is given by the condition adduced, will be seen at once if we construct through μ as vertex cones that cut out different portions of space, and set up the condition with respect to the masses of these separate portions. We may put, indeed, for the *entire* space encompassing μ, $d^2 (\Sigma \, m \, r/\Sigma \, m)/dt^2 = 0$. But the equation in this case asserts nothing with respect to the motion of μ, since it holds good for all species of motion where μ is uniformly surrounded by an infinite number of masses. If two masses μ_1, μ_2 exert on each other a force which is dependent on their distance r, then $d^2r/dt^2 = (\mu_1 + \mu_2)f(r)$. But at the same time, the acceleration of the center of gravity of the two masses or the mean acceleration of the mass-system with respect to the masses of the universe (by the principle of reaction) remains $= 0$; that is to say,

$$\frac{d^2}{dt^2} \left[\ \mu_1 \ \frac{\Sigma mr_1}{\Sigma m} + \mu_2 \ \frac{\Sigma mr_2}{\Sigma m} \ \right] = 0.$$

When we reflect that the time-factor that enters into the acceleration is nothing more than a quantity that is the measure of the distances (or angles of rotation) of the bodies of the universe, we see that even in the simplest case, in which apparently we deal with the mutual action of only *two* masses, the neglecting of the rest of the world is *impossible*. Nature does not begin with elements, as we are obliged to begin with them. It is certainly fortunate for us, that we can, from time to time, turn aside our eyes from the overpowering unity of the All, and allow them to rest on individual details. But we should not omit, ultimately to complete and correct our views by a thorough consideration of the things which for the time being we left out of account.

8. The considerations just presented show that it is not necessary to refer the law of inertia to a special absolute space. On the contrary, it is perceived that the masses that in the common phraseology exert forces on each other as well as those that exert none, stand with respect to acceleration in quite similar relations. We may, indeed, regard *all* masses as related to each other. That *accelerations* play a prominent part in the relations of the masses, must be accepted as a fact of experience; which does not, however, exclude attempts to *elucidate* this fact by a comparison of it with other facts, involving the discovery of new points of view. In all the processes of nature the *differences* of certain quantities u play a determinative rôle. Differences of temperature, of potential function, and so forth, induce the natural processes, which consist in the equalization of these differences. The familiar expressions d^2u/dx^2, d^2u/dy^2, d^2u/dz^2, which are determinative of the character of the equalization, may be regarded as the measure of the departure of the condition of any point from the mean of the conditions of its environment—to which mean the point tends. The accelerations of masses may be analogously conceived. The great distances between masses that stand in no especial force-relation to one another, change *proportionately to each other*. . . .

9. We have attempted in the foregoing to give the law of inertia a different expression from that in ordinary use. This expression will, so long as a sufficient number of bodies are apparently fixed in space, accomplish the same as the ordinary one. It is as easily applied, and it encounters the same difficulties. In the one case we are unable to come at an absolute space, in the other a limited number of masses only is within the reach of our knowledge, and the summation indicated can consequently not be fully carried out. It is impossible to say whether the new expression would still represent the true condition of things if the stars were to perform rapid movements among one another. The general experience cannot be constructed from the particular case given us. We must, on the contrary, *wait* until such an experience presents itself. Perhaps when our

physico-astronomical knowledge has been extended, it will be offered somewhere in celestial space, where more violent and complicated motions take place than in our environment. The most important result of our reflections is, however, *that precisely the apparently simplest mechanical principles are of a very complicated character, that these principles are founded on uncompleted experiences, nay on experiences that never can be fully completed, that practically, indeed, they are sufficiently secured, in view of the tolerable stability of our environment, to serve as the foundation of mathematical deduction, but that they can by no means themselves be regarded as mathematically established truths but only as principles that not only admit of constant control by experience but actually require it.*

4

TWO SYSTEMS OF MECHANICS:

Heinrich Hertz •

The most direct, and in a sense the most important, problem which our conscious knowledge of nature should enable us to solve is the anticipation of future events, so that
we may arrange our present affairs in accordance with such
anticipation. As a basis for the solution of this problem we
always make use of our knowledge of events which have
already occurred, obtained by chance observation or by
prearranged experiment. In endeavoring thus to draw inferences as to the future from the past, we always adopt
the following process. We form for ourselves images or
symbols of external objects; and the form which we give
them is such that the necessary consequents of the images
in thought are always the images of the necessary consequents in nature of the things pictured. In order that this
requirement may be satisfied, there must be a certain conformity between nature and our thought. Experience
teaches us that the requirement can be satisfied, and hence
that such a conformity does in fact exist. When from our
accumulated previous experience we have once succeeded
in deducing images of the desired nature, we can then in
a short time develop by means of them, as by means of
models, the consequences which in the external world only

• [This selection is excerpted from the Introduction to Hertz's *The
Principles of Mechanics,* translated by D. E. Jones and J. T. Walley
(London: 1899; New York: Dover Publications, Inc., 1956), origi-
nal German edition, 1894.]

arise in a comparatively long time, or as the result of our own interposition. We are thus enabled to be in advance of the facts, and to decide as to present affairs in accordance with the insight so obtained. The images which we here speak of are our conceptions of things. With the things themselves they are in conformity in *one* important respect, namely, in satisfying the above-mentioned requirement. For our purpose it is not necessary that they should be in conformity with the things in any other respect whatever. As a matter of fact, we do not know, nor have we any means of knowing, whether our conceptions of things are in conformity with them in any other than this *one* fundamental respect.

The images which we may form of things are not determined without ambiguity by the requirement that the consequents of the images must be the images of the consequents. Various images of the same objects are possible, and these images may differ in various respects. We should at once denote as inadmissible all images which implicitly contradict the laws of our thought. Hence we postulate in the first place that all our images shall be logically permissible—or, briefly, that they shall be permissible. We shall denote as incorrect any permissible images, if their essential relations contradict the relations of external things, i.e., if they do not satisfy our first fundamental requirement. Hence we postulate in the second place that our images shall be correct. But two permissible and correct images of the same external objects may yet differ in respect of appropriateness. Of two images of the same object that is the more appropriate which pictures more of the essential relations of the object—the one which we may call the more distinct. Of two images of equal distinctness the more appropriate is the one which contains, in addition to the essential characteristics, the smaller number of superfluous or empty relations—the simpler of the two. Empty relations cannot be altogether avoided: they enter into the images because they are simply images—images produced by our mind and necessarily affected by the characteristics of its mode of portrayal.

The postulates already mentioned are those which we assign to the images themselves: to a scientific representation of the images we assign different postulates. We require of this that it should lead us to a clear conception of what properties are to be ascribed to the images for the sake of permissibility, what for correctness, and what for appropriateness. Only thus can we attain the possibility of modifying and improving our images. What is ascribed to the images for the sake of appropriateness is contained in the notations, definitions, abbreviations, and, in short, all that we can arbitrarily add or take away. What enters into the images for the sake of correctness is contained in the results of experience, from which the images are built up. What enters into the images, in order that they may be permissible, is given by the nature of our mind. To the question whether an image is permissible or not, we can without ambiguity answer yes or no; and our decision will hold good for all time. And equally without ambiguity we can decide whether an image is correct or not; but only according to the state of our present experience, and permitting an appeal to later and riper experience. But we cannot decide without ambiguity whether an image is appropriate or not; as to this differences of opinion may arise. One image may be more suitable for one purpose, another for another; only by gradually testing many images can we finally succeed in obtaining the most appropriate.

Those are, in my opinion, the standpoints from which we must estimate the value of physical theories and the value of the representations of physical theories. They are the standpoints from which we shall here consider the representations which have been given of the Principles of Mechanics. We must first explain clearly what we denote by this name.

Strictly speaking, what was originally termed in mechanics a principle was such a statement as could not be traced back to other propositions in mechanics, but was regarded as a direct result obtained from other sources of knowledge. In the course of historical development it inevitably came to pass that propositions, which at one time and under special circumstances were rightly denoted as principles, wrongly retained these names. Since Lagrange's time it has frequently been remarked that the principles of the center of gravity and of areas are in reality only propositions of a general nature. But we can with equal justice say that other so-called principles cannot bear this name, but must descend to the rank of propositions or corollaries, when the representation of mechanics becomes based upon one or more of the others. Thus the idea of a mechanical principle has not been kept sharply defined. We shall therefore retain for such propositions, when mentioning them separately, their customary names. But these separate concrete propositions are not what we shall have in mind when we speak simply and generally of the principles of mechanics: by this will be meant any selection from amongst such and similar propositions, which satisfies the requirement that the whole of mechanics can be developed from it by purely deductive reasoning without any further appeal to experience. In this sense the fundamental ideas of mechanics, together with the principles connecting them, represent the simplest image which physics can produce of things in the sensible world and the processes which occur in it. By varying the choice of the propositions which we take as fundamental, we can give various representations of the principles of mechanics. Hence we can thus obtain various images of things; and these images we can test and compare with each other in respect of permissibility, correctness, and appropriateness.

I

The customary representation of mechanics gives us a first image. By this we mean the representation, varying in detail but identical in essence, contained in almost all textbooks which deal with the whole of mechanics, and in almost all courses of lectures which cover the whole of this science. This is the path by which the great army of students travel and are inducted into the mysteries of mechanics. It closely follows the course of historical development and the sequence of discoveries. Its principal stages are distinguished by the names of Archimedes, Galileo, Newton, Lagrange. The conceptions upon which this representation is based are the ideas of space, time, force, and mass. In it force is introduced as the cause of motion, existing before motion and independently of it. Space and force first appear by themselves, and their relations are treated of in statics. Kinematics, or the science of pure motion, confines itself to connecting the two ideas of space and time. Galileo's conception of inertia furnishes a connection between space, time, and mass alone. Not until Newton's laws of motion do the four fundamental ideas become connected with each other. These laws contain the seed of future developments; but they do not furnish any general expression for the influence of rigid spacial connections. Here d'Alembert's principle extends the general results of statics to the case of motion, and closes the series of independent fundamental statements which cannot be deduced from each other. From here on everything is deductive inference. In fact the above-mentioned ideas and laws are not only necessary but sufficient for the development of the whole of mechanics from them as a necessary consequence of thought; and all other so-called principles can be regarded as propositions and corollaries deduced by special assumptions. Hence the above ideas and laws give us, in the sense in which we have used the words, a first system of principles of mechanics, and at the same time the first general image of the natural motions of material bodies.

Now, at first sight, any doubt as to the logical permissibility of this image may seem very far-fetched. It seems almost inconceivable that we should find logical imperfections in a system which has been thoroughly and repeatedly considered by many of the ablest intellects. But before we abandon the investigation on this account, we should do well to inquire whether the system has always given satisfaction to these able intellects. It is really wonderful how easy it is to attach to the fundamental laws considerations which are quite in accordance with the usual modes of expression in mechanics, and which yet are an undoubted hindrance to clear thinking. Let us endeavor to give an example of this. We swing in a circle a stone tied to a string, and in so doing we are conscious of exerting a force upon the stone. This force constantly deflects the stone from its straight path. If we vary the force, the mass of the stone, and the length of the string, we find that the actual motion of the stone is always in accordance with Newton's second law. But now the third law requires an opposing force to the force exerted by the hand upon the stone. With regard to this opposing force the usual explanation is that the stone reacts upon the hand in consequence of centrifugal force, and that this centrifugal force is in fact exactly equal and opposite to that which we exert. Now is this mode of expression permissible? Is what we call centrifugal force anything else than the inertia of the stone? Can we, without destroying the clearness of our conceptions, take the effect of inertia twice into account—firstly as mass, secondly as force? In our laws of motion, force was a cause of motion, and was present *before* the motion. Can we, without confusing our ideas, suddenly begin to speak of forces which arise through motion, which are a consequence of motion? Can we behave as if we had already asserted anything about forces of this new kind in our laws, as if by calling them forces we could invest them with the properties of forces? These questions must clearly be answered in the negative. The only possible explanation is that, properly speaking, centrifugal force is not a force at all. Its name, like the name *vis viva*, is accepted as a historic tradition; it is convenient to retain it, although we should rather apologize for its retention than endeavor to justify it. But, what now becomes of the demands of the third law, which requires a force exerted by the inert stone upon the hand, and which can only be satisfied by an actual force, not a mere name?

I do not regard these as artificial difficulties wantonly raised: they are objections which press for an answer. Is not their origin to be traced back to the fundamental laws? The force spoken of in the definition and in the first two laws acts upon a body in one definite direction. The sense of the third law is that forces always connect two bodies, and are directed from the first to the second as well as from the second to the first. It seems to me that the conception of force assumed and created in us by the third law on the one hand, and the first two laws on the other hand, are slightly different. This slight difference may be enough to produce the logical obscurity of which the consequences are manifest in the above example. It is not necessary to discuss further examples. We can appeal to general observations as evidence in support of the above-mentioned doubt.

As such, in the first place, I would mention the experience that it is exceedingly difficult to expound to thoughtful hearers the very introduction to mechanics without being occasionally embarrassed, without feeling tempted now and again to apologize, without wishing to get as quickly as possible over the rudiments, and on to examples which speak for themselves. I fancy that Newton himself must have felt this embarrassment when he gave the rather forced definition of mass as being the product of volume and density. I fancy that Thomson and Tait must also have felt it when they remarked that this is really more a definition of density than of mass, and nevertheless contented themselves with it as the only definition of mass. Lagrange, too, must have felt this embarrassment and the wish to get on at all costs; for he briefly introduces his Mechanics with the explanation that a force is a cause which imparts "or tends to impart" motion to a body; and he must certainly have felt the logical difficulty of such a definition. I find further evidence in the demonstrations of the elementary propositions of statics, such as the law of the parallelogram of forces, of virtual velocities, etc. Of such propositions we have numerous proofs given by eminent mathematicians. These claim to be rigid proofs; but, according to the opinion of other distinguished mathematicians, they in no way satisfy this claim. In a logically complete science, such as pure mathematics, such a difference of opinion is utterly inconceivable.

Weighty evidence seems to be furnished by the statements which one hears with wearisome frequency, that the nature of force is still a mystery, that one of the chief problems of physics is the investigation of the nature of force, and so on. In the same way electricians are continually attacked as to the nature of electricity. Now, why is it that people never in this way ask what is the nature of gold, or what is the nature of velocity? Is the nature of gold better known to us than that of electricity, or the nature of velocity better than that of force? Can we by our conceptions, by our words, completely represent the nature of any thing? Certainly not. I fancy the difference must lie in this. With the terms "velocity" and "gold" we connect a large number of relations to other terms; and between all these relations we find no contradictions which offend us. We are therefore satisfied and ask no further questions. But we have accumulated around the terms "force" and "electricity" more relations than can be completely reconciled amongst themselves. We have an obscure feeling of this and want to have things cleared up. Our confused wish finds expression in the confused question as to the nature of force and electricity. But the answer which we want is not really an answer to this question. It is not by finding out more and fresh relations and connections that it can be answered; but by removing the contradictions existing between those already known, and thus perhaps by reducing their number. When these painful contradictions are removed, the question as to the nature of force will not have been answered; but our minds, no longer vexed, will cease to ask illegitimate questions.

I have thrown such strong doubts upon the permissibility of this image that it might appear to be my intention to contest, and finally to deny, its permissibility. But my intention and conviction do not go so far as this. Even if the logical uncertainties, which have made us solicitous as to our fundamental ideas, do actually exist, they certainly have not prevented a single one of the numerous triumphs which mechanics has won in its applications. Hence, they cannot consist of contradictions between the essential characteristics of our image, nor, therefore, of contradictions between those relations of mechanics which correspond to the relations of things. They must rather lie in the unessential characteristics which we have ourselves arbitrarily worked into the essential, content given by nature. If so, these dilemmas can be avoided. Perhaps our objections do not relate to the content of the image devised, but only to the form in which the content is represented. It is not going too far to say that this representation has never attained scientific completeness; it still fails to distinguish thoroughly and sharply between the elements in the image which arise from the necessities of thought, from experience, and from arbitrary choice. This is also the opinion of distinguished physicists who have thought over and discussed these questions, although it cannot be said that all of them are in agreement. This opinion also finds confirmation in the increasing care with which the logical analysis of the elements is carried out in the more recent textbooks of mechanics. We are convinced, as are the authors of these textbooks and the physicists referred to, that the existing defects are only defects in form; and that all indistinctness and uncertainty can be avoided by suitable arrangement of definitions and notations, and by due care in the mode of expression. In this sense we admit, as everyone does, the permissibility of the content of mechanics. But the dignity and importance of the subject demand, not simply that we should readily take for granted its logical clearness, but that we should endeavor to show it by a representation so perfect that there should no longer be any possibility of doubting it.

Upon the correctness of the image under consideration we can pronounce judgment more easily and with greater certainty of general assent. No one will deny that within the whole range of our experience up to the present the correctness is perfect; that all those characteristics of our image, which claim to represent observable relations of things, do really and correctly correspond to them. Our assurance, of course, is restricted to the range of previous experience: as far as future experience is concerned, there will yet be occasion to return to the question of correctness. To many this will seem to be excessive and absurd caution: to many physicists it appears simply inconceivable that any further experience whatever should find anything to alter in the firm foundations of mechanics. Nevertheless, that which is derived from experience can again be annulled by experience. This overfavorable opinion of the fundamental laws must obviously arise from the fact that the elements of experience are to a certain extent hidden in them and blended with the unalterable elements which are necessary consequences of our thought. Thus the logical indefiniteness of the representation, which we have just censured, has one advantage. It gives the foundations an appearance of immutability; and perhaps it was wise to introduce it in the beginnings of the science and to allow it to remain for a while. The correctness of the image in all cases was carefully provided for by making the reservation that, if need be, facts derived from experience should determine definitions or vice versa. In a perfect science such groping, such an appearance of certainty, is inadmissible. Mature knowledge regards logical clearness as of prime importance: only logically clear images does it test as to correctness; only correct images does it compare as to appropriateness. By pressure of circumstances the process is often reversed. Images are found to be suitable for a certain purpose; are next tested as to their correctness; and only in the last place purged of implied contradictions.

If there is any truth in what we have just stated, it seems only natural that the system of mechanics under consideration should prove most appropriate in its applications to those simple phenomena for which it was first devised, i.e., especially to the action of gravity and the problems of practical mechanics. But we should not be content with this. We should remember that we are not here representing the needs of daily life or the standpoint of past times; we are considering the whole range of present physical knowledge, and are, moreover, speaking of appropriateness

in the special sense defined in the beginning of this introduction. Hence we are at once bound to ask—Is this image
perfectly distinct? Does it contain all the characteristics
which our present knowledge enables us to distinguish in
natural motions? Our answer is a decided—No. All the motions of which the fundamental laws admit, and which
are treated of in mechanics as mathematical exercises, do
not occur in nature. Of natural motions, forces, and fixed
connections, we can predicate more than the accepted fundamental laws do. Since the middle of this century we have
been firmly convinced that no forces actually exist in nature
which would involve a violation of the principle of the
conservation of energy. The conviction is much older that
only such forces exist as can be represented as a sum of
mutual actions between infinitely small elements of matter.
Again, these elementary forces are not free. We can assert
as a property which they are generally admitted to possess
that they are independent of absolute time and place. Other
properties are disputed. Whether the elementary forces can
only consist of attractions and repulsions along the line connecting the acting masses; whether their magnitude is
determined only by the distance or whether it is also
affected by the absolute or relative velocity; whether the
latter alone comes into consideration, or the acceleration or
still higher differential coefficients as well—all these properties have been sometimes presumed, at other times questioned. Although there is such difference of opinion as to the
precise properties which are to be attributed to the elementary forces, there is a general agreement that more of such
general properties can be assigned, and can from existing
observations be deduced, than are contained in the fundamental laws. We are convinced that the elementary forces
must, so to speak, be of a simple nature. And what here
holds for the forces, can be equally asserted of the fixed
connections of bodies which are represented mathematically by equations of condition between the coordinates
and whose effect is determined by d'Alembert's principle.
It is mathematically possible to write down any finite or
differential equation between coordinates and to require
that it shall be satisfied; but it is not always possible to
specify a natural, physical connection corresponding to such
an equation: we often feel, indeed sometimes are convinced, that such a connection is by the nature of things
excluded. And yet, how are we to restrict the permissible

equations of condition? Where is the limiting line between them and the conceivable ones? To consider only finite equations of condition, as has often been done, is to go too far; for differential equations which are not integrable can actually occur as equations of condition in natural problems.

In short, then, so far as the forces, as well as the fixed relations, are concerned, our system of principles embraces all the natural motions; but it also includes very many motions which are not natural. A system which excludes the latter, or even a part of them, would picture more of the actual relations of things to each other, and would therefore in this sense be more appropriate. We are next bound to inquire as to the appropriateness of our image in a second direction. Is our image simple? Is it sparing in unessential characteristics—ones added by ourselves, permissibly and yet arbitrarily, to the essential and natural ones? In answering this question our thoughts again turn to the idea of force. It cannot be denied that in very many cases the forces which are used in mechanics for treating physical problems are simply sleeping partners, which keep out of the business altogether when actual facts have to be represented. In the simple relations with which mechanics originally dealt, this is not the case. The weight of a stone and the force exerted by the arm seem to be as real and as readily and directly perceptible as the motions which they produce. But it is otherwise when we turn to the motions of the stars. Here the forces have never been the objects of direct perception; all our previous experiences relate only to the apparent position of the stars. Nor do we expect in future to perceive the forces. The future experiences which we anticipate again relate only to the position of these luminous points in the heavens. It is only in the deduction of future experiences from the past that the forces of gravitation enter as transitory aids in the calculation, and then disappear from consideration. Precisely the same is true of the discussion of molecular forces, of chemical actions, and of many electric and magnetic actions. And if after more mature experience we return to the simple forces, whose existence we never doubted, we learn that these forces which we had perceived with convincing certainty were after all not real. More mature mechanics tells us that what we believed to be simply the tendency of a body toward the earth, is not really such: it is the result, imagined only

as a single force, of an inconceivable number of actual
forces which attract the atoms of the body toward all the
atoms of the universe. Here again the actual forces have
never been the objects of previous experience; nor do we
expect to come across them in future experiences. Only
during the process of deducing future experiences from the
past do they glide quietly in and out. But even if the forces
have only been introduced by ourselves into nature, we
should not on that account regard their introduction as inappropriate. We have felt sure from the beginning that unessential relations could not be altogether avoided in our
images. All that we can ask is that these relations should,
as far as possible, be restricted, and that a wise discretion
should be observed in their use. But has physics always
been sparing in the use of such relations? Has it not rather
been compelled to fill the world to overflowing with forces
of the most various kinds—with forces which never appeared in the phenomena, even with forces which only
came into action in exceptional cases? We see a piece of iron
resting upon a table, and we accordingly imagine that no
causes of motion—no forces—are there present. Physics, which
is based upon the mechanics considered here and necessarily
determined by this basis, teaches us otherwise. Through the
force of gravitation every atom of the iron is attracted by
every other atom in the universe. But every atom of the
iron is magnetic, and is thus connected by fresh forces with
every other magnetic atom in the universe. Again, bodies
in the universe contain electricity in motion, and this latter
exerts further complicated forces which attract every atom
of the iron. Insofar as the parts of the iron themselves contain
electricity, we have fresh forces to take into consideration;
and in addition to these again various kinds of molecular
forces. Some of these forces are not small: if only a part of
these forces were effective, this part would suffice to tear
the iron to pieces. But, in fact, all the forces are so adjusted
amongst each other that the effect of the whole lot is zero;
that in spite of a thousand existing causes of motion, no
motion takes place; that the iron remains at rest. Now if
we place these conceptions before unprejudiced persons,
who will believe us? Whom shall we convince that we
are speaking of actual things, not images of a riotous imagination? And it is for us to reflect whether we have really
depicted the state of rest of the iron and its particles in a
simple manner. Whether complications can be entirely

avoided is questionable; but there can be no question that a system of mechanics which does avoid or exclude them is simpler, and in this sense more appropriate, than the one here considered; for this latter not only permits such conceptions, but directly obtrudes them upon us.

Let us now collect together as briefly as possible the doubts which have occurred to us in considering the customary mode of representing the principles of mechanics. As far as the form is concerned, we consider that the logical value of the separate statements is not defined with sufficient clearness. As far as the facts are concerned, it appears to us that the motions considered in mechanics do not exactly coincide with the natural motions under consideration. Many properties of the natural motions are not attended to in mechanics; many relations which are considered in mechanics are probably absent in nature. Even if these objections are acknowledged to be well founded, they should not lead us to imagine that the customary representation of mechanics is on that account either bound to or likely to lose its value and its privileged position; but they sufficiently justify us in looking out for other representations less liable to censure in these respects, and more closely conformable to the things which have to be represented.

II

There is a second image of mechanical processes which is of much more recent origin than the first. Its development from, and side by side with, the latter is closely connected with advances which physical science has made during the past few decades. Up to the middle of this century its ultimate aim was apparently to explain natural phenomena by tracing them back to innumerable actions-at-a-distance between the atoms of matter. This mode of conception corresponded completely to what we have spoken of as the first system of mechanical principles: each of the two was conditioned by the other. Now, toward the end of the century, physics has shown a preference for a different mode of thought. Influenced by the overpowering impression made by the discovery of the principle of the conservation of energy, it likes to treat the phenomena which occur in its domain as transformations of energy into new forms, and to regard as its ultimate aim the tracing back of the phenomena to the laws of the transformation of energy. This mode of treatment can also be applied from the beginning to the elementary phenomena of motion. There thus arises a new and different representation of mechanics, in which from the start the idea of force retires in favor of the idea of energy. It is this new image of the elementary processes of motion which we shall denote as the second; and to it we shall now devote our attention. In discussing the first image we had the advantage of being able to assume that it stood out plainly before the eyes of all physicists. With the second image this is not the case. It has never yet been portrayed in all its details. So far as I know, there is no text-book of mechanics which from the start teaches the subject from the standpoint of energy, and introduces the idea of energy before the idea of force. Perhaps there has never yet been a lecture on mechanics prepared according to this plan. But to the founders of the theory of energy it was evident that such a plan was possible; the remark has often been made that in this way the idea of force with its attendant difficulties could be avoided; and in special scientific applications chains of reasoning frequently occur which belong entirely to this mode of thought. Hence we can very well sketch the rough outlines of the image; we can give the general plan according to which such a representation of mechanics must be arranged. We here start, as in the case of the first image, from four independent fundamental ideas; and the relations of these to each other will form the contents of mechanics. Two of them—space and time— have a mathematical character; the other two—mass and energy—are introduced as physical entities which are present in given quantity, and cannot be destroyed or increased. In addition to explaining these matters, it will, of course, also be necessary to indicate clearly by what concrete experiences we ultimately establish the presence of mass and energy. We here assume this to be possible and to be done. It is obvious that the amount of energy connected with given masses depends upon the state of these masses. But it is as a general experience that we must first lay down that the energy present can always be split up into two parts, of which the one is determined solely by the relative positions of the masses, while the other depends upon their absolute velocities. The first part is defined as potential energy, the second as kinetic energy. The form of the dependence of kinetic energy upon the velocity of the moving bodies is in all cases the same, and is known. The form of the dependence of potential energy upon the position of the bodies cannot be generally stated; it rather constitutes the special nature and characteristic peculiarity of the masses under consideration. It is the problem of physics to ascertain from previous experience this form for the bodies which surround us in nature. Up to this point there come essentially into consideration only three elements—space, mass, energy, considered in relation to each other. In order to settle the relations of all the four fundamental ideas, and thereby the course in time of the phenomena, we make use of one of the integral principles of ordinary mechanics which involve in their statement the idea of energy. It is not of much importance which of these we select; we can and shall choose Hamilton's principle. We thus lay down as the sole fundamental law of mechanics, in accordance with experience, the proposition that every system of natural bodies moves just as if it were assigned the problem of attaining given positions in given times, and in such a manner that the average over the whole time of the difference between kinetic and potential energy shall be as small as possible. Although this law may not be simple in form, it nevertheless represents without ambiguity the transformations of energy, and enables us to predetermine completely the course of actual phenomena for the future. In stating this new law we lay down the last of the indispensable foundations of mechanics. All that we can further add are only mathematical deductions and certain simplifications of notation which, although expedient, are not necessary. Among these latter is the idea of force, which does not enter into the foundations. Its introduction is expedient when we are considering not only masses which are connected with constant quantities of energy but also masses which give up energy to other masses or receive it from them. Still, it is not by any new experience that it is introduced, but by a definition which can be formed in more than one way. And accordingly the properties of the force so defined are not to be ascertained by experience, but are to be deduced from the definition and the fundamental laws. Even the confirmation of these properties by experience is superfluous, unless we doubt the correctness of the whole system. Hence the idea of force as such cannot in this system involve any logical difficulties: nor can it come in question in estimating the correctness of the system; it can only increase or diminish its appropriateness.

Somewhat after the manner indicated would the principles of mechanics have to be arranged in order to adapt them to the conception of energy. The question now is, whether this second image is preferable to the first. . . .

In order that an image of certain external things may in our sense be permissible, not only must its characteristics be consistent amongst themselves but they must not contradict the characteristics of other images already established in our knowledge. On the strength of this it may be said to be inconceivable that Hamilton's principle, or any similar proposition, should really play the part of a fundamental law of mechanics, and be a fundamental law of nature. For the first thing that is to be expected of a fundamental law is simplicity and plainness, whereas Hamilton's principle, when we come to look into it, proves to be an exceedingly complicated statement. Not only does it make the present motion dependent upon consequences which can only exhibit themselves in the future, thereby attributing intentions to inanimate nature; but, what is much worse, it attributes to nature intentions which are void of meaning. For the integral whose minimum is required by Hamilton's principle, has no simple physical meaning; and for nature it is an unintelligible aim to make a mathematical expression a minimum, or to bring its variation to zero. The usual answer, which physics nowadays keeps ready for such attacks, is that these considerations are based upon metaphysical assumptions; that physics has renounced these, and no longer recognizes it as its duty to meet the demands of metaphysics. It no longer attaches weight to the reasons which used to be urged from the metaphysical side in favor of principles which indicate design in nature, and thus it cannot lend ear to objections of a metaphysical character against these same principles. If we had to decide upon such a matter we should not think it unfair to place ourselves rather on the side of the attack than of the defense. A doubt which makes an impression on our mind cannot be removed by calling it metaphysical; every thoughtful mind as such has needs which scientific men are accustomed to denote as metaphysical. Moreover, in the case in question, as indeed in all others, it is possible to show what are the sound and just sources of our needs. It is true we cannot *a priori* demand from nature simplicity, nor can we judge what in her opinion is simple. But with regard to images of our own creation we can lay down requirements. We are justified in deciding that if our images are well adapted to the things, the actual relations of the things must be represented by simple relations between the images. And if the actual relations between the things can only be represented by complicated relations, which are not even intelligible to an unprepared mind, we decide that these images are not sufficiently well adapted to the things. Hence our requirement of simplicity does not apply to nature, but to the images thereof which we fashion; and our repugnance to a complicated statement as a fundamental law only expresses the conviction that, if the contents of the statement are correct and comprehensive, it can be stated in a simpler form by a more suitable choice of the fundamental conceptions. The same conviction finds expression in the desire we feel to penetrate from the external acquaintance with such a law to the deeper and real meaning which we are convinced it possesses. If this conception is correct, the objection brought forward does really justify a doubt as to the system; but it does not apply so much to its permissibility as to its appropriateness, and comes under consideration in deciding as to the latter. However, we need not return to the consideration of this.

If we once more glance over the merits which we were able to claim for this second image, we come to the conclusion that as a whole it is not quite satisfactory. Although the whole tendency of recent physics moves us to place the idea of energy in the foreground, and to use it as the cornerstone of our structure, it yet remains doubtful whether in so doing we can avoid the harshness and ruggedness which were so disagreeable in the first image. In fact I have discussed this second mode of representation at some length, not in order to urge its adoption, but rather to show why, after due trial, I have felt obliged to abandon it.

5

HERTZ ON CLASSICAL MECHANICS:
Henri Poincaré •

1. *Definition of force.* The first attempt at coordinating the facts of mechanics we shall call *the classical system.* It is, says Hertz, "the royal highway whose principal way-stations bear the names of Archimedes, Galileo, Newton and Lagrange. The fundamental notions that we find at the point of departure are those of *space, time, force* and *mass.* Force, in this system, is regarded as the cause of motion. It exists prior to motion and is independent of it."

I shall try to explain for what reasons Hertz was dissatisfied with this manner of considering things.

We have, first of all, the difficulties one encounters when one wishes to define the fundamental notions. What is *mass?* Newton replies that it is the product of volume by density. It would be better to say, reply Thomson and Tait, that density is the quotient of mass divided by volume. What is *force?* It is, replies Lagrange, a cause which produces motion of a body or which tends to produce it. Kirchhoff will say that it is the product of mass by *acceleration.* But then, why not say that mass is the quotient of force divided by acceleration?

• [This selection is extracted from Poincaré's review of Hertz's *Principles of Mechanics,* which appeared in the *Revue générale des sciences,* t.8, pp. 734–43 (1897), and was subsequently reprinted in Poincaré's *Oeuvres* (Paris: 1952), t.vii. It is especially translated for this volume by Arnold Miller of the Department of French, Columbia University.]

These difficulties are inextricable.

To say that force is the cause of motion is to talk metaphysics, and this definition, if we were content to look no further, would be absolutely sterile. For a definition to be of some use, it must tell us how to *measure* force. Moreover, that is all it need do. It is not at all necessary that it tell us what force is in itself, nor whether it is the cause or the effect of motion.

We must therefore first define the equality of two forces. When will we say that two forces are equal? They are equal, we may be tempted to reply, when, applied to the same mass, they impart to it the same acceleration, or when, directly opposed to each other, they are in equilibrium. This definition is nothing but an optical illusion, however. You cannot unhook a force applied to a body and hook it to another body as you would unhook a locomotive and attach it to another train. It is therefore impossible to know what acceleration a given force, applied to a given body, would impart to another given body, *if* it were applied to it. It is impossible to know how two forces which are not directly opposed would behave *if* they were directly opposed.

It is this definition that is embodied, so to speak, when we measure a force with a dynamometer, or by setting it in equilibrium with a weight. Two forces F and F', which I shall suppose for the sake of simplicity to be directed vertically upwards, are applied respectively to two bodies C and C'; I suspend the same body weighing P, first to body C, then to body C'; if equilibrium results in both cases, I shall conclude that the two forces F and F' are equal to each other, since they are both equal to the weight of body P.

But am I sure that the body P has kept the same weight when I transferred it from the first body to the second? Far from it; *in fact, I am sure of the contrary.* I know that the intensity of gravity varies from one point to another, that it is stronger, for example, at the pole than at the equator. The difference is doubtless very small, and in practice I shall disregard it. But a well-made definition ought to have mathematical rigor; this rigor does not exist. What I have said about the weight would clearly apply to the force of the spring of a dynamometer, which will vary with the temperature and a multitude of other circumstances.

This is not all. We cannot say that the weight of body

P is applied to body *C* and results in direct equilibrium with force *F*. What is applied to body *C* is the action *A* of body *P* on body *C*. Body *P* itself is acted upon, on the one hand, by its own weight, and on the other, by the reaction *R* of body *C* on *P*. In the last analysis, force *F* equals force *A*, because the two are in equilibrium; force *A* equals *R*, by virtue of the principle of the equality of action and reaction; finally, force *R* equals the weight of *P*, because the two are in equilibrium. It is from these three equalities that we deduce as a consequence the equality of *F* and the weight of *P*.

We are therefore obliged to bring into the definition of the equality of two forces the principle of the equality of action and reaction. *On this account, this principle should no longer be regarded as an experimental law, but as a definition.*

Thus, to recognize the equality of two forces, we find ourselves in possession of two rules: equality of two forces in equilibrium; equality of action and reaction. But, as we have seen above, these two rules do not suffice. We must have recourse to a third rule and assume that certain forces —for example, the weight of a body—are constant in magnitude and in direction. But this third rule, as I have said, is an experimental law; it is only approximately true; *it is a bad definition.*

So we come back to Kirchhoff's definition: *force is equal to mass multiplied by acceleration.* This "Newtonian law" ceases in its turn to be regarded as an experimental law. It is nothing but a definition. But this definition is still insufficient, since we do not know what mass is. It does indeed permit us to calculate the relationship between two forces applied to the same body at different instants; but it tells us nothing about the relationship between two forces applied to two different bodies.

To complete this definition, we must again have recourse to Newton's third law (equality of action and reaction), again regarded, not as an experimental law, but as a definition. Two bodies *A* and *B* act upon each other. The acceleration of *A* multiplied by the mass of *A* is equal to the action of *B* on *A*. Likewise, the product of the acceleration of *B* by its mass is equal to the reaction of *A* on *B*. Since, by definition, the action is equal to the reaction, the masses of *A* and *B* are in inverse ratio to the accelerations of these two bodies. This defines the relationship between these two masses and experiment must determine whether this relationship is constant.

All would be well if the two bodies A and B were the only ones present and were exempt from the action of the rest of the world. But nothing of the kind is true. The acceleration of A is due not only to the action of B, but to that of a multitude of other bodies C, D, ... To apply the preceding rule, we must therefore resolve the acceleration of A into several components and determine which one of these components is due to the action of B.

This resolution would be possible if we *assumed* that the action of C on A is simply added to that of B on A, that the presence of body C does not modify the action of B on A, that the presence of B does not modify the action of C on A; if we assumed, consequently, that any two bodies attract each other, that their mutual action is directed along the straight line that joins them and depends only on their distance; if we assumed, in a word, *the hypothesis of central forces.*

It is well known that, to determine the masses of celestial bodies, we use an entirely different principle. The law of gravitation tells us that the attraction of two bodies is proportional to their masses. If r is their distance, m and m' their masses, and k a constant, their attraction will be $\dfrac{kmm'}{r^2}$.

What we are measuring, then, is not mass, considered as a relationship between force and acceleration, but attractive mass; not the inertia of a body, but its attractive power.

This is an indirect procedure, use of which is theoretically not indispensable. It could very well have been the case that attraction was inversely proportional to the square of the distance without being proportional to the product of the masses. We would have had the attraction equal to $\dfrac{f}{r^2}$, but not

$$f = kmm'.$$

If this were so, we could nonetheless measure the masses of the celestial bodies by observing their *relative* motion.

But have we the right to assume the hypothesis of central forces? Is this hypothesis rigorously true? Is it certain that it will never be contradicted by experience? Who would dare say so? And if we must abandon this hypothesis, the whole laboriously constructed edifice will crumble.

We no longer have the right to speak of the component of the acceleration of A that is due to the action of B. We have no way of distinguishing it from the component due to the action of C or of another body. The rule for the measurement of masses becomes inapplicable.

What remains, then, of the principle of the equality of action and reaction? If the hypothesis of central forces is rejected, this principle must then be stated as follows: The geometric resultant of all forces applied to the various bodies of a system exempt from all exterior action will be null. Or, in other words, *the motion of the center of gravity of this system will be rectilinear and uniform.*

Here, it would seem, is a way of defining mass. The position of the center of gravity depends, clearly, on the values attributed to the masses. These values will have to be distributed in such a way that the motion of this center of gravity is rectilinear and uniform. This will always be possible if Newton's third law is true, and it will be possible, in general, in only one way.

But there exists no system exempt from all exterior action. All parts of the Universe are subject, more or less strongly, to the action of all the other parts. *The law of the motion of the center of gravity is rigorously true only if it is applied to the Universe as a whole.*

But then, in order to find the values of the masses, we would have to observe the motion of the center of gravity of the Universe. The absurdity of this consequence is manifest. We know only relative motion. The motion of the center of gravity of the Universe will remain for us an eternal unknown.

So nothing is left and our efforts have been fruitless. We are driven to the following definition, which is only an admission of impotence: *Masses are coefficients which it is convenient to introduce into our calculations.*

We could reconstruct all of mechanics, attributing different values to all masses. This new mechanics would contradict neither experience nor the general principles of dynamics (principle of inertia, proportionality of forces to masses and to accelerations, equality of action and reaction, rectilinear and uniform motion of the center of gravity, principle of areas).

However, the equations of this new mechanics would be *less simple*. It is evident, though, that only the first terms would be less simple, i.e., those terms which we have already come to know by experiment. Perhaps one could alter the masses by small amounts without causing the *complete* equations to gain or lose in simplicity.

I have gone into this discussion at even greater length than Hertz himself, for I was concerned to show clearly that Hertz was not simply picking a trivial quarrel with Galileo and Newton. We must conclude that with the classical system *it is impossible to give a satisfactory idea of force and mass*.

2. *Various objections.* Hertz then asks whether the principles of mechanics are rigorously true. "In the opinion of many physicists," he says, "it will appear inconceivable that any experience, however remote, will ever be able to alter the unshakable principles of mechanics; and yet, that which arises from experience can always be corrected by experience."

After what we have just said, these fears will seem superfluous. The principles of dynamics at first appear to us as experimental truths; but we have been obliged to use them as definitions. It is *by definition* that force is equal to the product of mass by acceleration. This principle is therefore beyond the reach of any ulterior experience. It is likewise by definition that action equals reaction.

But then, one may say, these unverifiable principles are absolutely devoid of all meaning. Experience cannot contradict them; but they cannot tell us anything useful. So what is the good of studying dynamics?

This too-hasty condemnation would be unjust. There is in Nature no system that is *perfectly* isolated, perfectly exempt from all exterior action, but there are *approximately* isolated systems.

If we observe such a system, we can study not only the relative motion of its various parts with respect to each other, but the motion of its center of gravity with respect to the other parts of the Universe. We then observe that the motion of this center of gravity is *approximately* rectilinear and uniform, in conformity to Newton's third law.

Here we have an experimental truth, but one that is not disconfirmable by experience. For what, in point of fact, would more precise experiments tell us? They would tell us that the law was only approximately true; but this we already knew.

We can now understand how experience has served as the basis for the principles of mechanics and yet will never be able to contradict them.

But let us return to Hertz's argument. The classical system is incomplete, since not all motions compatible with the principles of dynamics are realized in Nature, nor are they even realizable. Indeed, it is evident that the principle of areas and the principle of the motion of the center of gravity are not the only laws governing natural phenomena. It would of course be unreasonable to demand that dynamics should embrace in a single formula all the laws that physics has discovered or will be able to discover. But it is nonetheless true that one must regard as incomplete and insufficient a system of mechanics in which the principles of the conservation of energy is not even mentioned.

"Our system," Hertz concludes, "does embrace *all* natural motions, but at the same time it embraces many others that are not natural. A system which will exclude some of these motions will be in better conformity with the nature of things and will therefore constitute a step forward." An example of such a system is the energetic system. . . . This system introduces quite naturally the fundamental principle of the conservation of energy.

It may perhaps not be easy to understand what prevents us from simply annexing this fundamental principle to the other principles of the classical system.

But Hertz poses another question:

The classical system gives us a picture of the external world. Is this picture *simple?* Has it avoided parasitical features introduced arbitrarily alongside essential features? Are we sure that the forces that we are led to introduce are not in reality useless gear-wheels, turning in a vacuum?

On this table rests a piece of iron. An unprejudiced observer might believe that, since there is no motion, there is no force. How mistaken he would be! Physics teaches us that every atom of the iron is attracted by all the other atoms in the Universe. Moreover, each atom of the iron is magnetic and is therefore subject to the action of all the magnets in the Universe. All the electric currents in the world also act on this atom. Then there are electrostatic forces, molecular forces, etc.

If some of these forces acted alone, their effect would be enormous. The piece of iron would fly in fragments. Fortunately, they are all acting and counterbalancing each other, so that nothing at all happens. Your unprejudiced observer, who sees only one thing, a piece of iron at rest, will of course conclude that all these forces exist only in your imagination.

All these suppositions are, doubtless, not in the least absurd, but a system that would rid us of them would be, on that account alone, better than our own.

It is impossible not to be struck by the scope of this objection. Moreover, to show that it is not purely artificial, permit me to remind you of a controversy that occurred several years ago between two very eminent scientists, Von Helmholtz and M. Bertrand, over the mutual actions of currents. In the course of trying to translate Von Helmholtz's theory into classical language, M. Bertrand came up against insoluble contradictions. Each element of the current was supposed to be acted upon by a couple. But a couple is composed of two parallel, equal, and oppositely directed forces. M. Bertrand calculated that each of the two components must be considerable—great enough to bring about the destruction of the wire; and he concluded that the theory must be rejected. Von Helmholtz, on the contrary, being a partisan of the energetic system, saw no difficulty in this.

Thus, according to Hertz, the classical system must be abandoned:

1. because a good definition of force is impossible;

2. because it is incomplete;

3. because it introduces parasitical hypotheses; and these hypotheses can often give rise to purely artificial difficulties, which are nevertheless serious enough to give pause to the best minds. . . .

6

GEOMETRY AND SPACE:
Henri Poincaré •

In an article I published in the *Revue générale des sciences*, ⁙. ii., p. 774, on the subject of non-Euclidean geometry, I wrote the following sentences:

Beings with a mind made like ours, with the same senses that we have, but without any prior education, could receive from a properly selected world impressions such that they would be led to construct a geometry different from Euclid's and to localize the phenomena of that exterior world in a non-Euclidean space or even in a four-dimensional space.

For us, educated in this present world, if we were suddenly transported into that new world, we would have no difficulty in relating its phenomena to our Euclidean space.

A man who devoted his life to it could perhaps succeed in picturing to himself a fourth dimension.

I did not follow this up with any further clarification and it must have astonished several readers; it seems to me therefore that it is necessary to develop my thought and that I owe some explanations to the public.

Geometric space and representative space. We often say that the images of external objects are localized in space, and even that only on that condition can they be formed.

• [This selection first appeared as an article, "*L'Espace et la géométrie,*" in *Revue de métaphysique et de morale*, 1895 t.iii, pp. 631–46. It was especially translated for this volume by William Ryding of the Department of French, Columbia University.]

We also say that this space, which thus serves as a *frame* prepared in advance for our sensations and representations, is identical with that of the geometricians and that it possesses all the same properties.

To all the good people who [think that way], the sentence cited above must indeed have seemed quite extraordinary. But we ought to see whether they might not be under some illusion that a thorough analysis might dispel.

First, what are, strictly speaking, the properties of space? I mean the space that is the object of geometry and which I call *geometric space*. Here are some of the more essential:

1. It is continuous;
2. It is infinite;
3. It has three dimensions;
4. It is homogeneous, that is to say that all its points are identical to one another;
5. It is isotropic, that is to say that all the straight lines passing through a given point are identical to one another.

•   •   •   •

Solid bodies and geometry. Among the objects that surround us, there are some that frequently undergo displacements susceptible to correction by a *correlative* movement of our own bodies; they are the *solid bodies.*

Other objects, whose form is variable, only exceptionally undergo similar displacements (change of position without change of form). When a body moves and in so doing *changes its form*, we can no longer by appropriate movements bring our sense organs back into the same *relative* situation with respect to that body; we can no longer, consequently, re-establish the original set of impressions.

It is only later on and after a series of new experiences that we learn to seperate bodies of variable form into smaller elements such that each of them moves in approximate accordance with the laws of motion of solid bodies. We thus distinguish "deformations" from other changes of state; in these deformations each element undergoes a simple change of position, which can be corrected, but the modification of the ensemble is more profound and can no longer be corrected by a correlative movement.

Such an idea is already very complex and could only have appeared relatively late. It could moreover not have arisen if the observation of solid bodies had not already taught us to distinguish changes of position.

If, therefore, there were no solid bodies in nature, there would be no geometry.

Another remark also merits a moment of attention. Let us imagine a solid body first occupying position a and passing afterward to position b; in its first position, it would cause us to receive a set of impressions A, and in its second position a set of impressions B. Now let there be a second solid body having qualities entirely different from the first, for example a different color. Now let us suppose that it passes from position a, where we receive the set of impressions A', to position b, where we receive the set of impressions B'.

In general set A will have nothing in common with set A', nor set B with set B'. The passage from set A to set B and that from set A' to set B' are therefore two changes which in themselves have in general nothing in common.

And yet we consider both these changes as displacements, and what is more, we consider them as the *same* displacement. How can that be?

It is simply because we can correct both by the same correlative movement of our body.

It is therefore the correlative movement which constitutes the *only link* between two phenomena that it would not otherwise have occurred to us to compare.

On the other hand, our bodies, thanks to the number of their joints and muscles, can go through a host of different movements; but not all are capable of "correcting" a modification of external objects; those only are capable of it in which our whole body, or at the very least, all the sense organs involved, move *en bloc*, that is to say, like a solid body without varying their relative positions.

In summary:

1. We are first led to distinguish two categories of phenomena: Some, involuntary, not accompanied by muscular sensations, are attributed by us to exterior objects; they are external changes. Others, whose qualities are opposite and which we attribute to the movements of our own body, are internal changes.

2. We notice that certain changes of each of these categories can be corrected by a correlative change in the other category.

3. We distinguish, among external changes, those that have also a correlative in the other category; we call these displacements; and likewise among the internal changes we

distinguish those that have a correlative in the first category.

We have thus defined, thanks to this reciprocity, a particular class of phenomena that we call displacements. *It is the laws of these phenomena that are the object of geometry.*

The law of homogeneity. The first of these laws is that of homogeneity. Let us suppose that, by an external change *a*, we were to pass from a set of impressions *A* to set *B*, then that this change were corrected by a voluntary correlative movement *b* such that we were brought back to set *A*.

Let us suppose now that another external change *a'* caused us again to pass from set *A* to set *B*.

Experience teaches us that this change *a'* is, like *a*, susceptible to correction by a voluntary movement *b'*, and that this voluntary movement *b'* corresponds to the same muscular sensations as the movement *b* which corrected *a*. It is this fact that we normally have in mind when we say that *space is homogeneous and isotropic.*

We can also say that a movement that occurs once can be repeated a second time, a third time, and so on, without its properties varying.

Those readers who know the article I wrote in this journal on the nature of mathematical reasoning will perhaps remember the importance that I attribute to the possibility of indefinitely repeating a single operation.

It is from this repetition that mathematical reasoning draws its strength; it is thanks to the law of homogeneity which it has taken from geometric facts.

To be complete, we should annex to the law of homogeneity a host of other analogous laws into the details of which I do not wish to enter, but which mathematicians subsume into a single word by saying that displacements form a "group."

The number of dimensions. I feel more difficulty in explaining my thought concerning the origin of the notion of point and the number of dimensions: it is markedly different from opinions generally accepted and it is not easy to state it in ordinary language.

We understand displacements in terms of the passage from a set of impressions *A* to a different set *b;* but among these displacements we distinguish some such that the initial set *A* and the final set *B* conserve certain common qualities. I do not wish to go into further detail nor to seek to determine in exactly what these common qualities consist.

I am satisfied to note that we are led to distinguish certain special displacements such that we may say they leave fixed one of the points of space.

That is the origin of the idea of point.

The set of all displacements constitutes what we call a group; the set of those displacements that leave fixed a point of space constitutes a partial or subgroup.

It is in the relation of this group and subgroup that we must seek the explanation of the fact that space has three dimensions.

The group total is of the order 6, that is to say that any such displacement can be considered as a combination of six elementary and independent movements.

The subgroup is of the order 3, that is to say that any displacement belonging to this subgroup, or, in other words, any displacement which leaves fixed a point of space, can be considered a combination of three elementary and independent movements.

The difference $6 - 3$ represents the number of dimensions.

The Non-Euclidean world. If geometric space were a frame imposed on *each* of our sensations, considered individually, it would be impossible to represent an image stripped of that frame, and we could change nothing in our geometry.

But that is not the case; geometry is only the résumé of the laws in accordance with which images succeed one another. Nothing prevents our imagining a series of representations, in every way similar to our ordinary representations, but succeeding one another according to laws different from those to which we are accustomed.

We can therefore conceive that beings whose education took place in a milieu where these laws were inoperative could have a geometry very different from ours.

Let us imagine, for example, a world enclosed in a great sphere and subject to the following laws:

The temperature is not uniform; it is maximal in the center, and diminishes in proportion as we move away, reducing to absolute zero when we get to the sphere in which the world is enclosed.

I will further specify the precise law according to which the temperature varies. Let R be the radius of the limiting sphere; let r be the distance from a given point to the center of this sphere. The absolute temperature will be proportional to $R^2 - r^2$.

I will suppose, in addition, that in this world, all bodies have the same coefficient of expansion such that the length of any rule will be proportional to the absolute temperature.

Finally I will suppose that an object transported from one point to another whose temperature is different, immediately assumes calorific equilibrium in its new environment.

Nothing in these hypotheses is contradictory or unimaginable.

A mobile object will then become smaller and smaller as it approaches the limiting sphere.

First let us observe that although this world is limited from the point of view of our habitual geometry, it will appear infinite to its inhabitants.

Indeed, when they wish to approach the limiting sphere, they get colder and become smaller and smaller. The steps they take are therefore also smaller and smaller, so that they can never reach the limiting sphere.

If, for us, geometry is only the study of the laws by which invariable solids move, for these imaginary beings, it would be a study of the laws by which solids move *deformed by those differences of temperature* I have just mentioned

True, in our world natural solids also submit to variations of form and volume due to heating and cooling. But we neglect these variations in laying the foundation of geometry, for in addition to their being very weak, they are irregular and consequently seem to us to be accidental.

In this hypothetical world, this would not be the case, and these variations would follow regular and simple laws.

Moreover, the diverse solid particles making up the bodies of the inhabitants would also undergo the same variations of form and volume.

I will add one further hypothesis. I will assume that light crosses diversely refracting media in such a way that the index of refraction is inversely proportional to $R^2 - r^2$. It is easy to see that in these conditions, light rays would be not rectilinear but circular.

To justify the foregoing, it remains to be shown that certain changes occurring in the position of exterior objects could be *corrected* by correlative movements of the sensory beings who inhabit this imaginary world; and in such a way as to restore the original group of impressions felt by these sensory beings.

Let us suppose that an object moves, while changing shape, not as an invariable solid, but as a solid undergoing unequal dilations in exact accord with the law of temperature that I proposed above. Permit me, in the interest of succinct language, to call such a movement a *non-Euclidean displacement*. . .

If a sensory being were in the area, his impressions would be modified by the displacement of the object, but he could re-establish them by making suitable movements. It suffices that finally the object and the sensory being, considered as forming a single body, should have undergone one of those particular displacements that I have just called non-Euclidean.

Although from the point of view of our habitual geometry bodies are deformed in this displacement and their diverse parts are no longer in the same relative position, nevertheless we shall see that the impressions of that sensory being have again become the same.

Indeed, although the mutual distances of the diverse parts could and did vary, nevertheless the parts originally in contact have returned into contact. Therefore the tactile impressions have not changed.

Furthermore, taking into account the hypothesis set forth above as to the refraction and curve of light rays, the visual impressions will also have remained the same.

These imaginary beings will thus be led like us to classify the phenomena they witness, and to distinguish among them those "changes of position" that are susceptible to correction by a voluntary correlative movement.

If they were to found a geometry, it would not be like ours, the study of the movements of our invariable solids, it would be that of the changes of position that they will thus have distinguished, and which are none other than the "non-Euclidean displacements"; *it will be non-Euclidean geometry.*

Thus, beings like us, educated in such a world, would not have the same geometry as we.

The four-dimensional World. In the same way as a non-Euclidean world, we can represent a world having four dimensions.

The sense of sight, even with a single eye, joined to muscular sensations relative to movements of the eyeball could suffice to our knowing a three-dimensional world.

The images of exterior objects come and paint themselves on the retina, which is a two-dimensional tabula; these are perspectives.

But, since these objects are mobile, and since the same

is true of our eye, we see successively different perspectives of the same body, taken from several different points of view.

We notice at the same time that the passage from one perspective to another is often accompanied by muscular sensations.

If the passage from perspective A to perspective B and that from perspective A' to perspective B' are accompanied by the same muscular sensations, we consider them to be operations of the same kind.

Studying afterward the laws according to which these operations combine, we recognize that they form a group having the same structure as that of the movements of invariable solids.

Now, we have seen that it is from the properties of this group that we have deduced the notions of geometric and of three dimensions.

Thus we understand how the idea of a three-dimensional space was able to arise from the spectacle of these perspectives, even though each of them has only two dimensions, because *they succeed one another in accordance with certain laws.*

In the same way that we can make on a plane the perspective of a figure having three dimensions, we can make that of a four-dimensional figure on a tabula with three (or two) dimensions. It is only a game for the geometrician.

We can even take from a single figure several perspectives from several different viewpoints.

We can easily represent these perspectives since they have only three dimensions.

Let us imagine that the diverse perspectives of a single object succeed one another; that the passage from one to the other is accompanied by muscular sensations.

We will naturally consider two of these passages as two operations of the same kind when they are associated with the same muscular sensations.

Then nothing prevents our imagining that these operations might combine following any law that we wish, for example in such a way as to form a group having the same structure as that of an invariable four-dimensional solid.

In all this there is nothing we cannot represent and nevertheless these sensations are precisely those that a being furnished with a two-dimensional retina would feel if he could move in four-dimensional space.

It is in this sense that we may say that we can represent the fourth dimension.

Conclusions. We say that experience plays an indispensable role in the genesis of geometry; but it would be an error to conclude that geometry is an experimental science, even in part.

If it were experimental it would be only approximate and provisional. And what a crude approximation!

Geometry would only be the study of the movements of solids; but in reality it is not concerned with natural solids, it has as its object certain ideal solids, absolutely invariable, which are only a simplified and very distant image of the natural ones.

The notion of ideal bodies is drawn entirely from our minds and experience is only an occasion that invites us to construct such a notion.

The object of geometry is the study of a particular "group"; but the general concept of group pre-exists in our minds, at least potentially. It is imposed on us, not as a form of sensibility, but as a form of understanding.

Still, among all possible groups, we must choose that one which will be, so to speak, the *standard* to which we will refer natural phenomena.

Experience guides us in this choice which it does not impose on us; it makes us recognize not what is the truest geometry, but what is the most *convenient*. It will be noticed that I have been able to describe the fantastic worlds that I imagined above *without ceasing to use the language of ordinary geometry.*

Indeed, we should not have to change anything if we were to be transported to such a world.

Beings who were educated there would no doubt find it more convenient to create a geometry different from ours, better adapted to their impressions. As for us, in the face of the same impressions, it is certain that we would find it more convenient not to change our habits.

7

COORDINATIVE DEFINITIONS, RIGID BODIES, AND THE RELATIVITY OF SPACE:

Hans Reichenbach ˙

COORDINATIVE DEFINITIONS

Defining usually means reducing a concept to other concepts. In physics, as in all other fields of inquiry, wide use is made of this procedure. There is a second kind of definition, however, which is also employed and which derives from the fact that physics, in contradistinction to mathematics, deals with real objects. Physical knowledge is characterized by the fact that concepts are not only defined by other concepts but also coordinated to real objects. This coordination cannot be replaced by an explanation of meanings, it simply states that *this concept* is coordinated to *this particular thing*. In general this coordination is not arbitrary. Since the concepts are interconnected by testable relations, the coordination may be verified as true or false, if the requirement of uniqueness is added, i.e., the rule that the same concept must always denote the same object.

˙ [This selection is excerpted from Chapter 1, Sections 4, 5, and 8, of Hans Reichenbach's *The Philosophy of Space and Time* (New York: Dover Publications, Inc., 1957), translated by Maria Reichenbach and John Freund from *Philosophie der Raum-Zeit Lehre,* which first appeared in 1928. Printed by permission of Maria Reichenbach and Dover Publications.]

The method of physics consists in establishing the uniqueness of this coordination, as Schlick has clearly shown. But certain preliminary coordinations must be determined before the method of coordination can be carried through any further; these first coordinations are therefore definitions which we shall call *coordinative definitions*. They are *arbitrary*, like all definitions; on their choice depends the conceptual system which develops with the progress of science.

Wherever metrical relations are to be established, the use of coordinative definitions is conspicuous. If a distance is to be measured, the unit of length has to be determined beforehand by definition. This definition is a coordinative definition. Here the duality of conceptual definition and coordinative definition can easily be seen. We can define only by means of other concepts what we mean by a unit; for instance: "A unit is a distance which, when transported along another distance, supplies the measure of this distance." But this statement does not say anything about the size of the unit, which can only be established by reference to a physically given length such as the standard meter in Paris. The same consideration holds for other definitions of units. If the definition reads, for instance: "A meter is the forty-millionth part of the circumference of the earth," this circumference is the physical length to which the definition refers by means of the insertion of some further concepts. And if the wave-length of cadmium light is chosen as a unit, cadmium light is the physical phenomenon to which the definition is related. It will be noticed in this example that the method of coordinating a unit to a physical object may be very complicated. So far nobody has seen a wave-length; only certain phenomena have been observed which are theoretically related to it, such as the light and dark bands resulting from interference. In principle, a unit of length can be defined in terms of an observation that does not include any metrical relations, such as "that wave-length which occurs when light has a certain redness." In this case a sample of this red color would have to be kept in Paris in place of the standard meter. The characteristic feature of this method is the coordination of a concept to a physical object. These considerations explain the term "coordinative definition." If the definition is used for measurements, as in the case of the unit of length, it is a *metrical* coordinative definition.

The philosophical significance of the theory of relativity

consists in the fact that it has demonstrated the necessity for metrical coordination definitions in several places where empirical relations had previously been assumed. It is not always as obvious as in the case of the unit of length that a coordinative definition is required before any measurements can be made, and pseudo-problems arise if we look for truth where definitions are needed. The word "relativity" is intended to express the fact that the results of the measurements depend upon the choice of the coordinative definitions. It will be shown presently how this idea affects the solution of the problem of geometry.

After this solution of the problem of the unit of length, the next step leads to the comparison of two units of lengths at different locations. If the measuring rod is laid down, its length is compared only to that part of a body, say a wall, which it covers at the moment. If two separate parts of the wall are to be compared, the measuring rod will have to be transported. It is assumed that the measuring rod does not change during the transport. It is fundamentally impossible, however, to detect such a change if it is produced by universal forces. Assume two measuring rods which are equal in length. They are transported by different paths to a distant place; there again they are laid down side by side and found equal in length. Does this procedure prove that they did not change on the way? Such an assumption would be incorrect. The only observable fact is that the two measuring rods are always equal in length at the place where they are compared to each other. But it is impossible to know whether on the way the two rods expand or contract. An expansion that affects all bodies in the same way is not observable because a direct comparison of measuring rods at different places is impossible.

An optical comparison, for instance by measuring the angular perspective of each rod with a theodolite, cannot help either. The experiment makes use of light rays and the interpretation of the measurement of the lengths depends on assumptions about the propagation of light.

The problem does not concern a matter of *cognition* but of *definition*. There is no way of knowing whether a measuring rod retains its length when it is transported to another place; a statement of this kind can only be introduced by a definition. For this purpose a coordinative definition is to be used, because two physical objects distant from each other are *defined* as equal in length. It is not the *concept* equality of length which is to be defined, but a *real object* corresponding to it is to be pointed out. A physical structure is coordinated to the concept equality of length, just as the standard meter is coordinated to the concept unit of length.

This analysis reveals how definitions and empirical statements are interconnected. As explained above, it is an observational fact, formulated in an empirical statement, that two measuring rods which are shown to be equal in length by local comparison made at a certain space point will be found equal in length by local comparison at every other space point, whether they have been transported along the same or different paths. When we add to this empirical fact the definition that the rods shall be called equal in length when they are at *different places*, we do not make an inference from the observed fact; the addition constitutes an independent convention. There is, however, a certain relation between the two. The physical fact makes the convention unique, i.e., independent of the path of transportation. The statement about the uniqueness of the convention is therefore empirically verifiable and not a matter of choice. One can say that the factual relations holding for a local comparison of rods, though they do not require the definition of congruence in terms of transported rods, make this definition admissible. Definitions that are not unique are inadmissible in a scientific system.

This consideraton can only mean that the factual relations may be used for the simple definition of congruence where any rigid measuring rod establishes the congruence. If the factual relations did not hold, a special definition of the unit of length would have to be given for every space point. Not only at Paris, but also at every other place a rod having the length of a "meter" would have to be displayed, and all these arbitrarily chosen rods would be called equal in length by definition. The requirement of uniformity would be satisfied by carrying around a measuring rod selected at random for the purpose of making copies and displaying these as the unit. If two of these copies were transported and compared locally, they would be different in length, but this fact would not "falsify" the definition. In such a world it would become very obvious that the concept of congruence is a definition; but we, in our simple world, are also permitted to choose a definition of congruence that does not correspond to the actual behavior of rigid rods.

Thus we could arrange measuring rods, which in the ordinary sense are called equal in length, and, laying them end to end, call the second rod half as long as the first, the third one a third, etc. Such a definition would complicate all measurements, but epistemologically it is equivalent to the ordinary definition, which calls the rods equal in length. In this statement we make use of the fact that the definition of a unit at only one space point does not render general measurements possible. For the general case the definition of the unit has to be given in advance as a function of the place (and also of the time). *It is again a matter of fact that our world admits of a simple definition of congruence because of the factual relations holding for the behavior to rigid rods; but this fact does not deprive the simple definition of its definitional character.*

The great significance of the realization that congruence is a matter of definition lies in the fact that by its help the epistemological problem of geometry is solved. . . .

We are now left with the problem: which coordinative definition should be used for physical space? Since we need a geometry, a decision has to be made for a definition of congruence. Although we must do so, we should never forget that we deal with an arbitrary decision that is neither true nor false. Thus the geometry of physical space is not an immediate result of experience, but depends on the choice of the coordinative definition.

In this connection we shall look for the most adequate definition, i.e., one which has the advantage of logical simplicity and requires the least possible change in the results of science. The sciences have implicitly employed such a coordinative definition all the time, though not always consciously; the results based upon this definition will be developed further in our analysis. It can be assumed that the definition hitherto employed possesses certain practical advantages justifying its use. In the discussion about the definition of congruence by means of rigid rods, this coordinative definition has already been indicated. The investigation is not complete, however, because an exact definition of the *rigid body* is still missing.

RIGID BODIES

Experience tells us that physical objects assume different states. Solid bodies have an advantage over liquid ones because they change their shape and size only very little when affected by outside forces. They seem, therefore, to be useful for the definition of congruence. However, if the result of the previous considerations is kept in mind, this relative stability is no ground on which to base a preference for solid bodies. As was explained, the form and size of an object depends on the coordinative definition of congruence; if the solid body is used for the coordinative definition, the statement that it does not change its shape must not be regarded as a cognitive statement. It can only be a definition: we define the shape of the solid body as unchangeable. But how can the solid body be defined? In other words, if the physical state of *being solid* were defined differently, under what conditions would the solid body be called *rigid?* If the conservation of shape is not permissible as a criterion, what criteria may be used?

The problem becomes more complicated because we cannot solve it by merely pointing to certain real objects. Although the standard meter in Paris was cited previously as the prototype of such a definition, this account was a somewhat schematic abstraction. Actually no object is the perfect realization of the rigid body of physics; it must be remembered that such an object may be influenced by many physical forces. Only after several corrections have been made, for example, for the influence of temperature and elasticity, is the resulting length of the object regarded as adequate for the coordinative definition of the comparison of lengths. The standard meter in Paris would not be accepted as the definition of the unit of length, if it were not protected from influences of temperature, etc., by being kept in a vault. If an earthquake should ever throw it out of this vault and deform its diameter, nobody would want to retain it as the prototype of the meter; everybody would agree that the standard meter would no longer be a meter. But what kind of definition is this, if the definition may some day be called false? Does the concept of coordinative definition become meaningless?

The answer is: it does not become meaningless, but, as we shall see, its application is logically very complicated. The restrictions that affect the arbitrariness of the coordinative definition have two sources. One restriction lies in the demand that the obtained metric retain certain older physical results, especially those of the "physics of daily life." Nobody could object on logical grounds if the bent rod would be taken as the definition of the unit of length; but then we must accept the consequence that our house, our body, the whole world has become larger. Relative to the coordinative definition it has, indeed, become larger, but such an interpretation does not correspond to our habitual thinking. We prefer an interpretation of changes involving an individual thing on the one side and the rest of the world on the other side that confines the change to the small object. The theory of motion uses the same idea; the fly crawling around in the moving train is called "moving" relative to the train, and the train is called "moving" relative to the earth. Provided that we realize that such a description cannot be justified on logical grounds, we can employ it without hesitation because it is more convenient; yet it must not be regarded as "more true" than any other description. We must not assume that a deformation of the standard meter by an earthquake is equivalent to a change in any absolute sense; actually it is only a change in the *difference* in size between the rod and the rest of the world. There is, of course, no objection to the use of such restrictions on coordinative definitions, because their only effect is an adaptation of the scientific definition to those of everyday life.

These restrictions are more numerous than might be anticipated offhand. Geometrical concepts abound in our daily life. We call the floor and ceiling plane, the corners of our rooms rectangular, a taut string straight. It is clear that these terms can only be definitions and have nothing to do with cognition, as one might at first believe. But by means of these definitions we have arrived at a very simple physics of everyday life. It would logically be permissible to define the taut string as curved, but then we would have to introduce a complicated field of force which pulls the string to the side and prevents it from adjusting itself to the shortest line in spite of the elastic tension, comparable to a stretched chain bending under the influence of gravity; such a convention would complicate physics unnecessarily. However, this is the only objection that can be raised against this description; the statement that a taut string is straight is not empirical but only a more convenient definition.

On the other hand, these restrictions do not constitute strict rules; they merely confine coordinative definitions to certain limits. Direct observation is inexact and we admit the possibility of small inaccuracies of observation. Scientifically speaking nobody will deny that the floor is a little curved, or that a tightened string sags slightly. Such a statement would mean that science does not really use the floor and the string but other physical objects as standards for its coordinative definition, and that, compared to these other things, small deviations occur. The physics of everyday life furnishes only limits for coordinative definitions; it does not intend to establish them strictly.

For everyday physics this strictness is not possible, and the task of scientific physics is therefore to give a strict formulation of the coordinative definition within these limits. This aim of precision is the reason for the important role played by correction factors and supplementary forces in the measurement of lengths. The principle according to which the strict definition is achieved must now be investigated more closely. What is the rigid body of physics? It must be defined strictly without the use of the concept of change in size.

For this purpose the concepts *rigid* and *solid* must be distinguished. Solid bodies are bodies having a certain physical state which can be defined ostensively; it differs from the liquid and gaseous state in a number of observable ways. The solid body can be defined without the use of the concept of change in size. Rigid bodies, however, are those bodies that constitute the physical part in the coordinative definition of congruence and that by definition do not change their size when transported. By the use of the concept *solid body* a definition of the concept *rigid body* can be given that does not employ congruence.

Definition: *Rigid bodies are solid bodies which are not affected by differential forces, or concerning which the influence of differential forces has been eliminated by corrections; universal forces are disregarded.*

This definition will be discussed presently. Let us first deal with the last clause. May we simply neglect universal forces? But we do not neglect them: we merely set the universal forces equal to zero by definition. Without such a rule the rigid body cannot be defined. Since there is no demonstrable difference produced by universal forces, the conception that the transported measuring rod is deformed by such forces can always be defended. No object is rigid relative to universal forces. . . .

THE RELATIVITY OF GEOMETRY

With regard to the problem of geometry we have come to realize that the question which geometry holds for physical space must be decided by measurements, i.e., empirically. Furthermore, this decision is dependent on the assumption of an arbitrary coordinative definition of the comparison of length. Against this conception arguments have been set forth which endeavor to retain Euclidean geometry for physical space under any circumstances and thus give it a preference among all other geometries. On the basis of our results we can discuss these arguments; our analysis will lead to the relativity of geometry.

One of the arguments maintains it is a mistake to believe that the choice of the coordinative definition is a matter left to our discretion. The measurements of geometry as carried through in practice presuppose quite complicated measuring instruments such as the theodolite; therefore these measurements cannot be evaluated without a theory of the measuring instruments. The theory of the measuring instruments, however, presupposes the validity of Euclidean geometry and it constitutes a contradiction to infer a non-Euclidean geometry from the results.

This objection can be met in the following way. Our conception permits us to start with the assumption that Euclidean geometry holds for physical space. Under certain conditions, however, we obtain the result that there exists a universal force F that deforms all measuring instruments in the same way. However, we can invert the interpretation: we can set F equal to zero by definition and correct in turn the theory of our measuring instruments. We are able to proceed in this manner because a transformation of all measurements from one geometry into another is possible and involves no difficulties. It is correct to say that all measurements must be preceded by a definition; we expressed this fact by the indispensability of the coordinative definition. The mistake of the objection consists in the belief that this definition cannot be changed afterwards. Just as we can measure the temperature with a Fahrenheit thermometer and then convert the results into Celsius, measurements can be started under the assumption of Euclidean geometry and later converted into non-Euclidean measurements. There is no logical objection to this procedure.

In practice the method is much simpler. It turns out that the non-Euclidean geometry obtained under our coordinative definition of the rigid body deviates quantitatively only very little from Euclidean geometry when small areas are concerned. In this connection "small area" means "on the order of the size of the earth"; deviations from Euclidean geometry can be noticed only in astronomic dimensions. In practice, therefore, it is not necessary to correct the theory of the measuring instruments afterwards, because these corrections lie within the errors of observation. The following method of inference is permissible: we can prove by the assumption that Euclidean geometry holds for small areas that in astronomic dimensions a non-Euclidean geometry holds which emerges infinitesimally into Euclidean geometry. No logical objection can be advanced against this method, which is characteristic of the train of thought in modern physics. It is carried through in practice for astronomic measurements designed to confirm Einstein's theory of gravitation.

The objection is connected with the *a priori* theory of space that goes back to Kant and today is represented in various forms. Not only Kantians and Neo-Kantians attempt to maintain the *a priori* character of geometry: the tendency is also pronounced in philosophical schools which in other respects are not Kantian. It is not my intention to give a critical analysis of Kant's philosophy in the present book. In the course of the discussion on the theory of relativity, it has become evident that the philosophy of Kant has been subject to so many interpretations by his disciples that it can no longer serve as a sharply defined basis for present day epistemological analysis. Such an analysis would clarify less the *epistemological* question of the structure of space than the *historical* question of the meaning and content of Kant's system. The author has presented his own views on this problem in another publication; the present investigation is aimed at philosophical clarification and will not concern itself with historical questions. Therefore, I shall select only those arguments of Kant's theory of space, the refutation of which will further our understanding of the problem. Although in my opinion the essential part of Kant's theory will thereby be covered, I do not claim a historically complete evaluation of it in this book.

The ideas expressed in the preceding considerations attempted to establish Euclidean geometry as *epistemologically a priori*; we found that this *a priori* cannot be maintained and that Euclidean geometry is not an indispensable pre-supposition of knowledge. We turn now to the idea of the *visual a priori;* this Kantian doctrine bases the preference for Euclidean geometry upon the existence of a certain manner in which we visualize space.

The theory contends that an innate property of the human mind, the ability of visualization, demands that we adhere to Euclidean geometry. In the same way as a certain self-evidence compels us to believe the laws of arithmetic, a visual self-evidence compels us to believe in the validity of Euclidean geometry. It can be shown that this self-evidence is not based on logical grounds. Since mathematics furnishes a proof that the construction of non-Euclidean geometries does not lead to contradictions, no *logical* self-evidence can be claimed for Euclidean geometry. This is the reason why the self-evidence of Euclidean geometry has sometimes been derived, in Kantian fashion, from the human ability of visualization conceived as a source of knowledge.

Everybody has a more or less clear notion of what is understood by visualization. If we draw two points on a piece of paper, connect them by a straight line and add a curved connecting line, we "see" that the straight line is shorter than the curved line. We even claim to be certain that the straight line is shorter than any other line connecting the two points. We say this without being able to prove it by measurements, because it is impossible for us to draw and measure all the lines. The power of imagination compelling us to make this assertion is called the ability of *visualization.* Similarly, the Euclidean axiom of the parallels seems to be visually necessary. It remains for us to investigate this human quality and its significance for the problem of space.

The analysis will be carried through in two steps. Let us first assume it is correct to say that a special ability of visualization exists, and that Euclidean geometry is distinguished from all other geometries by the fact that it can easily be visualized. The question arises: what consequences does this assumption have for physical space? Only after this question has been answered can the assumption itself be tested. . . .

Let us turn to the first question, which has to be reformulated in order to relate it clearly to the epistemological problem.

Mathematics proves that every geometry of the Riemannian kind can be mapped upon another one of the same kind. In the language of physics this means the following:

Theorem θ: "Given a geometry *G′* to which the measuring instruments conform, we can imagine a universal force *F* which affects the instruments in such a way that the actual geometry is an arbitrary geometry *G*, while the observed deviation from *G* is due to a universal deformation of the measuring instruments."

No epistemological objection can be made against the correctness of theorem *θ*. Is the visual *a priori* compatible with it?

Offhand we must say yes. Since the Euclidean geometry G_0 belongs to the geometries of the Riemannian kind, it follows from theorem *θ* that it is always possible to carry through the visually preferred geometry for physical space. Thus we have proved that we can always satisfy the requirement of visualization.

But something more is proven by theorem *θ* which does not fit very well into the theory of the visual *a priori*. The theorem asserts that Euclidean geometry is not preferable on epistemological grounds. Theorem *θ* shows all geometries to be equivalent; it formulates the *principle of the relativity of geometry*. It follows that it is meaningless to speak about one geometry as the *true* geometry. We obtain a statement about physical reality only if in addition to the geometry *G* of the space its universal field of force *F* is specified. Only the combination

$$G + F$$

is a testable statement.

We can now understand the significance of a decision for Euclidean geometry on the basis of a visual *a priori*. The decision means only the choice of a specific coordinative definition. In our definition of the rigid body we set $F = 0$; the statement about the resulting *G* is then a univocal description of reality. This definition means that in "$G + F$" the second factor is zero. The visual *a priori*, however, sets $G = G_0$. But then the empirical component in the results of measurements is represented by the determination of *F*; only through the combination

$$G_0 + F$$

are the properties of space exhaustively described.

There is nothing wrong with a coordinative definition established on the requirement that a certain kind of geometry is to result from the measurements. We ourselves renounced the simplest form of the coordinative definition.

which consists in pointing to a measuring rod; instead we chose a much more complicated coordinative definition in terms of our distinction between universal and differential forces. A coordinative definition can also be introduced by the prescription what the result of the measurements is to be. "The comparison of length is to be performed in such a way that Euclidean geometry will be the result"—this stipulation is a possible form of a coordinative definition. It may be compared to the definition of the meter in terms of the circumference of the earth: "The unit is to be chosen in such a way that 40 million times this length will be equal to the circumference of the earth."

Although it may be admitted that Euclidean geometry is unique in that it can be easily visualized, the theory of the visual *a priori* does not disprove the theory of the relativity of geometry and of the necessity for coordinative definitions of the comparison of length. On the contrary, it is only this theory that can state precisely the epistemological function of visualization: the possibility of visualization is a ground for subjective preference of one particular coordinative definition. But the occurrence of visualization does not imply anything about the space of real objects.

In this connection another argument in support of the preference for Euclidean geometry is frequently adduced. To be sure, this argument is not related to the problem of visualization, but like the visual *a priori* it attributes a specific epistemological position to Euclidean geometry; therefore we shall consider it here. It is maintained that Euclidean geometry is the *simplest* geometry, and hence physics must choose the coordinative definition $G = G_0$ rather than the coordinative definition $F = 0$. This point of view can be answered as follows: physics is not concerned with the question which *geometry* is simpler, but with the question which *coordinative definition* is simpler. It seems that the coordinative definition $F = 0$ is simpler, because then the expression $G + F$ reduces to G. But even this result is not essential, since in this case simplicity is not a criterion for truth. Simplicity certainly plays an important part in physics, even as a criterion for choosing between physical hypotheses. The significance of simplicity as a means to knowledge will have to be carefully examined in connection with the problem of induction, which does not fall within the scope of this book.

Geometry is concerned solely with the simplicity of a

definition, and therefore the problem of empirical significance does not arise. It is a mistake to say that Euclidean geometry is "more true" than Einstein's geometry or vice versa, because it leads to simpler metrical relations. We said that Einstein's geometry leads to simpler relations because in it $F = 0$. But we can no more say that Einstein's geometry is "truer" than Euclidean geometry, than we can say that the meter is a "truer" unit of length than the yard. The simpler system is always preferable; the advantage of meters and centimeters over yards and feet is only a matter of economy and has no bearing upon reality. *Properties of reality are discovered only by a combination of the results of measurement with the underlying coordinative definition.* Thus it is a characterization of objective reality that (according to Einstein) a three-dimensional non-Euclidean geometry results in the neighborhood of heavenly bodies, if we define the comparison of length by transported rigid rods. But only the *combination* of the two statements has objective significance. The same state of affairs can therefore be described in different ways. In our example it could just as well be said that in the neighborhood of a heavenly body a universal field of force exists which affects all measuring rods, while the geometry is Euclidean. Both combinations of statements are equally true, as can be seen from the fact that one can be transformed into the other. Similarly, it is just as true to say that the circumference of the earth is 40 million meters as to say that it is 40 thousand kilometers. The significance of this simplicity should not be exaggerated; this kind of simplicity, which we call *descriptive simplicity*, has nothing to do with truth.

Taken alone, the statement that a certain geometry holds for space is therefore meaningless. It acquires meaning only if we add the coordinative definition used in the comparison of widely separated lengths. The same rule holds for the geometrical shape of bodies. The sentence "The earth is a sphere" is an incomplete statement, and resembles the statement "This room is seven units long." Both statements say something about objective states of affairs only if the assumed coordinative definitions are added, and both statements must be changed if other coordinative definitions are used. These considerations indicate what is meant by *relativity of geometry*.

This conception of the problem of geometry is essentially the result of the work of Riemann, Helmholtz, and Poincaré and is known as *conventionalism*. While Riemann prepared the way for an application of geometry to physical reality by his mathematical formulation of the concept of space, Helmholtz laid the philosophical foundations. In particular, he recognized the connection of the problem of geometry with that of rigid bodies and interpreted correctly the possibility of a visual representation of non-Euclidean spaces. It is his merit, furthermore, to have clearly stated that Kant's theory of space is untenable in view of recent mathematical developments. Helmholtz' epistemological lectures must therefore be regarded as the source of modern philosophical knowledge of space. It is Einstein's achievement to have applied the theory of the relativity of geometry to physics. The surprising result was the fact that the world is non-Euclidean, as the theorists of relativity are wont to say; in our language this means: if $F = 0$, the geometry G becomes non-Euclidean. This outcome had not been anticipated, and Helmholtz and Poincaré still believed that the geometry obtained could not be proved to be different from Euclidean geometry. Only Einstein's theory of gravitation predicted the non-Euclidean result which was confirmed by astronomical observations. The deviations from Euclidean geometry, however, are very small and not observable in everyday life.

Unfortunately, the philosophical discussion of conventionalism, misled by its ill-fitting name, did not always present the epistemological aspect of the problem with sufficient clarity.[1] From conventionalism the consequence was derived that it is impossible to make an objective statement about the geometry of physical space, and that we are dealing with subjective arbitrariness only; the concept of geometry of real space was called meaningless. This is a misunderstanding. Although the statement about the geometry is based upon certain arbitrary definitions, the statement itself does not become arbitrary: once the definitions have been formulated, it is determined through objective reality alone

[1] This is also true of the expositions by Poincaré, to whom we owe the designation of the geometrical axioms as conventions (*Science and Hypothesis,* New York: Dover Publications, Inc. 1952, p. 50) and whose merit it is to have spread the awareness of the definitional character of congruence to a wider audience. He overlooks the possibility of making objective statements about real space in spite of the relativity of geometry and deems it impossible to "discover in geometric empiricism a rational meaning" (*op. cit.,* p. 79).

which is the actual geometry. Let us use our previous example: although we can define the scale of temperature arbitrarily, the indication of the temperature of a physical object does not become a subjective matter. By selecting a certain scale we can stipulate a certain arbitrary number of degrees of heat for the respective body, but this indication has an objective meaning as soon as the coordinative definition of the scale is added. On the contrary, it is the significance of coordinative definitions to lend an objective meaning to physical measurements. As long as it was not noticed at what points of the metrical system arbitrary definitions occur, all measuring results were undetermined; only by discovering the points of arbitrariness, by identifying them as such and by classifying them as definitions can we obtain objective measuring results in physics. *The objective character of the physical statement is thus shifted to a statement about relations.* A statement about the boiling point of water is no longer regarded as an absolute statement, but as a statement about a relation between the boiling water and the length of the column of mercury. There exists a similar objective statement about the geometry of real space: *it is a statement about a relation between the universe and rigid rods.* The geometry chosen to characterize this relation is only a mode of speech; however, our awareness of the relativity of geometry enables us to formulate the objective character of a statement about the geometry of the physical world as a statement about relations. In this sense we are permitted to speak of *physical geometry.* The description of nature is not stripped of arbitrariness by naive absolutism, but only by recognition and formulation of the points of arbitrariness. The only path to objective knowledge leads through conscious awareness of the role that subjectivity plays in our methods of research.

8

LOGICAL AND PHILOSOPHICAL FOUNDATIONS OF THE SPECIAL THEORY OF RELATIVITY:

Adolf Grünbaum ·

1. INTRODUCTION

Since the publication of Hans Reichenbach's definitive books on the philosophy of the theory of relativity during the second decade of this century,[1] additions have been made to the literature on the special theory of relativity which call for critical evaluation as part of an up-to-date analysis of that theory's multiple philosophical, definitional, and experimental foundations. Specifically, my assessment of the current status of the kinematics of special relativity will include an appraisal of each of the following items: (i) E. T. Whittaker's philosophical interpretation of the Lorentz transformations which inspired his very recent claim that Einstein's contribution to the kinematics of what Whittaker calls "the relativity

· [This is a revised version of "Logical and Philosophical Foundations of the Special Theory of Relativity," *American Journal of Physics*, Vol. 23, 1955, pp. 450–64, printed by permission of Adolf Grünbaum and the *American Journal of Physics*. The editors are grateful to Professor Grünbaum for having especially revised this article for the present volume.]

[1] [The notes to this selection, because of their length and complexity, have been placed at the end of the essay.]

theory of Poincaré and Lorentz" consisted merely in calculating the expressions for aberration and for the Doppler
effect; [2] (ii) P. W. Bridgman's thesis that the philosophical
innovations of special relativity lend support to the homocentric and subjectivistic form of operationism espoused by him;
(iii) the contention made a few years ago by the distinguished experimental physicist H. E. Ives, whose observation
of the transverse Doppler effect first confirmed the relativistic
clock retardation, that the Lorentz transformations require
revision on the alleged ground that Einstein's principle of
the constancy of the speed of light is a paradox resting on a
pseudo-operational procedure; (iv) the empirical support
received by special relativity from the Kennedy-Thorndike
experiment of 1932, the Ives-Stilwell experiment of 1938, and
from the discovery in 1955 of the systematic errors that account for D. C. Miller's observations of fringe displacements;
(v) Moon and Spencer's challenge of the relativistic interpretation of the data furnished by double stars (de Sitter) and
of the other experimental results generally adduced as evidence for the truth of relativity theory; and (vi) H. Dingle's
recurring assertion that Einstein's theory has rendered untenable the view that "physics is the description of the
character of an independent external world."

In addition to taking issue with E. T. Whittaker, P. W.
Bridgman, H. E. Ives, P. Moon and D. E. Spencer, and H.
Dingle, this essay will seek to dispel the following misunderstandings which still linger on: (1) the view that, *in the
first instance*, the basis for the relativity of simultaneity must
be sought in the relative motion of inertial systems; (2) the
belief that the null-result of the Michelson-Morley experiment furnishes a sufficient experimental basis for what I shall
call, for brevity, the "light principle", i.e., the principle that
the speed of light is the same constant, independent of direction, position and time in all inertial systems; this erroneous
idea is often coupled with the further mistaken supposition
that, upon a suitable choice of zeros of time, the light principle alone permits the deduction of the Lorentz transformations, so that all the novel affirmations of relativistic kinematics are then held to derive their essential experimental
warrant from the Michelson-Morley experiment, and (3)
the inference that since two different Galilean observers give
formally the same description of the behavior of a single
identical light pulse, emitted upon the coincidence of their
origins, the respective expanding spherical forms of this dis-

turbance which they are said to "observe" in their respective systems are constituted by the self-same point-events or the self-same configuration of photons. Sometimes the attempt is made to buttress the false conclusion of this fallacious inference by the irrelevant though true remark that while judgments can contradict one another, sense-data cannot. As if the claim that the light pulse spreads spherically in each inertial system were warranted by immediate sense-data alone and did not already presuppose a theory concerning the intersystemic and intrasystemic status of simultaneity.

2. THE RELATIVITY OF SIMULTANEITY

During the reign of the absolutistic Newtonian theory, space and time were held to have a structure independent of the existence of matter or the occurrence of physical events. According to this conception of space and time as indifferent, merely accidental "containers" of physical things and events, (a) the *identity* of points in the physical container space in which bodies are located and of the instants of receptacle time at which physical events occur is autonomous and *not* derivative: physical things and events do *not* first define, by their own identity, the points and instants which constitute their loci or the loci of other things and events, and (b) receptacle space and time each have their own *intrinsic* metric, which exists quite independently of the presence of material rods and clocks in the universe, devices whose function is *at best* the purely epistemic one of enabling us to ascertain the intrinsic metrical relations of the receptacle space and time contingently containing them. Thus, for example, even when material clocks run uniformly, they merely *record* but do not *define* the temporal metric.

But with the advent of Riemann, Poincaré and Mach, it became clear that empty space and time are amorphous and that if they are to have a topology and a metric, such structure will derive its existence and character from relations between bodies and physical events. It is not an independently structured receptacle space or time, therefore, which endows events with their spatio-temporal particularity. Instead, the existence of a structure of space or time presupposes that, to begin with, there exist in the universe recognizable qualitative and relational differences among physical events and things which confer individuality upon them independently of any system of coordinates and prior to the construction of any such system. Thus, the theory of relativity assumes that physical events and things first define, by their own identity, the points and instants which we call their loci or the loci of other things or events. As against the absolutistic container-theory, this conception is "relational" in the sense of regarding space and time as systems of relations between physical events and things.

Accordingly, the temporal order among noncoincident physical events must derive from *their* properties and relations. Hence we seek the attributes, if any, in virtue of which such events sustain unambiguously relations of earlier, later, and simultaneous. Let us find the basis of the temporal order within a class of events sufficiently comprehensive to include events in different galaxies. It would clearly not be feasible even to attempt to establish an unambiguous temporal order in this class of events by means of the readings, at the respective loci of these events, furnished by clocks previously synchronized via the transport of a master clock. And even if the required transport were feasible, the attempt would fail to yield an unambiguous temporal order, since the resulting readings would depend on the path and mode of transport of the master clock.[3] Consequently, a different criterion of time order is needed.

Within our class of events, consider those pairs which have the property of being the termini of actual or physically possible causal chains. If in such pairs one and only one of the two events does or could constitute the emission of a pulse of radiation (or of a material particle) while the other is or could be the corresponding absorption or reception, then we define the emission-event E_1 as sustaining the relation "earlier than" to the absorption event E_2.[4] This relation and also its converse "later than" are asymmetric, so that neither relation would be sustained by a pair of events in which each member can be the emission-event for a causal influence reaching the other, as in the case of Newtonian instantaneous action-at-a-distance.

If the physical basis for relations of earlier and later among events lies in the possibility of their being the appropriate termini of influence chains, we ask: are the physically possible causal chains of nature such as to define a unique set of temporal relations in which every pair of events has an unambiguous place? Consider the various relations of temporal order between a single event E_2, at a given point P_2, on the one hand, and each of a set of different events at a different point P_1, on the other. Since the motion of the indicator of a dial clock is a causal chain, the presence of such a clock at P_1 can define the local temporal order in the class of events at that point. Let E_1, E_x, E_y, E_z, E, E_α, E_β, E_γ, E_3, be ordered members of this class—the direction from left to right being the positive time direction—such that t_1 is the time of E_1, t_3 the time of E_3 and $\frac{1}{2}$ $(t_3 + t_1)$ the time of E. And suppose further that among these events at P_1, the event E_1 coincides with the emission of a light ray whose arrival at P_2 coincides with E_2 and whose instantaneous reflection at P_2 issues in its return to P_1 so as to coincide with event E_3 there (see the world-line diagram, Fig. 1).

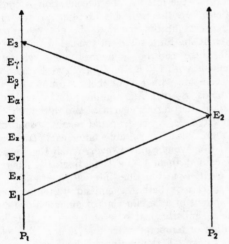

Figure 1. World-line diagram

The question before us concerns the time relations of the various events at P_1 to E_2 at P_2 which we can now ascertain in virtue of our definition of "earlier." Letting " $<$ " be short for "earlier than," we know that

$$E_1 < E_2 < E_3,$$
and that
$$E_1 < E < E_3,$$

the latter relation also holding, of course, if "E" is replaced by any of the symbols "E_x," "E_y," "E_z," "E_α," "E_β," "E_γ." But these combined relations do not furnish any information concerning the time relations of E_2 to any one of the events at P_1 lying within the open interval between E_1 and E_3. The existence of the latter relations will therefore depend upon the physical possibility that there be direct causal chains which could link E_2 to the events in the open interval at P_1.

Newtonian physics asserts that there can be such chains To be sure, it would admit that a light signal emitted at P will always require a positive time interval $t_3 - t_1$ to return to P_1 and that therefore no electromagnetic chain will furnish the required link. But it would go on to invoke its second law of motion, which asserts that, no matter what the velocity, the ratio of the force to the acceleration is constant and that particles can therefore be brought to arbitrarily high speeds in excess of the speed c of light by appropriately large forces acting for a sufficient time. Thus, in the Newtonian world, there can be influence chains whose emission would coincide with E_x, E_y, or E_z at P_1 and whose arrival at P_2 would coincide with E_2 but there are none for which the converse holds. E_2 can then significantly be said to be later than each of the former events. And although no signal emanating from E_α, E_β, or E_γ could reach P_2 soon enough to coincide there with E_2, suitable influence chains emanating from the latter event can, however, reach the former events and thus exhibit them to be later than E_2. There will be only one event E in the time interval $t_3 - t_1$ at P_1 which is such that it can be both the emission-terminus and the reception-terminus of a certain kind of influence chain of which E_2 can be a similarly dual type of terminus. It follows from our definition of temporal order that E is neither earlier nor later than E_2, and E thus uniquely divides the events at P_1 into those which are earlier than E_2 and those which are later. E is therefore the only event at P_1 which can justifiably be called "simultaneous" with E_2. This concept of simultaneity finds mathematical expression in Newton's law of universal gravitation and in his third law of motion, which affirm the existence of instantaneous action-at-a-distance interactions, i.e., of two-way causal chains whose emission coincides with their return and which are therefore said to travel at infinite speed (barring Wheeler-Feynman interactions and generally assuming that time is topologically open rather than closed).

We see that in a world of arbitrarily fast causal chains,

the concept of absolute simultaneity would have a perfectly clear physical meaning in the temporal description of nature given by a relational theory of time. Contrariwise, as we shall now show in detail, Einstein's denial of the existence of indefinitely rapid causal chains via his affirmation of the limiting role of light propagation in the class of influence chains deprives the concept of absolute simultaneity of its physical meaning even within a single inertial system. And it will be seen that the conventionality of simultaneity arising from Einstein's claim does not depend for its validity upon there being disagreement among different Galilean observers as to the simultaneity of pairs of noncoinciding events.

Although there were experiments by W. Kaufmann and others during the years 1902 to 1906 on the deflection of electrons (β-rays) in electric and magnetic fields which yielded a mass-variation with velocity incompatible with Newtonian dynamics, these experiments were unable to decide between the nonrelativistic formulas of Abraham's dynamics, which allow particle velocities exceeding the velocity of light *in vacuo* [5] and the dynamical equations issuing from Einstein's fundamental paper of 1905, which rule out causal chains faster than light *in vacuo*. Experiments which clearly support Einstein on this point were not successfully carried out until a good many years after 1905.[6] It was reflection, initiated by a thought-experiment he had carried out at the age of 16, which led Einstein to postulate the limiting character of light propagation. He writes: "If I pursue a beam of light with the velocity c (velocity of light in a vacuum), I should observe such a beam of light as a spatially oscillatory electromagnetic field at rest. However, there seems to be no such thing, whether on the basis of experience or according to Maxwell's equations." [7] Thus the very consideration which suggested that there are no preferred inertial systems for electromagnetic phenomena also indicated that a material object cannot attain the speed of light! [8] This claim concerning the limiting character of the speed of light is a fundamental axiom of the theory and is *not* a theorem depending for its deduction on the relativistic law for the addition of velocities, as we are sometimes told. For (i) this addition law itself depends for its own deduction on the Lorentz transformations, and these, as we shall see, could *not* be affirmed in Einstein's theory without the conventionality and intersystemic relativity of simultaneity assured by the limiting postulate about light, and (ii) the addition law shows only that if the velocities to be added are less than that of light, then we cannot obtain a velocity greater than c by adding them.

We must now define simultaneity for a universe in which the assumption of arbitrarily fast causal chains fails to hold. But since the metrical concept of velocity presupposes that we know the meaning of a transit time and since such a time, in turn, depends upon a prior criterion of clock synchronization or simultaneity, we must first formulate the limiting property of electromagnetic chains without using the concept of simultaneity of noncoincident events. We can then state the consequences of this property for the definition of simultaneity. Accordingly, we give the following nonmetrical formulation of Einstein's limiting postulate: no kind of causal chain (moving particles, radiation) emitted *in vacuo* at a given point P_1 together with a light pulse can reach any other point P_2 earlier—as judged by a local clock at P_2 which merely orders events there in a metrically arbitrary fashion—than this light pulse.[9]

We now apply this postulate to the special case of two points P_1 and P_2 which are fixed in a reference frame S and which are connected by a chain of light signals in the manner shown in our world-line diagram above. It is then clear at once that instead of E being the only event at P_1 which is neither earlier nor later than E_2 at P_2, as in the Newtonian world, on Einstein's hypothesis each one of the entire superdenumerable infinity of point-events in the open interval between E_1 and E_3 at P_1 fails to have a determinate time-relation to E_2. For none of these events at P_1 can then be said to be either earlier or later than E_2: no signal originating at any of these events can reach P_2 soon enough to coincide there with E_2, and no causal chain emitted at P_2 upon E_2's occurrence can reach P_1 prior to the occurrence of E_3. But to say that none of these events at P_1 is either earlier or later than E_2 is to say that no one of them is objectively any more entitled to be regarded as simultaneous with E_2 than is any of the others. It is therefore only by convention or definition that some one of these events comes to be simultaneous with E_2. Unlike the Newtonian situation, in which there was only a single event E which could be significantly held to be simultaneous with E_2, the physical facts postulated by relativity require the introduction, within a single inertial frame S, of a convention stipulating which particular pair of causally nonconnectible events will be called "simultaneous." This conventionality of simultaneity prevails within a single inertial system, because the simultaneity criterion of the system involves the choice of a particular numerical value between t_1 and t_3 as the temporal name to be assigned to E_2. Accordingly, depending on the particular event at P_1 that is chosen to be simultaneous with E_2, upon the occurrence of E_2 we set the clock at P_2 to read

(1) $$t_2 = t_1 + \epsilon \, (t_3 - t_1),$$

where ϵ has the particular value between 0 and 1 appropriate to the choice we made. If, for example, we choose ϵ such that E_y becomes simultaneous with E_2, then all of the events between E_1 and E_y become definitionally (i.e., not objectively) earlier than E_2 while all of the events between E_y and E_3 become definitionally later than E_2. Clearly, we could alternatively choose ϵ such that instead of becoming simultaneous with E_2, E_y would become earlier than E_2 or later in the same frame S. This freedom to decree definitionally the relations of temporal sequence merely expresses the objective indeterminateness of the time relations between causally nonconnectible events and, of course, such freedom can be exercised only with respect to such pairs of events.

It is apparent that no fact of nature found in the objective temporal relations of physical events precludes our choosing a value of ϵ between 0 and 1 which differs from ½. But it is only for the value ½ that the velocity of light in the direction P_1P_2 becomes equal to the velocity in the opposite direction P_2P_1 in virtue of the then resulting equality of the respective transit times $t_2 - t_1$ and $t_3 - t_2$. A choice of $\epsilon = \frac{3}{4}$, for instance, would make the velocity in the direction P_1P_2 only ⅓ as great as the return velocity. Couldn't one argue, therefore, that the choice of a value of ϵ is not a matter of convention after all, the grounds being that only the value $\epsilon = ½$ accords with such physical facts as the isotropy of space and with the methodological requirement of inductive simplicity, which enjoins us to account for observed facts by minimum postulational commitments? And, in any case, must we not admit (at least among friends!) that the value ½ is more "true"? The contention that either the isotropy of space or Occam's "razor" are relevant here is profoundly in error, and its advocacy arises from a failure to understand the import of Einstein's statement that "we establish *by definition* that the 'time' required by light to travel from A to B equals the 'time' it requires to travel from B to A." [10] For, in the first place, since no statement concerning a transit-time or velocity derives its meaning from mere facts but also requires a prior *stipulation* of the criterion of clock synchronization, a choice of $\epsilon \neq \frac{1}{2}$, which renders the transit-times (velocities) of light in opposite directions *un-equal*, cannot possibly conflict with such physical isotropies and symmetries as prevail *independently* of our descriptive conventions.[11] And, in the second place, the canon of simplicity which we are pledged to observe in all of the inductive sciences is not implemented any better by the choice $\epsilon = \frac{1}{2}$ than by any one of the other allowed fractional values. For no distinct hypothesis concerning physical facts is made by the choice $\epsilon = \frac{1}{2}$ as against one of the other permissible values. There can therefore be no question of having propounded a hypothesis making lesser postulational commitments by that special choice. On the contrary, it is the postulated fact that light is the fastest signal which assures that *each* one of the permissible values of ϵ will be equally compatible with all possible matters of fact which are independent of how we decide to set the clock at P_2. Thus, the value $\epsilon = \frac{1}{2}$ is not simpler than the other values in the inductive sense of assuming less in order to account for our observational data but only in the *descriptive* sense of providing a *symbolically* simpler representation of these data. But this greater symbolic simplicity arising from the value $\frac{1}{2}$ expresses itself not only in the *equality* of the velocities of light in opposite directions—the ratio of the outgoing and return velocities being in general $\dfrac{1-\epsilon}{\epsilon}$ —but also shows its unique descriptive advantages by assuring that synchronism will be both a symmetric and a transitive relation upon using *different* clocks in the same system.[12]

These considerations now enable us to see that physical facts which are independent of descriptive conventions do *not* dictate discordant judgments by different Galilean observers concerning the simultaneity of given events.

Consider the familiar example of the two vertical bolts of lightning which strike a moving train at points A' and B', respectively, and the ground at points A and B, respectively, A and A' being to the left of B and B', respectively. Let the distance AB in the ground system be $2d$. If we now define simultaneity in the ground-system by the choice $\epsilon = \frac{1}{2}$, then the velocity of light traveling from A to the midpoint C of AB becomes equal to the velocity of light traveling in the opposite direction BC.[13] And if the arrivals of these two oppositely directed light pulses coincide at C, then the ground observer will say that the bolt at AA' struck simultaneously with the bolt at BB', say at $t = 0$. Will the train observer's observations of the lightning flashes *compel* him to say that the bolts did *not* strike simultaneously? Decidedly not! To be sure, since the train is moving, say, to the left relatively to the ground, it will be impossible that the two horizontal pulses which meet at the midpoint C in the ground-system also meet at the midpoint C' of the train system, which was adjacent to the point C when the ground-system clock at C read $t = 0$. Hence the flash from A' will arrive at C' *earlier* than the one from B'. But this fact will hardly require the train observer to say that the point A' was struck by lightning *earlier* than the point B', *unless* the train observer *too* has chosen *equal* values of ϵ such as $\frac{1}{2}$ to set the clocks at A' and at B' to be each simultaneous with the clock at C' in his own system, a choice which then commits him to say that the time required by light from the left to traverse the distance $A'C'$ is the same as the transit-time of light from the right for an equal distance $B'C'$.[14] But, apart from descriptive convenience, what is to prevent the train observer from choosing suitable values $\epsilon \neq \frac{1}{2}$ $(0 < \epsilon < 1)$ such that he too will say that the lightning bolts struck simultaneously, just as the ground observer did? Such a choice can always be made by the train observer. For suppose that the clocks at A' and at B' were respectively synchronized from the midpoint C' on the basis of any proper positive fractional values $\epsilon_{A'}$ and $\epsilon_{B'}$ that satisfy the equation

$$(2) \qquad \epsilon_{A'} - \epsilon_{B'} = \beta, \qquad \text{where } \beta \equiv \frac{v}{c}.$$

Then the train observer at C' would judge the bolts at A' and B' to have struck simultaneously and would account for the time-difference $\dfrac{2d \cdot \beta}{c\sqrt{1 - \beta^2}}$ between the arrivals of the light-pulses from them at C' by the corresponding difference between the one-way velocities of the pulses along $A'C'$ and $B'C'$ respectively. Thus, if $\beta < \frac{1}{2}$ and we choose $\epsilon_{B'} = \frac{1}{2}$, then $\epsilon_{A'}$ will have the fractional value $\frac{1}{2} + \beta$ and the train-system time t' of the *simultaneous* occurrences of the bolts at A' and B' is $t' = \dfrac{d \cdot v}{c^2 \sqrt{1 - \beta^2}}$.

That this judgment of simultaneity in the train system need not be confined to a train observer at the midpoint C' of $A'\,B'$ emerges from the following considerations: the lightning-flashes at A' and B' not being themselves signal connectible, light pulses originating with these flashes will always meet on the moving train at some point D' different from C' but lying between A' and B' at a distance $d\sqrt{\dfrac{c + v}{c - v}}$ from A' and at a lesser distance $d\sqrt{\dfrac{c - v}{c + v}}$ from B'. And in order to define the two flashes to have occurred simultaneously, the train observer need only make appropriate choices of ϵ for synchronizing the clocks at A' and at B' with the clock at D' to define the ratio of the velocity of the light coming from the left to the velocity of the light coming from the right so as to be the same as the ratio $\dfrac{c + v}{c - v}$ of the distance $A'\,D'$ to the distance $D'\,B'$. Thus, for example, if again $\beta < \frac{1}{2}$, a choice of the proper fractional values $\epsilon_{B'} = \frac{1}{2}$ and $\epsilon_{A'} = \dfrac{c + 3v}{2\,(c + v)}$ would render the two bolts at A' and B' simultaneous in the judgment of an observer at D' and would assign to them the same time $t' = \dfrac{d \cdot v}{c^2 \sqrt{1 - \beta^2}}$ as had been assigned by the observer at C'.

The flash at AA' is causally absolutely nonconnectible with any of those events at point B in the ground-system which are members of the open time-interval I bisected by the flash at BB' and of duration $\dfrac{4d}{c}$ units of time in the ground-system. It is this absolute causal nonconnectibility that enables the ground-observer to say that the BB' flash was simultaneous with the AA' flash, as required by his choice of $\epsilon = \frac{1}{2}$, and *also* enables the train observer to implement his own separate choice of $\epsilon = \frac{1}{2}$ as follows: (i) it is *not* the flash at BB' that is simultaneous with the AA' flash, as the ground-system observer maintains by his assignment of $t = 0$ to both events, but a different I-interval event E_e at B which is absolutely earlier than the BB' flash, the ground-system clock at B reading the time $t = -\dfrac{2vd}{c^2}$ upon the occurrence of E_e, and (ii) the train-system time of the AA' flash and of the event E_e is $t' = -\dfrac{vd}{c^2\sqrt{1-\beta^2}}$, but the BB' flash occurs at the later train-system time $t' = +\dfrac{vd}{c^2\sqrt{1-\beta^2}}$.

It follows that the conventionality of simultaneity within each inertial system entailed by the aforementioned absolute causal nonconnectibility allows each Galilean observer to choose his own values of ϵ *either* so as to agree with the other observers on simultaneity *or* so as to disagree. If each separate Galilean frame does choose the value ½—which Einstein assumed in the formulation of the theory for the sake of the resulting descriptive simplicity—then the relative motion of these frames indeed makes disagreement in their judgments of simultaneity unavoidable, except in regard to pairs of events lying in the planes perpendicular to the direction of their relative motion.[15] But, in the first instance, it is not the relative motion of inertial systems but the limiting character of the velocity of light which gives rise to the relativity of simultaneity.

Moreover, this limiting property of light is evidently an objective property of the causal structure of the physical world, quite independent of man's presence in the cosmos and of his measuring activities. The resulting relativity of simultaneity is therefore expressive of a property of the causal relatedness of physical events and is *not*, in the first instance, *generated* by *our* inability to carry out those measuring *operations* that would define absolute simultaneity. Instead, the impossibility of such operations is a consequence of the more fundamental impossibility of the required causal relations between physical events. To be sure, operations of measurement are indispensable for *discovering* or *knowing* that particular physical events can or cannot sustain the causal relations which would define relations of temporal succession or of ordinal simultaneity between them. But the actual or physically possible causal relations in question are or are not sustained by physical events quite apart from *our* actual or hypothetical measuring operations and are *not* first *conferred* on nature by our operations. In short, it is because no relations of absolute simultaneity *exist* to be measured that measurement cannot disclose them; it is *not* the mere failure of measurement to disclose them that *constitutes* their nonexistence, much as that failure is *evidence* for their nonexistence.

Only a philosophical obfuscation of this state of affairs can make plausible the view that the relativity of simultaneity (or, for that matter, any of the other philosophical innovations of relativity theory) lends support to the subjectivism of homocentric operationism or of phenomenalistic positivism (for further details, see the references to other papers of mine given in footnote 33).

3. THE PRINCIPLE OF THE CONSTANCY OF THE SPEED OF LIGHT ("LIGHT PRINCIPLE")

In what sense can the null-result of the Michelson-Morley experiment legitimately be held to support the claim that the speed of light is the same constant c in all inertial systems, independent of the relative velocity of the source and observer, and of direction, position, and time?[16]

The null-result of the Michelson-Morley experiment merely showed that if *within* an inertial system, light-rays are jointly emitted from a given point in different directions of the system and then reflected from mirrors at equal distances from that point, as measured by rigid rods, then they will return together to their common point of emission. And it must be remembered that the equality of the round-trip times of light in different directions of the system is measured here not, of course, by material clocks but by light itself (absence of an interference fringe shift).[17] The repetition of this experiment at different times of the year, i.e., in different inertial systems, showed only that there is no difference within *any* given inertial system in the round-trip times as between different directions within that system. But the outcome of the Michelson-Morley experiment does *not* show at all either that (a) the round-trip (or one-way) time required by light to traverse a closed (or open) path of length $2\,l$ (or l) has the same numerical value in different inertial systems, as measured by material clocks stationed in these systems[18] or that (b) if, contrary to the arrangements in the Michelson-Morley and Kennedy-Thorndike experiments, the source of the light is outside the frame K in which its velocity is measured, then the velocity in K will be independent of the velocity of the source relative to K. In fact, the statement about the round-trip times made under (a) was first substantiated by the Kennedy-Thorndike experiment of 1932, as we shall see, and the assertion under (b) received its confirmation by observations on the light from double stars.[19] Yet the light principle certainly affirms both (a) and (b) and thus clearly claims more than is vouchsafed by the Michelson-Morley experiment. Accordingly, we can see that in addition to the result of the Michelson-Morley experiment, the light principle contains at least all of the following theses:

(i) The assertion given under (a), which undoubtedly goes beyond the null-result of the Michelson-Morley experiment. For brevity, we shall call it "the clock axiom" in order to allude to its reference to clock-times of travel. Although lacking experimental corroboration at the time of Einstein's enunciation of the light principle, this "clock axiom" was suggested by the fundamental assumption of special relativity that there are no preferred inertial systems.

(ii) The Einstein postulate regarding the maximal character of the velocity of light, which is the source of the conventionality and relativity of simultaneity within a given inertial system and as between different systems respectively. This postulate *allows* but does *not* entail that we choose the same value $\epsilon = \frac{1}{2}$ for all directions within any given system and also for each different system.

(iii) The claim that the velocity of light in any inertial system is independent of the velocity of its source.

To see specifically how the light principle depends for its validity upon the truth of all of these constituent theses, we now consider the consequences of abandoning any one of them while preserving the remaining two. To do so, we direct our attention to the one-way velocity of an outgoing light pulse that traverses a distance l in system S and also to the one-way velocity of such a pulse traversing a distance l in system S'. Let T_s and $T_{s'}$ be the respective outgoing transit times of these light pulses for the distances l in S and S', the corresponding round-trip times in these frames being τ_s and $\tau_{s'}$. In this notation, Eq. (1) of Sec. 2 becomes

$$T_s = \epsilon \tau_s \quad ,$$

and similarly for S'. Hence, the relevant one-way velocities of

light in these systems are, respectively, given by
$$v_s = (l/T_s) = (l/\epsilon\tau_s),$$
and

$$v_{s'} = (l/\epsilon\tau_{s'}).$$

Our problem is to determine, one by one, the consequences of assuming that of the three above ingredients of the light principle, only two can be invoked at a time in an attempt to assure that if $v_s = c$ in virtue of the observed value of τ_s and of a choice of $\epsilon = \frac{1}{2}$ for S, then $v_{s'}$ will also have the value c.

(i) In the absence of the clock axiom, it can well be that $\tau_s \neq \tau_{s'}$. In that case, the relations $v_s = (l/\frac{1}{2}\tau_s) = c$ and $v_{s'} = (l/\epsilon\tau_{s'})$ tell us that it will not be possible to make $v_{s'} = c$ by a choice of $\epsilon = \frac{1}{2}$ in S'. To be sure, it may still be possible then to choose an appropriately different value of ϵ for S' so as to make $v_{s'} = c$. But, much as the latter choice of ϵ might yield the value c for the outgoing one-way velocity of light in S', it would also inescapably entail a value different from c for the return-velocity. And such a result would not be in keeping with the light principle.

(ii) If, on the other hand, we guarantee that $\tau_s = \tau_{s'}$ by assuming the clock axiom but disallow the freedom to choose a value of ϵ for each inertial system by withdrawing the second constituent thesis above, then $v_{s'}$ could readily be different from c. For the illegitimacy of choosing ϵ to be $\frac{1}{2}$ in S' would then derive from physical facts incompatible with the conventionality of simultaneity which objectively fix the value of $T_{s'}$ as different from $\frac{1}{2}\tau_{s'}$.

(iii) The need for the third ingredient is obvious in the light of what has already been said.

It is of importance to note that even when all of the above constituent principles of the light principle are assumed, no fact of nature independent of our descriptive conventions would be contradicted, if we chose values of ϵ other than $\frac{1}{2}$ for each inertial system, thereby making the velocity of light different from c in both senses along each direction in all inertial systems. I have shown elsewhere [*American Journal of Physics*, Vol. 24, pp. 588–90, 1956] that this conclusion is not invalidated either by determinations of the one-way velocity of light on the basis of measurements of the half-wave-length of standing waves in cavity resonators or by measurements of the ratio of the electromagnetic and electrostatic units of charge. The assertion that the invariant velocity of light is *c* is therefore not, in its entirety, a purely factual assertion. But we saw that it is nonetheless a consequence of a presumed physical fact that the specification of the velocity of light involves a stipulational element which, in combination with other factual principles, *allows* us to say that the velocity of light is *c*.

The importance of complete clarity on the logical status of the light principle is apparent from the fact that misunderstandings of it still issue in misconceived and irrelevant attacks upon it. A very recent case in point is a paper by the noted experimental physicist H. E. Ives ["Revisions of the Lorentz Transformations," *Proceedings of The American Philosophical Society* Vol. 95, p. 125, 1951], who rests his proposed revisions of the Lorentz transformations on the following argumentation, whose unsoundness is evident from the analysis given above: "Einstein . . . proposed two principles: the first, 'The Principle of Relativity,' is the same in name and content as Poincaré's principle of relativity of the year before [see footnote 8 of Sec. 2 above]; the second, 'The Principle of the Constancy of the Velocity of Light' . . . is that the velocity of light is the same on all relatively moving bodies. Adhering at the same time to the independence of the velocity of light from that of the source, Einstein thus asked the acceptance of a paradox. . . . He also decreed a pseudo-operational procedure for obtaining [the Lorentz transformations] . . . Distances were to be measured by rods laid end to end, distant clocks were to be set by light signals *ascribed* the velocity *c*. This proposed procedure . . . fell short of actually meeting the [operational] requirement. The assignment of a definite value to an unknown velocity, by fiat, without recourse to measuring instruments, is not a true physical operation, it is more properly described as a ritual . . . Einstein . . . invoked supposed experimental fact to support his principle. . . .

"This appeal to experiment to support a logical contradiction, is however invalid. The 'experience' cited [by Einstein] is the customary laboratory measurement of the velocity of light by signals sent out and back, while the Lorentz transformations describe signals sent in one direction. No precision measurement of this sort has been performed; it would require, as compared with the experimental equipment adequate for out and back measurement, additional instruments, whose behavior under manipulation would have to be established and taken account of. It is an unwarranted assumption that such a measurement would yield the value 'c'. . . . It develops that the velocity of light measured by signals sent in one direction is not 'the universal constant c.' The 'principle' of the constancy of the velocity of light is not merely 'un-understandable', it is not supported by 'objective matters of fact'; it is untenable, and, . . . unnecessary.

"On any randomly chosen material platform consider a light signal proceeding from one end, at which is a clock, to a reflector at the far end, and back to the clock. Because of the independence of the velocity of light from that of matter we may expect the velocity of light in the out and back directions, in terms of divisions on the platform, and the clock at the origin, to be in general different. Call the out and back velocity c_o and c_b. . . . A point of great importance may here be noted. It is that we do not need to assign definite individual values to c_o and c_b such for instance as calling them equal as is done in Einstein's arbitrary 'definition' of simultaneity. We carry these in our calculations as real although undetermined quantities. . . ."

4. THE EXPERIMENTAL CONFIRMATION OF THE KINEMATICS OF THE SPECIAL THEORY OF RELATIVITY

Since the Michelson-Morley experiment could hardly be regarded as empirical proof for the "clock axiom" contained in the light principle, it is fortunate that an experiment devised by Kennedy and Thorndike can be invoked as support for that axiom's relativistic denial of the existence of preferred inertial systems.[20] The apparatus used was essentially similar to that of the Michelson-Morley experiment, except for making the lengths L and l of the arms of the interferometer as *different* as possible in order to maximize the difference between the travel times of the partial beams. Assume that the apparatus has a velocity relative to the ether, which could not be detected under the particular conditions of the Michelson-Morley experiment in virtue of a *bona fide* Lorentz-Fitzgerald contraction. Then the difference $\dfrac{2(L-l)}{\sqrt{c^2-v^2}}$

between the travel times of the two partial beams is a
function of the diurnally and annually changing velocity v
of the apparatus (as well as of the length difference $L - l$
between the two arms), and if the period of the light source
does not itself depend upon this velocity relative to the fixed
ether, the changing time difference ought to give rise to
corresponding observable shifts in the fringe pattern.

Now, if the Kennedy-Thorndike experiment had yielded a
positive effect instead of the null-result which it did actually
yield, then it could have been cogently argued that the Michelson-Morley experiment was evidence for a *bona fide* Lorentz-Fitzgerald contraction, just as a fringe shift produced by
heating one of the arms of the interferometer could be held
to be evidence for the elongation of that arm. But, in view
of the *de facto* null outcome of the Kennedy-Thorndike
experiment, there is very good reason indeed to attribute the
absence of a diurnal or annual variation in the time-difference
between the two partial beams to a constancy, as between
different inertial systems, of the time required by each of the
partial beams to traverse its own closed path. And thus we
are entitled to say that the Kennedy-Thorndike experiment
has provided empirical sanction for the clock axiom.[21]

We recall that in 1905, there was no unambiguous experimental evidence supporting Einstein's postulate that light
is the fastest signal. But subsequent experiments showed
that the mass and kinetic energy of accelerated particles
become indefinitely large as their velocity approaches that
of light.[22]

There is therefore impressive empirical evidence for all
of the constituent theses of the light principle. It would be
an error, however, to suppose that the experimental justification of the light principle suffices also to substantiate the
Lorentz transformations. For these equations entail the clock
retardation, whereas the light principle alone does not. A
lucid demonstration of this fact has recently been given by
H. P. Robertson.[23] He considers a linear transformation
$$T: \quad (t', x', y', z') \quad \rightarrow \quad (t, x, y, z)$$
between a kind of primary inertial system Σ and a "moving"
inertial system S'. Upon having fixed 13 of the 16 coefficients
of this transformation by various conventions, symmetry
conditions, and a specification of the velocity v of S' relative

to Σ, Robertson is concerned with the experimental warrant for asserting that the remaining 3 coefficients have the values required by the Lorentz transformations. And he then shows that the Michelson-Morley and Kennedy-Thorndike experiments, which do succeed in completing the confirmation of the light principle, do *not* suffice to fix the remaining three coefficients of the transformation such that these have the values required by the Lorentz transformations. An additional experiment is needed to do so: the laboratory work of Ives and Stilwell (1938) furnished the lacking data by observations on high speed canal rays. And it was their confirmation of the transverse Doppler effect that constituted the first experimental proof of the clock retardation affirmed by the Lorentz transformations. Additional confirmation has been provided by data on the rate of disintegration of mesons.[24]

According to the special theory of relativity, the clock retardation is exhibited by all natural clocks, be they the material clocks which keep astronomical time or atomic clocks like cesium atoms, whose unit the theory assumed to have a time-invariant ratio to the astronomical unit. But this assumption of a constant ratio of the atomic and astronomical units of time has been questioned by Dirac, Milne, Jordan, and others, who have suggested that the ratio increases continuously by amounts of the order of $\frac{1}{T}$ per year, where T is "the age of the universe" in years. If T is about 4×10^9 years, the change at the present epoch is of the order of $1/10^9$. Changes of this order may soon be measurable over intervals of a few years, since Essen and Parry of the National Physical Laboratory in England have recently measured the natural resonant frequency of the cesium atom with a stated precision of 1 in 10^9 and hope for even higher accuracies.[25]

5. THE PHILOSOPHICAL ISSUE BETWEEN LORENTZ AND EINSTEIN

Many writers tell us that the Lorentz-Fitzgerald contraction hypothesis was an *ad hoc* explanation of the result of the Michelson-Morley experiment, claiming that Einstein, on the other hand, "explained" the Lorentz-Fitzgerald contraction. Thus they charge Lorentz with having formulated a hypothesis whose addition to classical physics could serve to explain only the otherwise embarrassing outcome of the

Michelson-Morley experiment while precluding, in principle, any other experimental test. The unfoundedness of this charge is already apparent from our discussion of the reasoning underlying the Kennedy-Thorndike experiment. And, as we saw, far from explaining the outcome of the Michelson-Morley experiment as a consequence of more fundamental principles, Einstein incorporated its null result as a physical axiom in his light principle.

It is a widespread error to suppose that Einstein nonetheless furnished an explanation for the Lorentz-Fitzgerald contraction by exhibiting the contraction of a moving rod to be a consequence of the relativity of simultaneity as between different frames on the basis of the Lorentz transformations. This error is inspired by the numerical equality of the contraction factors of these two kinds of contraction, the value being $(1 - \beta^2)^{1/2}$ in each case. But they are different, because the Lorentz-Fitzgerald contraction is measured in the very system in which the contracted arm is *at rest*, whereas the contraction that Einstein derived from the Lorentz transformations pertains to the length measured in a system relative to which the arm is *in motion*. More explicitly, the Lorentz-Fitzgerald contraction hypothesis asserts a comparison of the actual length of the arm, as measured by the round-trip time of light, to the greater length that the travel-time would have revealed, if the classical ether theory were true. Thus, using light as the standard for effecting the comparison, this hypothesis affirms that in the *same* system and under the same conditions of measurement, the metrical properties of the arm are different from the ones predicted by classical ether theory. And this difference or contraction is clearly quite independent of any contraction based on comparisons of lengths in different inertial systems. On the other hand, the contraction which Einstein deduced from the Lorentz transformations is based on a comparison of the length of a rod, as measured from an inertial system relative to which it is in motion, to the length of that same rod, as measured in its own rest system. Unlike the Lorentz-Fitzgerald contraction, this "Einstein contraction" is a *symmetrical* relation between the measurements made in any two inertial systems and is a consequence of the inter-systemic relativity of simultaneity, because it relates lengths determined from *different* inertial perspectives of measurement, instead of contrasting conflicting claims concerning the results obtained under the same conditions of measurement. What Einstein did explain, therefore, is this "metrogenic" contraction, a phenomenon which poses no greater logical difficulties than the differences in the angular sizes of bodies that are observed from different distances. Lest it be thought that the confusion of the two kinds of contraction just discussed is a thing of the past, I cite the following recent statements from Sir E. T. Whittaker's Tarner Lectures: "The Lorentz transformation . . . supplies at once an explanation of the Fitzgerald contraction. . .[26] the failure of all attempts to determine the velocity of the earth by comparing the Fitzgerald contraction in rods directed parallel and perpendicular to the terrestrial motion . . . is necessitated by the Postulate of Relativity. But there is no impossibility in principle at any rate, in observing the contraction, provided we can make use of an observation-post which is *outside* the moving system."[27] To be sure, if Whittaker's proviso of an ether-system observation post outside the moving earth be granted, then an observer at that post who interprets his data *pre*-relativistically would confirm the Lorentz-Fitzgerald contraction by finding that the "true" length of the moving arm, which he believes himself to be observing from his vantage point, is smaller than the "spurious" length measured by the rod of a terrestrial observer. But the relativistic explanation of the numerically equal Einstein contraction actually involved here *rejects*, as we shall see in detail, the very conceptions which alone give meaning to (a) construing the findings of the extraterrestrial observer as *equivalent* to a contraction *within* the moving system in the sense of Lorentz and Fitzgerald, and (b) asking the question as to *why* there is a *L–F* contraction *within* the moving system. And the relativistic deduction of the Einstein contraction from the Lorentz transformations can therefore have no bearing at all on *why* the Michelson-Morley experiment failed to fulfill the predictions of the classical ether theory.

We see that the locus of the philosophical difference between Lorentz and Einstein has been misplaced by the proponents of the *ad hoc* charge against Lorentz. To understand Einstein's philosophical innovation, we must take cognizance of the fact that the Lorentz-Fitzgerald contraction hypothesis was not the only addition to the ether theory made by Lorentz in order to account for the available body of experimental data. In addition, he had been driven to postulate with J. Larmor that just as rods are caused to contract in any inertial system moving relatively to the ether, so also clocks are *caused* by that very motion to modify their rates and to read a spurious "local" time (as distinct from the "true" time shown by the clocks in the ether-system). The conceptual framework of Lorentz' interpretation of the transformation equations known by his name was the absolutistic one in which the clocks and rods even in the privileged ether system merely *recorded* but did not *define* the topology and metric of container space and time. On this basis, Lorentz was led to reason somewhat as follows:

1. Since the horizontal arm of the Michelson-Morley experiment is shorter than a rod lying alongside it but conforming to the expectations of classical optics and its container theory of space, we must infer that when a unit rod in the ether system is transported to a moving system, it can no longer be a true unit rod but becomes shorter than unity in the moving system, and similarly for clocks.

2. The *deviation* from the classically expected behavior exhibited by rods and clocks must have a *cause* in the sense of being due to a perturbational influence. For in the absence of such a cause, the classically expected behavior would have occurred spontaneously.

Einstein left the Lorentz transformations formally unaltered. But the reasoning underlying his radical reinterpretation of their physical meaning was probably somewhat as follows:

As Riemann has pointed out, "in the case of a discrete manifold the criterion of length is already contained in the concept of this manifold but in a continuous manifold, it must be brought in from elsewhere."[28] This means that, contrary to the container theory, the length of a body is not a measure of an intrinsic amount of space between its end-points by themselves. More specifically, as Cantor has shown, the continuity of space assures that there are just as many points between the end-points of a long segment as between those of a short one. There is thus no intrinsic attribute of the spaces between these pairs of end-points which would endow each of their segments with a distinct length. The relational theory of space therefore rightly maintains that the length of a body *AB* is an attribute of the relation be-between two *pairs* of points: the termini of *AB* on the one hand and those of the chosen unit rod on the other. Similarly the length of a time-interval is a ratio of that interval to the unit defined by some periodic physical process. And it is inherent in this definition of length as a ratio that the unit rod be at rest relative to *AB* when performing its metrical function.[29]

But, on this new conception of length, one is not entitled to infer with Lorentz that a unit rod in the ether system will no longer be unity, *as a matter of physical fact*, once it has been transported to a moving system, and that such transport renders spurious the "local" readings of clocks in moving systems. For the relational conception *allows* us to *call* that same rod unity in the moving system *by definition*, and similarly for the units of time on clocks at rest in a moving system. If Lorentz had realized that the length of this rod in the moving system can be legitimately *decreed* by definition, and similarly for the periods of material clocks, then it would have been clear to him that the ground is cut from under his distinction between "true" and "local" (i.e., spurious) lengths and times and thereby from his idea that the horizontal arm in the Michelson-Morley experiment is actually shorter than the vertical arm. Thus, a coupling of the epistemological insights of the relational theory of length with the experimental findings of optics deprives reference to a preferred ether system of all objective physical significance and makes possible the enunciation of the principle of relativity.

We can understand Einstein's philosophical departure from the *second* step in Lorentz' reasoning by giving an analysis of Lorentz' invocation of a *cause* for the contraction revealed by the Michelson-Morley experiment.

Every physical theory tells us what particular behavior of physical entities or systems it regards as "natural" in the absence of *perturbational* influences. Concurrently, it specifies the influences or causes which it regards as responsible for any *deviations* from the assumedly "natural" behavior. But when such deviations are observed and a theory cannot designate the perturbations to which it proposes to attribute them, its assumptions concerning the character of the "natural" or unperturbed behavior become subject to doubt. For the reliability of our conceptions as to what pattern of occurrences is "natural" is no greater than the *scope* of the evidence on which they rest. And a theory's failure to designate the perturbing causes of the nonfulfillment of its expectations therefore demands the envisionment of the possibility that (a) the "natural" behavior of things is indeed different from what the theory in question has been supposing it to be and that (b) deviations from the assumedly natural behavior transpire *without* perturbational causes. Several examples from past and present scientific controversy attest to the mistaken search for the perturbational factors which are supposed to cause deviations from the pattern which a particular theory unquestioningly and tenaciously affirms to be the natural one. Thus, Aristotelian critics of Galileo, assuming that Aristotle's mechanics describes the natural behavior, asked Galileo to specify the cause which prevents a body from coming to rest and maintains its speed in the same straight line in the manner of Newton's first law of motion. It was axiomatic for them that uniform motion could not continue indefinitely in the absence of net external forces. In our own time, there are those who ask: if the "new cosmology" of Bondi and Gold is true, must there not be a divine interference (perturbation) in the natural order whereby the spontaneous accretion ("creation") of matter is caused?[30] The propounders of this question do not tell us, however, on what basis they take it for granted that the constancy of the mass (-energy) content of the universe is *cosmically* the natural state of affairs. Curiously enough, other theologians ask us to regard a state of "nothingness" (whatever that is!) as the natural state of the universe and thereby endeavor to create grounds for arguing that the mere existence and conservation of matter or energy require a divine creator and sustainer. But even if it should indeed turn out that the physical world is a three-dimensional expanding spherical space whose radius of curvature had a minimum value at one time and that the latter was a genuine beginning because it was not preceded by an earlier contraction of which the present expansion is an "elastic" rebound, then *every* phase of this expansion process must be held to be integral to the *natural* behavior of the universe. In that case, the inception of the expansion does not constitute evidence for the operation of a divine creator as perturbational cause, any more than any other phase of the expansion does. For there is absolutely no criterion for distinguishing those newly observed or inferred facts which merely compel the revision of previous generalizations and which the proponent of divine creation regards as part of the "natural order" from those to which he gratuitously attributes the status of being "outside" the "natural order" and of therefore being due to divine intervention in that order. We see that the theological concept of miracles attributes a supernatural origin to certain phenomena by the mere fiat of declaring that a certain set of limited empirical generalizations which do not allow for these phenomena define with *certainty* what is natural. As if observed events presented themselves to us with identification tags as to their "naturalness"! [31]

The basis for Einstein's philosophical objection to the second step in Lorentz' reasoning is now at hand: it was an error on Lorentz' part to persist, in the face of mounting contrary evidence, in regarding the classically expected behavior as the natural behavior. It was this persistence which forced him to explain the observed deviations from the classical laws by postulating the operation of a physically nondesignatable ether as a perturbational cause. Having used the relational theory of length and time to reject the conclusion of the first step in Lorentz' reasoning, Einstein was able to see that the unexpected results of the Michelson-Morley experiment do not require any perturbational causes at all, because they are integral to the "natural" behavior of things.

The character and significance of these fundamental philosophical differences between Einstein's conception of the Lorentz transformations, on the one hand, and the interpretation of earlier versions of these transformations by his predecessors Fitzgerald, Larmor, Poincaré (see footnote 8 in Sec. 2 above) and Lorentz, on the other, altogether escaped recognition by E. T. Whittaker in his very recent account of the history of the development of the special theory of relativity. Entitling his chapter on that theory "The Relativity Theory of Poincaré and Lorentz," he reaches the following unwarranted judgment concerning Einstein's contribution to the theory [32]: "In the autumn of the same year (1905), . . . Einstein published a paper which set forth the relativity theory of Poincaré and Lorentz with some amplifications, and which attracted much attention. He asserted as a fundamental principle the constancy of the velocity of light. . . . an assertion which at the time was widely accepted, but has been severely criticized by later writers [at this point, Whittaker refers to the paper by H. E. Ives whose logical inadequacies the reader will recall from the discussion in Sec. 3. above]. In this paper Einstein gave the modifications which must now be introduced into the formulas for aberration and the Doppler effect."

In conclusion, it should be noted that the term "relational" has been used advisedly throughout this paper in place of the more common term "operational" to characterize the relativistic conception of space and time. For I reject Bridgman's contention that we human beings are the ones who first confer properties and relations upon physical entities by our operations of measurement, and I do not think that the theory of relativity can be validly adduced in support of this homocentric form of operationism.[33] Einstein's theory asks us to conceive the topology and metric of space-time as systems of relations between physical events and things. But both these things and their relations are independent of man's presence in the cosmos. Our operations of measurement merely discover or ascertain the structure of space-time but they do *not* generate it.

NOTES

[1] H. Reichenbach, *Axiomatik der relativistischen Raum-Zeit-Lehre,* (Braunschweig: Vieweg, 1924), Vol. 72 of *Die Wissenschaft* (hereafter this work will be cited as *AR*); *The Philosophy of Space and Time* (New York: Dover, 1958). My treatment of several of the issues dealt with in this paper is greatly indebted to these books by Reichenbach.

[2] References to the relevant writings of the authors mentioned in this section will be given in the appropriate places later in this essay.

[3] See *AR*, Secs. 22–3.

[4] It might be objected at once that this definition is vitiated by circularity on the grounds that the sole basis for characterizing one of the two termini of a causal chain as *the* emission-terminus is that it is the earlier one of the two. There are two ways, however in which this circularity can be avoided:

(i) the temporal intuition of a local human observer is used at E_1 to certify that E_1 is an emission-event by virtue of being locally earlier than the events in its immediate spatial vicinity belonging to the same causal chain, a corresponding procedure being used to identify E_2 as an absorption-event. The function of the definition given above is then to define the relation "earlier than" for spatially-separated, distant events E_1 and E_2;

(ii) The alternative method for avoiding circularity, which I have developed in detail in other publications [cf. my contribution to P. A. Schilpp (Ed.), *The Philosophy of Rudolf Carnap, Library of Living Philosophers*, Vol. XI (Tudor, to be published); "Time and Entropy," *American Scientist 43*, 550, 1955, and "Das Zeitproblem," *Archiv für Philosophie, 7,* 165–208, 1957], is inspired by the view that since temporality is presumably a significant attribute of the physical world independently of human consciousness (i.e., prior to the advent of man, and after his disappearance from the cosmos), it ought to be possible (a) to specify the purely physical bases of the temporal relations between physical events without invoking man's conscious intuition in the axiomatic foundations, and then (b) to exhibit man's possession of the psychological deliverances of time as a consequence of his organism's participation in those purely physical processes which equip the inorganic sector of the universe with temporality. In this analysis of the physical basis of time, temporal betweenness and distant simultaneity are defined in terms of a symmetrical relation of causal connectedness between events belonging to reversible genidentical causal chains, taken in conjunction with the principle of causal continuity governing such chains. With the aid of these definitions, which are needed for giving meaning to the concepts of "closed system" and of the "entropy of an extended, closed system at a given time," it is possible to provide a noncircular criterion of the difference between the emission-event and the corresponding absorption-event of an irreversible causal chain such as the propagation of a light pulse: of the two termini of such a chain, the emission-event is characterized by being simultaneous with the lower entropy state of the closed system comprising the emitter and the absorber, the absorption-event being simultaneous with the correspondingly higher entropy state. But this entropic definition of "earlier than" requires a crucial refinement to take account of the non-monotonicity of the entropy-increase in a permanently closed system arising from the fundamental reversibility of microprocesses. For the relevant details, I refer the reader to H. Reichenbach, *The Direction of Time*, (Berkeley: Univ. California Press, 1956), Ch. III. For a non-entropic definition of "earlier than," see E. L. Hill and A. Grünbaum "Irreversible Processes in Physical Theory," *Nature, 179,* 1296, (1957).

[5] See M. Abraham, *Ann. d. Physik, 10,* 105, 1903. The qualification *in vacuo* is essential in characterizing the limiting velocity in the theory of relativity. For we know from the phenomenon of Cerenkov radiation (Cf. I. E. Tamm, *Am. Scientist 47,* 169, 1959), that a particle moving in a medium can possess a velocity which is greater than the velocity c' of light in that medium though less than the velocity c of light *in vacuo.*

6 See Møller, *The Theory of Relativity* (New York: Oxford University Press, 1952), pp. 85–9, and von Laue, *Die Relativitätstheorie* (Braunschweig: Fredrich Vieweg, 1952), Vol. I., p. 27.

7 Einstein, "Autobiographical Notes" in P. A. Schilpp (Ed.), *Albert Einstein: Philosopher-Scientist* (New York: Tudor, 1949), p. 53. M. Polanyi has claimed [cf. his *Personal Knowledge*, Chicago, 1958, pp. 9–15] that the pre-1905 experiments now generally cited as Einstein's decisive inspiration for developing the special theory of relativity (e.g. the Michelson-Morley experiment) played either a wholly subordinate role or were then not even known to Einstein. Cf. also G. Holton's forthcoming monograph *On the Origins of Relativity Theory*.

8 See Laue, footnote 6, p. 34n. It is of both historical and logical importance to note that in an address "The Principles of Mathematical Physics" delivered in St. Louis on September 24, 1904, and published in *The Monist, 15,* 1–24, 1905, (reprinted in the *Scientific Monthly, 82, 165,* April, 1956), H. Poincaré had already envisioned the construction of a new mechanics in which the velocity of light would play a limiting role. Although he concluded this paper with the remark that "as yet nothing proves that the (old) principles will not come forth from the combat victorious and intact" (p. 24), Poincaré did prophesy that "From all these results, if they are confirmed, would arise an entirely new mechanics, which would be, above all, characterizd by this fact, that no velocity could surpass that of light, any more than any temperature, could fall below the zero absolute, because bodies would oppose an increasing inertia to the causes, which would tend to accelerate their motion; and this inertia would become infinite when one approached the velocity of light" (p. 16). But, unlike Einstein, Poincaré failed to see the import of this new limiting postulate for the meaning of simultaneity: in the very same paper (p. 11), he speaks of spatially separated clocks as marking *the same hour at the same physical instant* (my italics). And he distinguishes between watches which mark "the true time" and those that mark only the "local time," a distinction which was also invoked, as we shall see, by Larmor and Lorentz. But Poincaré does note that a Galilean observer will not be able to detect whether his frame is one in which the clocks mark the allegedly spurious local time. Accordingly, he affirms "The principle of relativity, according to which the laws of physical phenomena should be the same, whether for an observer fixed, or for an observer carried along in a uniform movement of translation; so that we have not any means of discerning whether or not we are carried along in such a motion" (p. 5). For a useful, brief account of these pre-Einsteinian conceptions, cf. P. Bergmann, *Science, 123,* 3, 1956.

[9] It must be remembered that, in its metrical form, this postulate does not confine purely "geometric" velocities which are not the velocities of causal chains to the value c. For example, within any given inertial system K, special relativity allows us to subtract vectorially (as against by means of the Einstein velocity addition formula) a velocity $v_1 = .9c$ of body A in K and a velocity $v_2 = -.3c$ of body B in K to obtain 1.2c as the relative velocity of separation of A and B as judged by the K-observer [though not by an observer attached to either A or B!]. For no body or disturbance is thereby asserted to be traveling relative to any other at the velocity 1.2c of separation, and since the process of separation has no direction of propagation, it cannot be a causal chain. See Laue, footnote 6, pp. 40–1; L. Silberstein, *The Theory of Relativity* (New York: Macmillan, 1914), p. 164n; A. Sommerfeld, Notes in *The Principle of Relativity*, a collection of original memoirs, Dover reprint, p. 94; A. Grünbaum, *Phil. of Sci.*, *22*, 53, 1955; H. P. Robertson, *Mathematical Reviews*, *16*, 1166, 1955; G. D. Birkhoff, *The Origin, Nature and Influence of Relativity* (New York: Macmillan, 1925), p. 104, and J. Weber, *Am. J. Phys.*, *22*, 618, 1954.

[10] Einstein, *Ann. d. Physik*, *17*, Sec. 1, 1905.

[11] An example of such an independent kind of isotropy is the fact, discovered by Fizeau [see Møller, footnote 6, Chap. I, Sec. 8, and Chap. II, Sec. 16] that if, in a given inertial system, the emission of a light beam traversing a *closed* polygon in a given direction coincides with the emission of a beam traveling in the opposite direction, then the returns of these beams to their common point of emission will likewise coincide. We know from the experiments by Sagnac and by Michelson and Gale [cf. A. A. Michelson and H. G. Gale, *Astrophys. J.*, *61*, 140, 1925, and M. G. Trocheris, *Phil. Mag.*, *40*, 1143, 1949] that in a *rotating* system, this directional symmetry will *not* obtain. For a discussion of the philosophical status of such phenomena in the general theory of relativity, see A. Grünbaum, "The Philosophical Retention of Absolute Space in Einstein's General Theory of Relativity," *Philosophical Review*, *66*, 525, 1957.

[12] See AR, pp. 34–5, 38–9.

[13] The choice of $\epsilon = \frac{1}{2}$ is *not* the only choice which would assure the equality of the velocities in the opposite directions AC and BC. The same result could be achieved by using any other *equal* values of ϵ ($0 < \epsilon < 1$) to synchronize the clocks at A and B with the clock at C, although, in that case, the velocity along CA would *not* equal the velocity along AC, and similarly for the velocities along CB and BC.

14 If a train-observer moving to the *right* relatively to the ground chooses the same ϵ for synchronizing the clocks at A' and at B' with the one at C', he will, of course, say that point A' was struck *later* than B'.

15 Since $t' = \dfrac{t - \dfrac{v}{c^2} x}{\sqrt{1 - \beta^2}}$, spatially-separated events occurring at the same time t in system S will occur at different times t' in system S', unless they lie in the planes given by $x =$ constant. *Cf. AR*, pp. 55–6.

16 It will be recalled that, in opposition to the emission theory of light, the classical ether theory had already affirmed the independence of the velocity of light in the ether from that of its *source*, while affirming, however, its dependence on the observer's motion relative to the ether medium.

J. H. Rush has pointed out [*Sci. American, 193,* 62, August, 1955] that the *time* constancy of the velocity of light may have to be questioned: measurements over the past century have yielded three fairly distinct sets of values for c. For a comprehensive recent survey of measurements of the velocity of light, see E. Bergstrand, "Determination of the Velocity of Light," *Handbuch der Physik* (Ed. Flügge), Vol. 24, 1956, pp. 1–43.

17 Since the classically expected time difference in the second-order terms is only of the order of 10^{-15} second, allowance must be made for the absence of a corresponding accuracy in the measurement of the equality of the two arms. This is made feasible by the fact that, on the ether theory, the effect of any discrepancy in the lengths of the two arms should *vary*, on account of the earth's motion, as the apparatus is rotated. For details, see P. Bergmann, *Introduction to the Theory of Relativity* (New York: Prentice-Hall, 1946), pp. 24–6.

18 It is understood that the lengths $2\,l$ in the different frames are each ratios of the path to the same unit rod, which is transported from system to system in order to effect these measurements and which remains equal to unity *by definition* in the course of this transport.

19 See Tolman, *Relativity, Thermodynamics and Cosmology* (Oxford: Oxford University Press, 1934), pp. 16–17, and Laue, footnote 6, p. 25. Professor H. Feigl has kindly called my attention to a recent paper by P. Moon and D. E. Spencer [*J. Opt. Soc. Am., 43,* 635, 1953] in which this interpretation of the data furnished by double stars is contested. These authors contend that if light is postulated to travel in a Riebannian space of constant positive

curvature ($R = 5$ light years), then the data on binaries admit of being interpreted as according with the Ritz emission theory. On Ritz's assumption, the velocity of light in free space is always c with respect to the source, but, contrary to the relativistic light principle, its value in a frame K depends on the velocity of the source relative to K.

Moon and Spencer do not explain how their hypothesis would account for the findings of R. Tomaschek [*Ann. Physik 73*, 105, 1924], who repeated the Michelson-Morley experiment with stellar light and, contrary to the expectations of the Ritz theory [cf. W. Pauli, *Theory of Relativity*, New York: Pergamon Press, 1958, p. 8] obtained the same results as had been found by using terrestrial light. Nor do these investigators establish their entitlement to supplant the relativity of simultaneity by the absolutistic theory of time integral to their hypothesis. For further details, see Moon and Spencer, in *Phil. of Science, 23*, 216, 1956, and A. Grünbaum, *Phil. of Science, 24*, 77, 1957.

[20] See R. J. Kennedy and E. M. Thorndike, *Phys. Rev.*, 42, 400, 1932. As we shall see in footnote 21, however, these experimenters themselves did not conceive of their experiment as a test of the clock axiom.

J. P. Cedarholm and C. H. Townes have just reported their very recent cognate experiment [cf. "A New Experimental Test of Special Relativity," *Nature 184* (No. 4696, 1959), pp. 1350–1351]. They write: "The experiment compares the frequencies of two maser oscillators with their beams of ammonia molecules pointed in opposite directions, but both parallel to a supposed direction of motion through the ether. . . . A precision of one part in 10^{12} has been achieved in this frequency comparison, and failure to find a frequency change of the predicted type allows setting the upper limit on an ether drift as low as $1/1000$ of the orbital velocity of the Earth. . . . The present experiment sets an upper limit on an ether-drift velocity about one-fiftieth that allowed by previous experiments."

[21] Cf. A. Grünbaum, "The Falsifiability of the Lorentz-Fitzgerald Contraction Hypothesis," *British Journal for the Philosophy of Science, 10*, 48, 1959. The proviso that the period of the light source may *not* depend upon the velocity of the apparatus postulates a constant relation between the time-metric defined by light itself and that defined by material clocks. This relation is presupposed in using the null outcome of the Kennedy-Thorndike *optical* experiment as corroboration of the "clock axiom," as is evident from the fact that this axiom involves a claim concerning the behavior of *material* clocks. Awareness of the assumptions made in interpreting the result of the K-T experiment as we did is essential lest it be erroneously supposed that this optical ex-

periment gave *univocal* support to the relativistic "clock axiom": H. E. Ives has explained [*J. Opt. Soc. Am.* 27, 177, 1937] that the outcome of the K-T experiment also lends itself to several *non*-relativistic interpretations, if suitable other assumptions are made. In fact, the experimenters themselves intended it *not* as a test of what we have called the "clock axiom" in the light principle but rather as a test of the relativistic clock retardation.

Although we confront here an illustration of inconclusive falsifiability in the sense of P. Duhem, it would be an error to suppose with Duhem that the falsifiability of isolated empirical hypotheses is *always* unavoidably inconclusive: cf. A. Grünbaum, "The Duhemian Argument," *Philosophy of Science*, vol. 27, pp. 75–87, 1960.

22 See W. Gerlach, *Handbuch der Physik* (Berlin: Springer-Verlag, 1926), pp. 61ff., and Møller, footnote 6. Ch. III, Sec. 32. This interpretation has been challenged by V. Bush in a paper "The Force Between Moving Charges," *J. Math. and Phys.*, 5, 129, 1925–6 to which Professor Parry Moon has kindly called my attention. Bush offers a *non*-relativistic account of the experimental results obtained by Kaufmann, Bucherer and others with accelerated charged particles by assigning the reason for the variation of e/m with velocity to the charge rather than to the mass, postulating a velocity-dependent charge and an invariant mass. Significantly, Bush shares the relativistic affirmation that no electrons can exceed the velocity of light but links this fact *not* with a mass increase but rather with a postulate that "the force between charges becomes zero when their relative velocity is equal to the velocity of light" (p. 149). But, as we saw, the postulate of the limiting character of the velocity of light makes acceptance of the conventionality of simultaneity unavoidable. And the latter conventionality together with (a) the other constituents of relativistic kinematics and (b) very plausible conservation principles of dynamics entail the variation of *mass* with velocity. Bush does not adduce any experimental facts which support his hypothesis of charge variation while being incompatible with relativity. Neither does he remove one's *prima facie* doubts that the hypothesis of charge variation could actually be consistently incorporated in the body of well-confirmed physical principles. I therefore conclude that his citation of Miller's experiments (pp. 133, 135) as warrant for offering a non-relativistic hypothesis is not convincing.

It is noteworthy in this connection that on the basis of a recent analysis of Miller's data, Shankland, McCuskey, Leone, and Kuerti claim [*Revs. Modern Phys.*, 27, 167, 1955] that they are due to errors. For additional doubts concerning Miller's findings, see L. Essens's report in *Nature*, 175, 794, 1955. On the other hand, V. Hlavaty [*J. Rational Mech. and Analysis*, 5, 471, 1956] reaches the following conclusions: "Hence from the point of view of the unified field theory and under the assumption of the constant velocity of light, one has to expect either Michelson and Morley's result or Miller's result."

[23] H. P. Robertson, *Revs. Modern Phys.*, *21*, 378, 1949. An earlier proof of the compatibility of the light principle with the *denial* of the clock retardation was given by Reichenbach (see *AR*, pp. 79–83, esp. pp. 81–3), who exhibits a consistent set of coordinate transformations embodying both assertions.

[24] B. Rossi and D. B. Hall, *Phys. Rev.*, *59*, 223, 1941. The clock retardation continues to provoke ill-founded philosophical attacks on the theory of relativity: cf. F. Sandgathe's proposal to modify the theory [*Archiv für Phil.*, *5*, 241, 1955]. For a proof that the clock retardation does *not* give rise to the "clock paradox" in the context of the conditions to which the special theory of relativity is applicable, see A. Grünbaum, *Phil. of Science*, *21*, 249, 1954 [reprinted with distorting misprints in the *Proceedings of the Second International Congress of the International Union for the Philosophy of Science*, Zürich, 1954, vol. III, Editions du Griffon, Neuchâtel: 1955, pp. 55–60] and *Phil. of Science*, *22*, 53 and 233, 1955, and H. P. Robertson, *Mathematical Reviews*, 16, 1166, 1955.

[25] Cf. Essen and Parry, *Nature*, *176*, 280, 1955, and the comments by G. M. Clemence, *ibid.*, p. 1230, and in *Science*, *123*, 571, 1956. See also H. Lyons, *Sci. American*, *196*, 71, February, 1957.

[26] E. T. Whittaker, *From Euclid to Eddington* (London: Cambridge University Press, 1949), p. 63.

[27] See footnote 26, p. 64; italics supplied. The same error is repeated by Whittaker in his *A History of the Theories of Aether and Electricity* (New York: Nelson, 1953), Vol. 2, p. 37, which should be read in conjunction with his "G. F. Fitzgerald," *Sci. American, 189*, 98, November, 1953.

[28] Riemann, "Über die Hypothesen welche der Geometrie zu Grunde liegen", in *Gesammelte mathematische Werke*, Dedekind and Weber (Eds.), (Leipzig, 1876), p. 268. For a discussion of the range of validity of this statement by Riemann, cf. A. Grünbaum, "Conventionalism in Geometry," in: *The Axiomatic Method*, ed. by Henkin, Suppes, and Tarski, Amsterdam, 1959, pp. 204–22, esp. 208–209.

[29] B. Hoffmann has shown recently [*Phys. Rev.*, *89*, 49–52, 1953] that the usual affine tensor calculus of the general theory of relativity does not implement the conception that length is a

ratio, because it fails to yield invariance of the equations of physics under a change of scale. To achieve such implementation, Hoffmann proposes an enlargement of that tensor formalism assuring its conformity to an appropriate similarity principle.

It is perfectly clear that relations or relational properties of physical objects (which are expressed numerically as ratios) are fully as objective physically and exist just as independently of the human mind as simple properties of individual objects. Thus, the relation between a copper bar at rest in a system K and the unit rod in K might have the property that the copper bar has a length of 5 units in K. But the different relation of that bar's projection onto the x-axis of a system S, relative to which it is moving along that axis, to the unit rod of S may then yield a length of only 4.7 S-units It is incontestable that the differences among the various relations sustained by the bar do *not* render these relations subjective products of the physicist's mind, any more than they do the fact that the bar in question is a copper bar. In a futile attempt to defend a mentalistic metaphysics on the basis of relativity theory, Herbert Dingle denies this fact. Replying to decisive critiques of his views by P. Epstein [*Am. J. Phys. 10*, 1, 205, 1942, and *11*, 228, 1943,] and M. Born [*Phil. Quart., 3*, 139, 1953], Dingle offers the following argument [*The Sources of Eddington's Philosophy* (London: Cambridge University Press, 1954), pp. 11–12]: "The view that physics is the description of the character of an independent external world was simply no longer tenable . . . . Every relativist will admit that if two rods, A and B, of equal length when relatively at rest, are in relative motion along their common direction, then A is longer or shorter than B, or equal to it, exactly as you please. It is therefore impossible to evade the conclusion that its length is not a property of either rod; and what is true of length is true of every other so-called physical property. Physics is therefore (*sic!*) not the investigation of the nature of the external world." Far from having demonstrated that relativity physics is subjective, Professor Dingle has merely succeeded in exhibiting his unawareness of the fact that *relational* properties do not cease to be *bona fide* objective properties just because they involve relations between individuals rather than belong directly to individuals themselves. Only such unawareness can lead to his primitive thesis that the relations of physical entities to one another cannot constitute "the character of an independent external world."

30 The logical blunder which generates this question was committed in inverted form by Herbert Dingle. One of his reasons for rejecting the cosmology of Bondi and Gold is that it would allegedly require not merely a single act of miraculous divine interference, as Biblical creation *ex nihilo* does, but a continuous series of such acts. See A. Grünbaum, *Sci. American, 189*, 6–8, December, 1953.

[31] For further details on this issue, see A. Grünbaum, *Sci. Monthly*, *79*, 15–16, 1954.

[32] E. T. Whittaker, A *History of the Theories of Aether and Electricity* (New York: Nelson, 1953), Vol. 2, p. 40. Whittaker himself points out (p. 36) that even at the time of his death in 1928, Lorentz reportedly still favored the concepts of "true" time and absolute simultaneity. For Lorentz' own brief statement on this point, see his *The Theory of Electrons* (New York: Columbia University Press, 1909), pp. 329, 230. In regard to the role played by Lorentz and Poincaré as precursors of Einstein, von Laue gives evidence in a recent publication [*Naturwissenschaften*, *43*, 4, 1956] that Einstein was unaware of the groundwork they had done for the theory of relativity.

[33] For details, see A. Grünbaum, *Sci. Monthly 79*, 228, 1954, *Am. Scientist*, *43*, 555–8, 1955, and *Am. J. Phys.*, *22*, 499, 1954. Cf. also A. Grünbaum, "Geometry, Chronometry and Empiricism," in: *Minnesota Studies in the Philosophy of Science*, vol. III (ed. by Feigl and Maxwell), University of Minnesota Press (forthcoming). The first of these papers, "Operationism and Relativity," is reprinted in P. Frank (Ed.), *The Validation of Scientific Theories* (Boston: Beacon, 1958), pp. 84–94.

9

MEANING AND SCIENTIFIC
STATUS OF CAUSALITY:

Henry Margenau •

The disagreement with regard to the validity of the principle of causality, existing today among scientists, has its roots in the diversity of definitions of the principle itself rather than in a problematic scientific situation. As far as the formulation of quantum theory is complete, its bearing upon philosophical questions can be fixed with precision provided the questions are phrased intelligibly. But a question is intelligible from a scientific point of view only if it satisfies two conditions: (1) the meaning of its terms must be fixed; (2) it must be in accord with the conventions of the science to which the question is put.

The necessity of the first requirement is at once evident; if it were not satisfied the question would have several correct but self-conflicting answers, such as those to which the undisciplined discussion of philosophical problems usually leads. The second requirement, however, reflects a particular weakness of philosophy. Within the domain of the latter, words have retained a variability of meaning which, to be sure, makes for beauty and flexibility of expression, but impairs precision of speech. So persistent was the tendency toward figurative flourish that even in cases where

• [This selection is reprinted in its entirety from *Philosophy of Science*, Vol. 1, No. 2, 1934, pp. 133–48, by permission of Henry Margenau and the editors of *Philosophy of Science*.]

science had standardized the meaning of a term in a very systematic and useful way philosophers continued to use the term with its former diffuseness. When accused of this procedure they said they were speaking nontechnically and deplored politely the scientist's manner of degrading terms into technical ones. Indeed the difference between philosophy and the specialized sciences began when the latter caused their concepts to crystallize and agreed to name them universally and with care. Even now the distinction between science and philosophy is best described in saying that science proceeds by making the acceptance of its terms obligatory for all its pursuants, while philosophy allows its advocates to coin largely their own phraseology. This individualism frequently causes confusion and indefiniteness of philosophical attitude. To illustrate: whether causality is a category or not, is chiefly a matter of definition and nomenclature and may be answered correctly by yes and no; in fact, the question may be meaningless. Proponents for each of these three answers are to be found among modern philosophers. However, the question: Is mercury an element? has but one correct answer. Similarly, the term energy which has a perfectly definite scientific meaning is constantly used in phrases such as "mental energy" which signifies nothing unless ignorance of the laws of physics on the part of the speaker. Science has avoided such ambiguities. Hence we can effectively guard against them by using technical lingo wherever it is possible. In discussing causality it is necessary to formulate the problem in terms of physics as far as they are available.

Considerations like these are common with all scientists and many philosophers today; they constitute no unsympathetic critique of philosophy, or of the methods employed in philosophical investigations. For the solution of numerous problems, the methods of science, which, speaking figuratively, are nothing but the crystallized part of philosophy are not, or at least not yet, at hand. It is also true that the philosophical terminology is more strongly subjected to popular misuse than scientific language, and therefore prevented from being standardized. None of these arguments is sufficient, however, to justify the use of vague philosophical phrases where definite scientific terms present themselves.

Kant's formulations of the causality principle are to be rejected mainly for these reasons. When he says in the first edition of his "Critique of Pure Reason": *"Alles, was ge-*

schieht (anhebt zu sein), setzt etwas voraus, worauf es nach einer Regel folgt,"[1] this statement is not scientifically clear. *Regel* ["rule"] is entirely undefined; it is possible to find a rule for everything that is susceptible of description. On the other hand, if the word is to be interpreted as a means of knowing subsequent events in advance, there arises the difficulty of who is to know and employ the rule, together with all the other inconsistencies which will be encountered shortly in connection with similar formulations. Another possibility of interpretation places the emphasis upon the first part of the sentence and neglects the last as an inessential explanatory phrase. But then, if *voraussetzen* ["presupposes"] is taken in its temporal sense, Kant's statement amounts to nothing more than the assertion that the universe has no beginning in time, which is plainly not identical with the causality postulate.

Kant's modified formulation, as it appeared in the second edition of the same book, reads: "*Alle Veränderungen geschehen nach dem Gesetz der Verknüpfung von Ursache und Wirkung,*"[2] and is subject to the same criticism. Physics knows of no such law; as a matter of fact there is no plausible way of defining cause and effect. No laws of physics, if properly stated, involve reference to either of these concepts, and if the distinction of cause and effect is artificially impressed upon the phenomena which these laws regulate, then the laws do not even allow us to differentiate between the two. This fact follows at once from the well known property of reversibility possessed by all natural laws. Newton's law of gravitation, for instance, sets up a relation between an observation on the rate of change of the radial velocity between two masses on the one hand, and the distance between them on the other. But it contains no criterion to determine the causal status of these observations. There is no law of connection between cause and effect known to science; moreover, these concepts are foreign to physical analysis. Nor is it of any avail to inject them externally, for the meaning usually conveyed by the words in question is expressed more adequately and precisely by technical terms like boundary condition, initial and final state.

[1] ["Everything that happens (comes into being) presupposes something which it follows in accordance with a law."]

[2] ["All changes happen in accordance with the law of the connection of cause and effect."]

Most of the difficulties discussed so far are avoided in Laplace's statement of what he and many later scientists consider to be the essence of causality. He postulates the existence of a universal formula according to which all happenings take place, and expresses this state of affairs as follows (*Théorie analytique des probabilités*): "An intelligence knowing, at a given instant of time, all forces acting in nature, as well as the momentary positions of all things of which the universe consists, would be able to comprehend the motions of the largest bodies of the world and those of the smallest atoms in one single formula, provided it were sufficiently powerful to subject all data to analysis; to it, nothing would be uncertain, both future and past would be present before its eyes." This is certainly an intelligible proposition; it is excellent in its clarity and precision. All of its terms are well defined; the word force is to be understood in its accurate physical sense as the product of mass and acceleration, and "knowledge of a force" means knowledge of the differential equation which relates this product to a function of position, this function being also known. This spirit of Laplace's propositon pervades all of classical physics and has been eminently fruitful in the development of that science. Is the proposition true? In answering this question we shall find reason for abandoning this particular formulation of the causality principle.

Of course Laplace's statement is true. Imagine if possible a perfectly arbitrary universe with a god agitating it according to his ever-changing desires. Although we are still searching for a suitable definition of causality, it seems clear that this would constitute the model of a noncausal world. If we further suppose the happenings in this chaotic universe to be discernible and describable, then it must be possible also to represent them by means of equations. These equations will not necessarily contain analytic functions only, nor will they be differentiable. However, if things take place with reasonable smoothness and not too suddenly, if *natura non facit saltus*, the functions will possess the property of differentiability. It is then clear that differentiation will, in general, simplify the equations, for it will cause additive constants to disappear. An intelligence powerful enough to know all these differential equations together with the values of coordinates and derivatives at a given time, and able to solve them, would have a complete survey of all events, future and past. In Laplace's world this survey must be possible on the basis of a knowledge of all forces, i.e., differential equations of the second order. This, in itself, constitutes no further restriction upon our arbitrary universe, since there is nothing to prevent us from differentiating the equations twice; but it expresses a preference which should manifest itself in a universe satisfying this particular causality postulate. In such a world laws should take on an especially simple form if they are stated as second order differential equations. Thus it is seen that Laplace's postulate is not a stringent one; it is true for almost any imaginable universe. It imposes nothing upon a world which by itself runs smoothly, and is certainly a valid approximation to the course of events in the arbitrary, noncausal universe. In that sense the statement in question is true, but it does not seem to characterize causality. Whether or not nature is conveniently describable in terms of second order differential equations is an entirely different issue and must probably be affirmed —although there are cases of physical analysis where description by equations of higher order is customary.

The fact that the postulation of a universal formula, as phrased by Laplace, involves the hypothetical existence of an omniscient demon has been considered unsatisfactory by numerous investigators. An excellent critique of this point is to be found in P. Frank's recent book: *Das Kausalgesetz und seine Grenzen*. The appeal to a higher intelligence is certainly unscientific and to be avoided if possible. But it is not intrinsically bad if it merely serves to clarify the proposition. The question is: does Laplace's supposition of a superior intelligence constitute an essential point of his statement? Evidently not, for if the reference to this intelligence were omitted the assertion, weak as it may be, that nature be conveniently describable in terms of second order differential equations would still remain. But this can be progressively tested by experience and admits of definite verification. Hence it is not legitimate to say that the demon does not exist or is impossible and therefore reject the proposition. A real criticism should attack its meat and not its form. It may well be observed in this connection that a very common argument against causality fails for the same reason. This argument appeals to the uncertainty principle which does not permit all the simultaneous data necessary to integrate the universal formula to be known. Hence, it is concluded, the causality principle cannot be valid. Here, too, it is forgotten that the criticism is directed against an inessential point in Laplace's formulation which, as we have seen, fails to express the characteristics of a causal universe anyway.

The differential equations governing the processes in the arbitrary, lawless world which has been imagined will in general involve the time explicitly. Consequently the forces (which are always to be defined in terms of accelerations, not popularly as "pushes and pulls") will change with time in an essential manner, and not only through the coordinates on which they depend. In order to predict the future Laplace's demon not only would have to know the instantaneous values of all forces, he would require their complete form as functions of the space coordinates and of time. An entirely different situation arises if we postulate that the forces be functions of space coordinates and possibly their time derivatives only. This would constitute a very definite limitation upon natural processes, a limitation indeed which the world agitated by a god would fail to exhibit. For now the forces have the same instantaneous values whenever the coordinates and their derivatives assume a given set of values; this endows nature with a regularity which, it appears to us, is very nearly what causality is meant to convey. But this important feature hardly follows from Laplace's formulation and may, at any rate, be expressed more directly as we shall see presently.

Before continuing this trend of thought it seems necessary to deal with a definition of causality which is most widely accepted at present. The argument runs: Introducing a superior intelligence is not permissible because it is man who makes his science and it must be he who is to judge whether his world is causal or not. A universal formula without an individual knowing it is a vague phrase. Why not modify the proposition last considered by substituting man in place of the demon? The causality principle is then valid if it is possible for the scientist, on the basis of known laws, to reconstruct the past and to project the future when the present state of the world is completely known. We shall term this conception of causality, in which a clearly anthropomorphic attitude combines with utilitarian considerations, the positivistic one for want of a better name. It is quite in harmony with the modern trend of eliminating things that have merely logical status but no concrete meaning in terms of physical operations. Nevertheless it pays to examine it closely.

First it is defective from the point of view of intelligibility. The term "possible for the scientists," or, if it is preferred, "possible for the human mind" is objectionable. If it conveys its popular connotation, who is to decide the capabilities of the scientist or the human mind? Even though a present physical theory denies the possibility of knowing all data upon which a detailed analysis of the future depends, this possibility may be restored by later developments. It is true that this fault can be remedied by modifying the positivistic formulation of the causality principle and stating: Causality exists if no confirmed physical theory contradicts the acquisition of data by which a determination of future and past events can be made. However, this is very specific and has never been proposed, nor is it exempt from the criticism that follows. In line with the present argument we also note the occurrence of words like "law" and "theory" which, though they figure prominently in physical discussions, still lack universal definitions and are very far from being technical terms. Direct statements about nature are always clearer and less involved than terms like these which refer to our reasoning about nature, and are therefore better suited to define causality. If such considerations seem pedantic, one must answer that their neglect has caused more difficulties than has the actual solution of philosophical problems.

Yet they do not touch the principal weakness of the positivistic causality formulation. We propose to show that the latter may be satisfied by a non-causal universe. The point is simply this: causality has nothing to do with the question whether future events may be known in advance, its prerequisite is not that the scientist turn prophet. Suppose that the god who agitates his universe according to his inscrutable desires and without restrictions by law or order should give the scientist exact forewarnings of his actions, so that the latter is able to prophesy with accuracy. Would this make his playland a causal universe? Of course there is no rigid answer since we are still searching for a suitable definition of causality. But if we interpret correctly the universal implication of this concept regardless of its various formulations we feel that one must answer: no. It is commonly conceived, for instance, that the occurrence of mir-

acles contradicts causality; in fact disbelief in miracles
is usually justified by the causal constitution of the world.
The circumstance that many miracles have allegedly been
predicted is hardly sufficient to restore a skeptic's belief in them, and hence to reconcile their occurrence with
the causality postulate. We conclude: the positivistic formulation with its main emphasis upon human ability to know
in advance does not express the nucleus of what is understood by causality. Besides, it is anthropomorphic and reflects distinctly the present utilitarian color of our science.

Let us now put an end to criticism and select a definition
that will satisfy the outlined requirements more widely and
state the central part of·the concept in question. It will
be granted that the crucial feature which makes the arbitrary world noncausal is the irregularity arising from the
whims of the god, whether this irregularity may be known
or not. To be more specific it is the fact that in a noncausal
world the force between two electric charges varies, say, as
the inverse second power of the distance today, but possibly as the inverse tenth power tomorrow. Or even, while
they attract each other today, they may repel each other
tomorrow. We feel that causality is violated when a given
state A is not always followed by the same state B. A
definition of the word "state" is certainly necessary, but we
may reserve it until later. At present the customary intuitive
meaning will suffice. This property by which any given
state has associated with it a unique consequent state has
previously[3] been called "consistency of nature." To avoid
circumlocutions we shall continue to use this term. In more
adequate phraseology, and without the unsatisfactory reference to states, consistency of nature may be characterized
by saying: As a result of the constitution of nature, the
differential equations by means of which it is described do
not contain explicit functions of the time. This statement
is less definite than it seems because it does not contain directions as to the choice of variables appearing in
the equations, a vagueness which is the counterpart of the
indefinite meaning of "state." The existence of variables
must of course be supposed since they form the condition
under which description of nature is possible at all. But
then, if nature is consistent in this sense, the integrated
equations will not depend on time in an absolute manner;
more specifically if $x = f(t)$ is a solution, then $x = f(t - t_0)$

[3] H. Margenau, *The Monist*, Jan. 1932.

is another, so that the motion in question has an arbitrary beginning in time which becomes fixed only if accessory conditions are known. Furthermore, to use a previous example, the exponent in Coulomb's law of attraction will be invariable in time; if it is -2 to-day it will be -2 forever. The same should hold for all parameters appearing in the differential equations of physics if nature is consistent or causal.

It is to be remembered, however, that the occurrence of equations which do not satisfy this requirement, is not at once a proof against causality. In fact we often encounter such equations when a problem is not completely analyzed, for example in the case of forced oscillations. But here, as well as in all similar cases, the explicit time dependence could be eliminated by including in the analysis those parts of the system which produce the varying force, i.e., by "closing" the system. "Impressed forces" always indicate that the physical system in question is an open one. In fact a closed system is simply one to which causal analysis can be applied, that is one which can be described by differential equations not containing the time explicitly. Another point of importance is this: An equation which originally satisfied the causal requirement will, after a single integration, no longer do so. We express this state of affairs by saying that we now have an "equation of motion" and not a "law." (Incidentally it would be very desirable to standardize this particular meaning of the word law in natural science.) Nevertheless this introduces an uncertainty into our formulation of the causal principle, but one which cannot be avoided. It will occupy us when we discuss the analytic character of causality, its property as a nontautological proposition.

Consistency, the central issue of the causality postulate, banishes absolute time from the description of nature (equations of motion) by eliminating time explicitly from its *essential* representation (differential equations, laws). It is the only formulation which does so. The elimination is necessary because absolute time has no physical meaning. Another advantage is the simplicity of the consistency formula, which nevertheless involves everything implied in the usual conceptions of causality, such as the existence of unique laws, strict determinism as far as it is a concomitant of causality. (It does not imply, however, that future events be actually known or knowable by an individual.) Theorems of conservation (energy, momentum), generally felt to be in some way connected with the causality principle but unaffected by its customary formulations, follow at once as analytical consequences from the fact that the differential equations do not involve the time explicitly.

The principle of consistency, and hence of causality, has no meaning if it can be applied only to the universe as a whole. For in that case the number of describing variables would probably be infinite and the description in terms of differential equations loses its sense. Using the more intuitive definition according to which a state A is always followed by the same state B the failure is evident when we realize that state A may occur only once. Causality is then an empty phrase unless the universe is periodic. But the same would be true of all the laws of physics, in fact of physics as a science, if its statements were inapplicable to small domains of nature. Hence the condition that causality shall have meaning is the same as that for the existence of science. The philosopher who argues that the consistency definition be void forgets that his argument nullifies science as a whole. As a matter of experience the universe *is separable* into smaller systems to which differential equations can be applied, and if these equations are of the type here postulated then nature is causal.

An observation of this kind carries little weight with those who feel too keenly that the processes in the universe are separable only to a rough approximation. One is entitled to discuss this attitude in earnest only if he is willing to accept all of its consequences which include the proposition that science is an illusion. But we note in the first place that it is by no means necessary for an arbitrary nature to be *roughly* or *approximately* separable into systems whose fates are independent; to say that it is imposes a definite restriction even if the separation is not completely possible. But let us consider more exactly how it is performed. Measurements on the force of attraction between two electric charges will not in general verify Coulomb's law. We observe that the force depends in some peculiar way upon the postion of external charges, which suggests to us that the measured effects are not entirely due to the system in question, namely the two test charges. This is expressed by stating that the system is not completely separated from its surroundings. Next we remove our system farther and farther from surrounding bodies and notice a gradual improvement in the consistency of the measurements. Now the situation would be very simple and satisfactory if progressive isolation produced better and better agreement between the observations. For then the condition of complete isolation, i.e., a closed system, could be defined by a simple limiting process much in the same manner as limits of functions are defined in mathematics. However, the situation is here of greater complexity, though still manageable. The agreement is improved only up to a certain point, and then further isolation fails to make itself felt. We have reached the limit of precision of our measurements. This limit of precision is a very definite thing which scientists have always considered very carefully. Quantum mechanics emphasizes it greatly and even renders its value in some instances calculable by means of the uncertainty relation. Nevertheless there is a well-known method of dealing with the ever-present divergence of observations: the theory of errors allows us to compute the most probable value of a measurement from any group of observations. It is the limit of this most probable value upon which we base the derivation of Coulomb's law, and not the limit to which actual observations tend. The latter does not exist, but the former does. Hence it is possible to define a state of separation, not by actual physical operations but by blending experimentation with reasoning. We wish to emphasize in this connection that physical concepts need not—and cannot—be defined solely in terms of experimental operations or observations; it is both customary and proper in scientific investigations to characterize an abstract state of affairs by its logical consequences if they are more simply expressible, whether they are observable or not. For example, when we state the second law of thermodynamics in the form: the entropy of the universe increases, then there is no way of testing the law as such; its evidence arises from considerations formally similar to those which have convinced us of the existence of closed systems to which differential equations are applicable.

By its definition, a closed or independent physical system is a causal one, because we call it closed when the laws governing its behavior do not involve the time. But strictly speaking, only closed systems are accessible to physical analysis. Thus it would seem that physics can never inform us of a failure of the causality principle. This brings us to a point of importance: Is the causal principle a tautology?

Here we are forced to make a large concession; an unbiased investigation must not fail to recognize its character as an analytic proposition. Kant, who thought of it as an *a priori* synthetic judgment, did not formulate it in a way in which its analytic character became apparent. It is certainly true that whenever a physical system does not appear to be closed, that is when the differential equations describing it contain the time explicitly (if it does not behave consistently), we conclude that the variables determining the state in question are not completely known. We then look immediately for hidden properties whose variation may have produced the inconsistencies, and whose inclusion in the analysis would eliminate them; moreover if we do not find any we invent them. This procedure is possible because in the consistency formulation of causality the term "state" is undefined. The corresponding indefiniteness in the more abstract formulation lies in the absence of specifications as to the number of variables entering into the differential equations on the one hand, and of the order of the equations on the other. If the number of variables is increased indefinitely, or if an indefinite number of differentiations is permitted, time dependence can be ultimately eliminated no matter how complicated the processes of nature, provided only that the equations of motion can be differentiated a sufficient number of times. But this requires no more than a certain smoothness and continuity which nature certainly satisfies. On the whole it seems, then, that the causality postulate reduces to a definition of what is meant by "state." It is an agreement to consider those quantities as composing the state of a system which enter into a time free differential equation describing its behavior.

This line of reasoning leads at once to the inevitable question: Why retain the proposition if it is merely tautological? Tautologies, as everybody knows, add nothing to the knowledge of nature; they expose a property already included in the term they are to explain; their careless use often produces vicious circles. All this is true in a sense; but to suppose that tautologies are always useless and to be avoided is a very common fallacy. Every definition is a tautology except the first time it is stated. To the writer the word tautology conveys something more objectionable than the good old "analytic judgment." Really the two are synonymous, and one must free himself from any intuitive bias that may cling to the former term. The principle of conservation of energy is a tautology in the proper sense of the word, yet nobody doubts its fruitfulness, and it is even customary to speak of its validity as though it were an actual proposition about the world. The point in question is this: The general definition of the principle contains no restriction as to the number of different kinds of energy which may be transformed into one another and whose sum is constant. If this number became indefinitely great as a consequence of invention whenever a new type was needed, the principle would hardly be applicable, it would merely define energies. As a matter of fact, however, nature permits us to get along with very few different types of energy, and its description in terms of energies is exceedingly useful and convenient. Therefore, while the energy principle in its logical formulation is a tautology which amounts to a definition of energies, the *analysis of nature in terms of this definition is advantageous.* Precisely the same is true with regard to causality. Its logical formulation is inevitably tautological and leads to a definition of physical "states," or a selection of variables in the differential equations. But this selection is useful and applicable, so that the causality principle, though tautological in its abstract form, does amount to a statement about nature. Moreover, it makes sense to say that nature is not causal, for this would be true if, in an attempt to describe nature in accordance with our definition of consistency, the resulting differential equations were found to contain very many variables or to be of very high order. One might, of course, arbitrarily restrict the latter and permit only equations of the second order, but we feel that this would do violence to the common conception of causality.

We have seen that the tautological character of the consistency postulate is no particular fault. Indeed the postulate may be transformed into a synthetic statement if this be desired, but somewhat at the expense of its precision; it might be phrased: Nature is so constituted that its description in terms of differential equations which do not involve the time explicitly (such description is admittedly possible!) is *convenient.* We merely state that Laplace's causality formulation is also tautological, while the one identifying causality of nature with human power to prophesy is not. But it stands to reason that the latter modification, missing, as it does, the central point of the casuality concept, pays too large a price for its nontautological form.

In formulating the principle of causality we have almost solved the question as to its validity. Classical physics was based upon it and therefore presents no argument against it. The influence of quantum mechanics upon its status has been considered in detail in two previous publications,[4] whose results may be stated briefly as follows: Classical analysis had come face to face with experiences which its usual methods failed to describe; in fact the treatment of certain problems threatened to become non-causal. At this very instant quantum mechanics achieved a revolutionary feat of great importance: it redefined the concept of physical states in a more abstract manner (in terms of mathematical functions satisfying certain requirements) and *thereby restored the causal character of physical analysis.* It was the conviction that the causality principle must be retained which inspired quantum mechanics, although some of its creators have not been altogether conscious of this fact. The impression that quantum mechanics violates the principle now arises whenever the older classical conception of states (positions and velocities of the component parts of a system) is carelessly carried over into the new field of description in which it has no meaning. The uncertainty principle forbids ultimate extrapolation to the quantities defining a state in the classical sense, but it does not prevent an ultimate extrapolation to Ψ-functions. To be quite impartial one should add that the trustworthiness of quantum mechanics even in questions of ultimate extrapolation to classical states is not entirely evident, for it is precisely in the very small domains of space (structure of the nucleus, structure of the electron, and its trembling motion) where its present axioms break down. Quantum mechanics does not constitute an argument against causality.

However, there comes news from other quarters which may upset the validity of the causal principle. If, as has been reported, the velocity of light, which is an essential parameter in the differential equations of physics, undergoes a slow variation in time, then a revision of the postulate may be in order.

Another significant objection has long been known although it is ordinarily overlooked. It has to do with spatial continuity of the universe. If the structure of nature's elements is continuous in space, and hence infinitely detailed,

[4] H. Margenau, *The Monist,* Jan. 1931; *ibid.,* April 1932.

the equations representing the behavior of any of its parts will of necessity contain an infinite number of variables. Hence causal analysis, as it proceeds into finer and finer details of structure, will meet the same obstacle which prevented it from exploring an inseparable universe as a whole. Two means are available for avoiding this difficulty; both have been employed. One is to adopt a field theory which fixes minutely the values of a physical quantity at every point of space, but fixes it by means of simple functions so that the scientist is enabled to dominate in one grand sweep all the intricacies of spatial structure. There are reasons, however, why this procedure is unsatisfactory. Unless the field functions used in physical theory are periodic they imply singularities which, while they are insignificant as far as many properties of nature are concerned, certainly do not exist. The other and probably the better way to escape the difficulty is to eliminate its roots, that is, to abandon the conception of a continuous universe. This is done in quantum theory by assuming the discrete existence of electrons, protons, neutrons, energy quanta, and the like. The magic formula here was to reduce the number of variables appearing in causal description by endowing finite parts of space with homogeneity, so that this finite portion requires no more elements of description than does a point. Here again, quantum theory comes to the rescue of the causality principle.

10

THE COPENHAGEN INTERPRETATION
OF QUANTUM THEORY:
Norwood Russell Hanson •

It is fashionable amongst philosophers to attack the "Copenhagen Interpretation" of quantum theory as being unrealistic,[1] unreflective,[2] or unnecessary.[3] This paper may be open to the same objections, but it aims to locate this "interpretation" in its historical and conceptual context, and to argue for quantum theory as it now stands.

I

The Bohr theory issues from seeds a century old. Controversy over the nature of light was analogous to our discussions about interpreting $| \Psi (q) |^2$. Grimaldi's undulatory theory, developed by Huygens, speculated about by Hooke, and confirmed by Young, Fizeau, and Foucault, encountered the opposition of corpuscularians like Newton, Biot, Bos-

• [This paper appeared in an expanded form in the *American Journal of Physics*, Vol. 27, No. 1, pp. 1–15, 1959. It was specially abridged for this volume by Professor Hanson. Printed by permission of Norwood Russell Hanson and *American Journal of Physics*.]

[1] H. Mehlberg, "The Observational Problem of Quantum Theory," read at the May 1958 meeting of the American Philosophical Association, Western Division.

[2] D. Bohm, *Phys. Rev.* Vol. 85, No. 166, p. 180, 1952.

[3] P. Feyerabend, "The quantum theory of measurement," in *Observation and Interpretation* (London: Butterworths Scientific Publications, 1957).

covich, and Laplace. The plot is intricate, but it resolves in the nineteenth century, when the work of Young and Foucault came to be seen as decisive *against* the particulate theory.

Young's work proves *only* that light is wavelike—not that it is in no way corpuscular. The latter conclusion follows only from assuming, in addition to Young's data, the disjunction "light is wavelike or corpuscular (*but never both at once*)." Newton would not have accepted this rider. Foucault, however, needed no such logical preface. He crushed a cornerstone of Newton's *Opticks* by proving that the velocity of light decreases as the density of its medium increases. This refutes the theory of particulate attraction with which Newton accounted for Snell's law.

A logical monument was built by the wave theorists to mark this defeat. Poisson, Green, MacCullagh, Neumann, Kelvin, Rayleigh, Kirchhoff, and, most notably, Clerk Maxwell developed the heritage of Young and Fresnel. The ideas of particle and wave came to be fashioned in logical opposition. Particle dynamics and electrodynamics matured as exclusive and incompatible theories. Why? Because of (1) the apparent logic of the "crucial" experiment of Foucault, and (2) the conviction that either one of these two theories could explain every type of energy transfer. Yet the theories could never be applied simultaneously to the same event. A particle is an entity with sharp coordinates, i.e., it is in one place at one time. No two particles can share the same place at t—this is the logic of punctiform masses in Newton's *Principia*. They collide and rebound, with a calculable energy exchange. It spreads boundlessly through its medium. The expression "wave motion at a geometrical point" would be, for Maxwell and Newton both, unintelligible. Moreover, two waves *can* be in the same place at once, as when surf waves cross at a point. Nor is there in wave motion anything like particulate collision, impact, and recoil. So obvious was this in the algebra of Maxwell and Lorentz, that one could treat any class of wave properties α, β, γ as the obverse of some comparable class of particularate properties, $\sim \alpha$, $\sim \beta$, $\sim \gamma$. It was unthinkable that an event should be at once describable both ways: not just *unimaginable*, but *notationally* impossible. In the only languages available for describing particle and wave dynamics such a joint description would have constituted a contradiction. Wave and particle ideas were now become conceptual opposites.

There is the kernel of the Copenhagen interpretation; because nature refused to live up to nineteenth-century expectations. Consider the discontinuous emission of energy from radiant blackbodies, the discovery that photoelectron energy rises with the *frequency* of the incident light, and is independent of intensity, the photon theory of Einstein, the effects discovered by Compton and Raman, and the first confirmations of the de Broglie-Schrödinger wave theory of matter by Davisson, Germer, and G. P. Thomson. All this showed that microparticles could be described only jointly —in particulate and wavelike terms simultaneously. Yet the only such terms available were the inflexible legacy of Maxwell's successors. From the necessity of describing nature thus arises all the conceptual constraints of quantum theory, including the Copenhagen interpretation.

In microphysics it is arbitrary whether one uses a wave or a particle language for descriptions,—just so one is aware that *both are jointly valid*. Several conclusions follow, which it is the merit of the Copenhagen school boldly to have adopted. The microphenomenon is a conspiracy of wave and particle properties. But after admitting this one must then maintain a symmetry between these modes of description in all further work. Thus in a two-electron interaction, the description may run: electron creates field; field acts on another electron. But we can always find a parallel particulate description: electron emits photon; photon is absorbed by another electron. Consider also proton-neutron interaction. In wave notation: neutron creates field; field acts on proton. But we will often say: neutron emits electron plus neutrino; electron and neutrino are absorbed by proton.

This resolution not to sacrifice either notation leads to a qualitative appreciation of the uncertainty relations. Because if the microphenomenon—an orbiting electron—is provisionally described as a cluster of the interference maxima of an otherwise undefined wave group, then precisely to locate it at the intersection of four coordinates would require an infinite number of further waves (of infinitely varying amplitudes and frequencies) so as to increase destructive interference along the line of propagation and "squeeze" the packet to a "vertical" line (in configuration space). This renders unknowable the particle's energy, which is intimately associated with the amplitude and frequency of the component phase waves. But if we would determine the particle's energy, then the phase waves must be decreased in number, allowing the "wavicle" to spread "monochromatically" through the whole configuration space.

Thus when micronature forced a wedding between the concepts classical physics had sundered, three disconcerting notions emerged as issue of the marriage: (1) Physicists were obliged not to overstress either phase of the new joint notation unless nature dictated this. (2) They became aware of a conceptual limitation—the uncertainty relations. (3) They saw the need of a single formalism which could integrate these inharmonious ideas, "wave" and "particle," into one algorithm.

Of the "old" quantum theories of 1913 and 1916 I shall remark only that they were classical models of the "Saturnian" atom proposed by Nagaoka and Rutherford into which was forced the idea of quantizing electronic orbits. Then de Broglie hammered together the wave and particle notations. He had no physical interpretation of these waves, and still has not. Schrödinger then took de Broglie's *ondes de phase* literally as classical fields of the Maxwell type. This interpretation was punctured by Born as we shall see. So the elegant wave mechanics of Schrödinger, and the observationally equivalent matrix mechanics of Heisenberg had to float in a cloud of uncertainty concerning just what experimental sense there is in $| \Psi (q) |^2$. Born dispelled this with the suggestion that the waves be taken as a measure of the probability of locating particles within a given volume element. Because it was operationally clear, and corroborated by every experiment, Born's view was adopted, and generalized for multiparticle distributions by Bohr, Heisenberg, Gordon, Jordan, Klein, Pauli, and, most significantly, by Dirac.[4]

In 1928 there appeared a great contribution to physical theory. Just as Newton welded the five independent laws of Kepler and Galileo, all of hydrodynamics, astronomy, ballistics, and optics—so also did Dirac unite in one powerful theory every idea of the particle physics of the Twenties. He provided a model for the hydrogen atom, explained Compton scattering, the Zeeman effect, and the empirically required electron spin; all these were forged into an algorithm whose purpose was to achieve a relativistically invariant theory for electrons. Dirac's adaptation of Jordan's

[4] P. A. M. Dirac, Proc. Phys. Soc., London, Vol. 112, p. 661 (1926); Vol. 113, p. 621 (1926); Vol. 114, p. 710 (1927); Vol. 117, p. 610 (1928); Vol. 118, p. 351 (1928).

operator calculus (itself a generalization of Heisenberg's matrix mechanics), makes the uncertainty relations a formal property of the notation. Dirac took an idea of Graves, developed in Heaviside's calculus, and already used by Born and Jordan, wherein an ordinary algebra is modified by the law $PQ - QP = n$. The properties of such a noncommutative system were understood by 1900. But to translate this into a systematic expression of the uncertainty relations implicit in the wave-particle fusion was pure genius. Dirac's paper established quantum mechanics as a unified description of nature. The theory was even more elevated when one of its consequences—first thought a blemish by Dirac (and even earlier (1926) by Gordon)—entailed unobserved entities with queer properties. This "blemish," which Dirac, Schrödinger, Weyl, and Oppenheimer tried to eradicate, was seen by Blackett to describe the new antielectrons which he and Occhialini and Anderson observed in 1932. Dirac's theory did everything; it integrated all available facts, provided a formalism, and was fertile in predictions; e.g., the antiproton and the antineutron have only recently been detected.

Many objections to the Copenhagen interpretation arise from not appreciating the historical role played by Dirac's paper. Here is the notational key to all subsequent quantum physics. Yet, in that paper (Dirac tells me) the Copenhagen interpretation figured essentially—not as some afterthought appended to his algebra, but basic to every operation with the notation. Feyerabend suggests that this need not have been so, that it would be possible to have a "minimum" interpretation of quantum theory, and hence of Dirac's paper. But in fact this is not the way in which this paper was written. This would not *be* the same paper were its assumptions "purified." Largely because of these realistic suppositions Dirac's theory had complete success (before the era of mesons). Critics of the Copenhagen interpretation often fail to see that to ask for an alternative account of micronature without providing one which works reinvites the chaos which Dirac ended. To command a physicist's attention with counterproposals, one must provide a better scientific theory, not just a restatement of the orthodox formalism plus metaphysical asides. Perhaps it *is* possible to have a minimum statement of quantum theory, with no more "interpretation" than is required barely to describe the facts. But this is what Dirac felt he had, and what

Copenhagen feels it now has, and why it views most counterproposals as observationally irrelevant superstructures. In 1952, Bohm conceded that his reinterpretation affected no known facts, but added philosophical notions of heuristic value.[5] *Bohr et Heisenberg n'ont pas besoin de cette hypothèse.*

Should philosophers discontinue attempts to develop proposals which counter the Copenhagen interpretation? No. But they might be less enthusiastic in their evaluations of such activity. What is objectionable is referring to the Copenhagen school as holding the field by authoritative dictatorship. As if *alternative* interpretations of quantum theory were being forcibly suppressed in favor of the naïve metaphysics of Bohr and Heisenberg! Patent nonsense. There is as yet *no* working alternative to the Copenhagen interpretation. Ask your nearest synchrotron operator. It therefore seems questionable to make every new speculation sound as if it *were* a clear alternative which could revolutionize the foundations of physics, if only elder statesmen would stop backing their favorite horse so uncritically. The issue is: *Until you formulate a new interpretation which works as well as does the old one, call your efforts by their proper name, "speculations."* This makes them no less worthwhile. If it be riposted that the Copenhagen interpretation is itself a speculation, then please let us distinguish those speculations which have proven themselves to *work* in theory and practice from those which have not yet been put to any test.

Consider an analogy. By 1860 the inability of celestial mechanics to explain aberrations in Mercury's perihelion became obvious. Leverrier had explained the perturbations of Uranus via Newtonian mechanics by supposing another planet, "Neptune," gravitationally responsible for the anomaly. Six years later he detected Mercury's precession. Leverrier appealed again to the "hidden planet" hypothesis.[6] The unseen object was confidently christened "Vulcan" and made responsible for the perturbations. But Vulcan does not exist. It cannot exist (it would require a straightline solution to the three-body problem, earth—sun—Vulcan, a solution demonstrably unstable). Although many nineteenth-century thinkers were upset by this failure, no one proposed that

[5] D. Bohm, *Phys. Rev.*, Vol. 85, No. 166, p. 180, 1952.

[6] U. J. J. Leverrier, *Recherches astronomiques* (L'Observatoire nationale de Paris Annales, 1855–1877).

Newtonian astronomy be abandoned. To do that then, would have been to stop thinking about celestial phenomena. One had to provide some equally useful astronomy, or accept the otherwise successful orthodox theory. Similarly in quantum theory.

Thus it is arguable that the Copenhagen limitations are built into the very wave-particle duality micronature has forced on us, and built also into the symmetry of explanations in terms of that duality. At least it remains to be shown that this is not so. Dr. Feyerabend would not agree. He distinguishes "Born's interpretation" which gives the formalism a physical meaning, from "Bohr's interpretation" which he characterizes as being itself a metaphysical addition to the bare theory. Let us suppose that he is correct: would it follow that "Admitting this implies that we are . . . free to invent and to consider other 'metaphysical' interpretations."[7] Not at all! For this obscures the historical, conceptual, and operationally successful role of the Bohr view *as opposed to other interpretations.* The metaphysics in Newton's *Principia* is not to be rated equally with the harangues of Hooke and *unintelligibilia* of Benton. The freedom for inventing alternative interpretations which Feyerabend imagines to follow on the discovery of a metaphysical strain in Bohr's view is unwarranted in the absence of an alternative formalism, and concrete experimental suggestions, on which to build the "new metaphysics."

There is a further related point: The design of apparatus makes clear that the only way of learning about particles is to interact with them at our macrophysical level. This is not merely a comment on experimental technique. The proposition, "To learn anything about a particle we must interact with it," has the same logical force as "Nothing can move faster than light," or "There cannot be a *perpetuum mobile,*" or "A temperature-registration of less than $-273°$ C is impossible." None of these state *mere* matters of fact. *Each involves the conceptual principles of entire physical theories.* Similarly: one must interact with microparticles to learn about them. The negation of this, although not self-contradictory, is physically unintelligible.

This entails what many philosophers persist in being unhappy about—that in particle physics the data never come to us packed with invariant properties, undistorted by the observing instrument. Data in microphysics can never be

[7] *Brit. J. Phil. Sci.,* Vol. 7, p. 356, 1957.

less than a compound of the microevent and some macro-physical system (a detector, or just ourselves). We have no concept of an alternative to this, as a cemetery of dead *gedan-kenexperiments* proves. Such an alternative would have to rest on using a detector whose quantum of perturbation is h, to get information about micronature in units smaller than $h!$ Inter-action is *the* information concept in quantum physics. If the basic unit of interaction is h, then all information patterns with which we describe the world must also be quantized in units of h imposed by the detector. Anything "beyond" this is undetectable—unknowable. The alternative to this can scarcely be made intelligible. Yet early critics of quantum theory readily supposed they had ideas of what electrons and protons are "really" like, technical limitations notwithstand-ing. They pointed to classical statistical mechanics. There, *experimental* limitations could affect the confidence with which we described new thermodynamical events. But they never altered our *concepts* of the matter involved; a hidden symmetry always lurked behind the statistics. (This confi-dence results from confounding "phenomenological thermo-dynamics" with "deductive thermodynamics," developed from the two principles of impotence.) It is, however, *the* feature of experimental microphysics that the degree and manner of the perturbation of the system by the detector is *in principle* incalculable.

This is not novel. Let's take statistical mechanics seriously. Boltzmann and Gibbs spring to mind. In his irresolvably statistical gas theory Boltzmann objects to Newtonian con-cepts of observation, as contrasted with what earlier physi-cists were entitled to count as such. He did not feel that gas theory required statistical formulation *only* because of experimental limitations. No; he viewed statistical mechanics as the *primary* discipline; it is directly connected with ob-servable parameters. Punctiform masses and ideal particle populations Boltzmann construed not as the starting point of physics, but as heuristic abstractions: these were dubious variables hidden within the total laboratory exploration of a physical event. They *are* notationally simpler and are in-dispensable in calculation. But the simplicity is merely formal, and should not be confounded with thinking about actual observational data. The development of kinetic theory might have proceeded more smoothly had early mechanics attended to what is *observable*, and not only to what is easier to con-ceive. There are no *special* mechanical problems about gases other than that they *must* be described as observed *en masse*. They will not be reduced to metaphysically prior abstractions. Boltzmann saw every observation as a function of the design of the apparatus and the observer's knowledge of the previous state of the system.

Imagine now a hot metal emitting electrons. A measuring apparatus registers, by the blackening of a point on a photographic plate, the emission of any electron with a velocity greater than v. Now adjust the apparatus so that electrons are emitted very infrequently. This measurement of the metal's temperature leads to an "objective" determination of one of its properties. We express this mathematically by regarding the "metal system" as a sample selected from a canonical ensemble.

But what does "objective" mean here? It means that *any* thermometer can be used as measuring instrument; that measurements do not depend on either thermometer or observer. Now if the total system, metal-plus-apparatus, is isolated from the rest of the universe, it has a constant energy not exactly known because of the canonical distribution. If, however, the metal is not isolated, its energy varies with time and oscillates in temperature equilibrium about a mean value indicated by the distribution. If now the canonical ensemble of the total system follows a Newtonian pattern, the ensemble evolves, containing an increasing proportion of states in which points on the plate are blackened. The probability that the measuring apparatus will respond at a certain place at t can be calculated, but the exact instant and place of an actual event cannot be predicted. Were every detail of this experiment known at the start, *à la Laplace*, we should be able to determine beforehand each point-blackening, *provided that the experimental system were isolated from the rest of the universe*. But in this case the statement of the temperature would be unintelligible. If, however, the experimental system is really part of the external world, then even complete knowledge of its details would not allow precise predictions, since we cannot know every detail of the remaining universe.

This total experimental system also contains a "subjective" element, despite those who suppose thermodynamics to carry no thumbprints of the observing instrument. In the absence of a detecting apparatus, the mathematics of the system changes continuously, as outlined. But introject a detector; it will *suddenly* register that a point on the plate is blackened. The representation is altered discontinuously, because here we have moved from the former situation containing a great range of mathematical possibilities to a new ensemble containing only the plate blackened at one point. For *that* event, *ex post facto*, the formal statistical representation originally appropriate has no further descriptive utility. The discontinuous change is not even hinted at in the Gibbs' equations characterizing the ensemble. It corresponds to the "reduction of wave packets" in quantum theory. Thus, characterizing an *experimental* system as a Gibbs' ensemble not only specifies *its* properties, but is also contingent on a detector's presence within that system. Hence the word "objective" in this context is questionable (and the same may be said of "subjective," too).

So one can assign an "objective" temperature to a body only on the evidence of the average velocity of its particles, some of which escape (altering "the body") and are recorded by a detector whose own properties are involved in the "reading." If one had Laplacean knowledge of the particles, one could predict every recording by the detector —place and time. But then one could no longer assign an *objective* temperature to the body; the *concepts* of temperature and entropy presuppose statistical disorder. Objective temperature and actual recordings are thus mutually exclusive, though complementary: the former requires randomness. The latter, by determining an event, curtails randomness to that extent. Again, every such recording, by changing the ensemble, reduces the probability function in the Gibbs' representation, a reduction unmentioned in the equations for the particles.

Against all this consider quantum mechanics. A microsystem can be represented by a wave function or by a statistical mixture of such functions (i.e., a density matrix). This corresponds to a Gibbs' ensemble. If the system interacts with the world, only the mixture (or matrix) representation is possible; we cannot know all details of the total macrophysical system (i.e., the universe). If the microsystem is closed, we may have a "pure case,"—represented by a vector in Hilbert space. This representation is completely "objective." It is unconnected with any observer's knowledge or detector's reaction. Calculations concerning this vector are valid or invalid according to objective rules. But such a representation is completely abstract. Its mathematical expressions, $| \Psi (q) |^2, | \Psi (p) |^2$, do not refer to experimental space or observable properties: they contain no physics whatever. The microsystem *qua* vector-group-in-Hilbert-space describes nature only when linked to possible experiments. We *must* consider the interaction of the system with the apparatus, the detecting instrument, the observer. We *must* use a statistical mixture in representing this joint, and discontinuously fluctuating, system.

Could this be avoided by isolating the microsystem and the observing apparatus from the macrophysical universe? No. Its placement within the universe is necessary for the apparatus to function as intended; its behavior must register in experiments if we are to get information from the apparatus. Again, this is not logical necessity. The denial of this does not reduce to *P-and-not-P*. (If it did, we would be discussing only the formal properties of an algorithm.) Still, this denial describes nothing intelligible. It is inconceivable that we should ever encounter a *perpetuum mobile*. So also is it inconceivable that the measuring apparatus should both perform its function, and also be isolated from the world. The joint system is therefore describable only by a statistical mixture of wave functions— a density matrix. It *inevitably* contains statements about the detector.

To deny this robs us of the concepts needed to experiment in microphysics at all. When detectors react within an experiment, the mathematical representation is altered discontinuously. One among various statistical possibilities has proved to obtain. This discontinuous "reduction of wave packets," underivable from Schrödinger's equation, is (as in Gibbs) a shifting from mathematical descriptions to experimental actualities. An observation reduces the original Ψ representing an ensemble of possibilities to a new Ψ, whose future possibilities will have been altered by the first observation. This shift from original to new Ψ is not in the wave equation. One *can* imagine all this projected back in time; but never so far back that the joint system can be thought separate from the world. (This would be incompatible with the validity of quantum mechanics for closed systems, and hence would leave us no concepts with which to think about quantum phenomena.)

Hence a system isolated from the macrophysical world cannot be described in classical terms. We *may* say that the state of the closed system described by a Hilbert vector is *objective*, although it does *not obtain*. Here, however, the classical idea of objectivity must be abandoned. The description of a microsystem by its Hilbert vector group complements its description in classical terms (just as a Gibbs' description of a microscopic state complements a statement of its temperature). The description of an event can be effected by classical concepts to just that approximation to quantum theory one needs for predictions in a given context; this is one version of the correspondence principle. Quantum theory can also be used, however. So the boundary between object-observed and instrument-observing can be pushed indefinitely toward the latter—just as I can always regard the temperature of a body as but a property of thermometers placed in a physical context containing the original body. The statistical nature of the laws of microphysics is again seen to be unavoidable.

So much for the history of the Copenhagen interpretation.

II

Consider now some representative attacks on this interpretation. The opposition has moved against Copenhagen on four fronts. The earliest discomfort concerned the statistical nature of quantum laws. How should one interpret the Ψ function in the fundamental Schrödinger equation? De Broglie's *ondes de phase* were never defined. Are they algebraic fictions, or physical existants? His theory of the pilot wave suggests the latter. But no experiment has ever revealed such pilot waves in electrons, protons, or neutrons. Exit de Broglie.

Abstract configuration space is not for Schrödinger either. He imagines an infinite number of interfering Maxwell waves, whose resultant wave maximum just *is* the particle in question. For him an electron is an "energy smear"; $|\Psi(q)|^2$ gives the measure of the spread and intensity of that smear. This view collapses in multibody collision problems. Here Schrödinger must entertain spaces of an indefinite number of dimensions (for N particles Ψ is a function of $3N$ coordinates)—an idea with no experimental interpretation, save in the "degenerate" case of one particle, where configuration space and physical space coincide. De Broglie, Schrödinger, and also Einstein and Jeffreys have always contended that quantum theory has not yet settled down. It is like mechanics in 1600, phenomenological and chaotic. Schrödinger seeks to rewrite microphysics as a classical field theory. Others pursue hydrodynamic models in which the singularities are localizations in a continuous substratum. These attempts, however, have all proved disappointing. At present we have *one* way of construing quantum phenomena, and this is in terms of the Copenhagen formulation. Show the physicist a detailed, physically intelligible alternative, and he will readily try it. But physicists use a formalism only so far as its parameters are testable; hence the Ψ function is usually taken to measure either the probability of finding a particle within a given volume element, or the probability that certain areas on a target detector will be more affected by particle impact than other areas. Or, Ψ may be related to determinations of the density of particles within a parallelepiped of the particle beam, etc. This doesn't minimize the reality of the wave aspect of microparticles. A pencil of β rays scattered by metal foil will leave target patterns describable only by the distribution implicit in the Ψ function of equations appropriate for β particles in such a situation. We possess *direct* evidence of the correctness of de Broglie's approximation in the diffraction of particle beams by crystal lattices. The resulting patterns obey Bragg's law and all other laws of diffraction by spatial gratings as are observed in x-ray diffraction, and with the exact wavelengths required by the law $\lambda K = p$ ($K =$ wave propagation vector). The "ultimate" property of individual particles responsible for this distribution remains for the Copenhagen theorist as it might have been for Newton: *I have not been able to discover the cause of these features of the distribution; it is enough that a particle will more probably strike in one place rather than in another, and that I have a formula for describing this probability.*[8]

Another charge has concerned uneasiness about the uncertainty relations. But it has been shown that this discomfort usually consists in failing to comprehend the reasons for our needing such a theory at all. One *could* generate all of quantum theory from a suitable statement of these relations alone. So they cannot be a peripheral blemish. They are the heart of quantum theory. How else to understand the achievement of Dirac's noncommutative operators?

A third discomfiture concerns this noncommutative algebra. Some can feel no confidence in a theory whose mathematics are managed according to: $QP - PQ = n$. This

[8] *Principia*, Conclusion: "I have not been able to discover the cause of those properties of gravity . . . it is enough that gravity does really exist, and act according to the laws we have explained."

echoes the dissatisfaction many felt with Heaviside's decision to represent dx/dt by p—any ordinary algebraic quantity. This also leads to a noncommutativity. Critics thought the operational calculus but a sloppy approximation to some more refined-but-then-uninvented theory. Still, the calculus does its job (e.g., in alternating current circuit theory) if one learns the rules of the algorithm. Similarly the Dirac calculus: it was more powerful in prediction and in explanation of microphenomena than any previous theory. Noncommutativity *per se* is no blemish; *here* it is an ingenious expression of what the data oblige us to think.

There are *genuine* formal improprieties within quantum theory, e.g., "renormalization" and negative probabilities ("ghost states"). True, some physicists have related these mathematical inelegancies to the structure of the Dirac theory. But even Heisenberg's most recent work is couched in a noncommutative algebra.

A final kind of discomfort with Copenhagen concerns an asymmetry in microphysical explanation and prediction. In classical physics explaining X is symmetrical with predicting X. If I explain X via the laws of a system S by reference to initial conditions α, β, γ . . . then I might as easily have predicted X on the basis of α, β, γ . . and operating on these via the rules of S. Thus a retrogradation of Mars is explained via celestial mechanics by referring to Mars' mean angular velocity, distance, mass, and coordinates at some past time. But conversely, at this time past, to have known Mars' coordinates, mass, distance, and velocity would have allowed one to predict via S that at certain future times Mars would be in apparent retrograde movement. For those who take this as the paradigm of explanation and prediction, disappointment with the quantum-theoretic situation is inevitable.

After a microphysical event X has occurred within our purview, we can give a complete explanation of its occurrence within the total quantum theory. But it is impossible to predict those features of X so easily explained *ex post facto*. This meshes with earlier points. Expressions of discomfort at this juncture are often ways of announcing that one likes his physics deterministic, orthodox, Newtonian.

III

Heisenberg has examined several counterinterpretations of quantum theory. These fall, roughly, into four classes:

1. The sighs of great men, who have not offered one scrap

of algebra to back up their advice. This is reminiscent of Hooke's charge that Newton had merely provided a formula for gravity, but had said nothing about its causes; to which Newton retorted that if Hooke had some *mathematical* contribution to make, he would listen—but not to metaphysical poetry alone.

2. *Hidden variable* formalisms each of which destroys the symmetry which has been the power of quantum theory.

3. Prose passages which fail to grasp the experimental necessity of interaction.

4. Pure mathematics, offering no hint about what an experiment which could abrogate, e.g., the uncertainty relations would be like.

The symmetry sacrifice is significant. These counterproposals all sacrifice symmetry in some form. Perhaps a Copenhagen-type interpretation is unavoidable if things like wave-particle duality and Lorentz invariance are genuine features of nature. Every experiment supports this idea. The theoretician always favors the theory which saves such symmetries. Recall Schrödinger's attempt to restate the Dirac electron theory, eliminating the negative energy solutions. Both Weyl and Oppenheimer showed his attempt to vary with the choice of Lorentz frames; exit Schrödinger. If we decide thus the fate of genuine theories, why not the same criterion for interpretations of theories?

IV

Professor Mehlberg has considered[9] Jordan's argument against early versions of the correspondence principle. He rejects Jordan's reasoning by first accepting perfect correspondence between classical and quantum mechanics, and then concluding that the latter cannot be limited in the "nonclassical" ways Bohr and Heisenberg have stressed.

Thus Mehlberg says:

since the validity of quantum theory is . . . admitted to range over the whole physical universe, . . . [all] . . . physical concepts would become unobjectifiable and the epistemological consequences of this pervasive unobjectifiability would appear to be crippling for the whole empirical method of

[9] H. Mehlberg, in the symposium "Philosophical Problems of Quantum Mechanics," at the May 1958 meeting of the American Philosophical Association, Western Division.

acquiring knowledge of physical objects on the basis of observation.

Mehlberg has adopted and exploited sentiments expressed by Weyl:

Thus we see a new quantum physics emerge of which the old classical laws are a limiting case in the same sense that Einstein's relativistic mechanics passes into Newton's . . . when *c* the velocity of light tends to ∞ .[10]

Theoretical treatises intend something special when they speak thus. No one is misled. But in contexts like Mehlberg's, misconceptions can arise. He has this perplexity: the motions of planets are explained in terms of "the old classical laws." In practice it is not possible to determine planetary states by sharp coordinates and momentum vectors, nor can one eliminate observer's error. Still, it is legitimate to speak of the planet as *having* exact coordinates and moments. Uncertainties in state determination are in principle eradicable. Thus *point particles are conceptual possibilities within classical particle physics.*

Within Dirac's theory, however, to speak of the exact coordinates and momentum of a particle at *t* is to make no assertion at all. What could such an assertion consist in? That a wave packet has been compressed to a point? This cannot even be false. *Point particles, therefore, are not conceptual possibilities within quantum physics.*

Yet we are told, by Weyl and Mehlberg, that quantum theory embraces classical physics as a limiting case. The justification for this is usually given in the classical connection between radiation and electrical oscillation when we consider the orbital frequency of the hydrogen atom's electron. ($\omega/2\pi = \gamma = 4\pi^2 me^4/h^3 n^3$.) Quantum theory gives a formula for this analogous to the classical connection. $\gamma = (2\pi^2 e^4/h^3)$ $(n_i^2 - n_f^2/n_i^2 n_f^2)$—for frequency of radiation connected with the transition $n_i \rightarrow n_f$. If this transition is small as against n_i, we write $\gamma = (4\pi^2 e^4 m/h^3 n_i^3)$ $(n_i - n_f)$. In the limiting case of large quantum numbers $\triangle N = 1$ gives a frequency identical with the classical frequency. The transition $\triangle N = 2$ gives the first harmonic.

Here a perplexity arises which may have affected Mehlberg. A cluster of symbols S expresses an intelligible assertion in classical mechanics, yet that same S does not do so

[10] Weyl, *Philosophy of Mathematics and Natural Science* (Princeton: Princeton University Press, 1949).

in quantum mechanics. Still, classical and quantum languages are said to be continuous—arbitrarily distinguished clusters of statements in but one language.

However, *statements and language don't work this way.* A well-formed sentence S, if it makes an assertion in one part of a language, does so in all parts. Technical notations are defined by rules determining which symbol-combinations can make intelligible assertions. When S can express a statement here, but not there, one concludes that the languages in these contexts were different and discontinuous. Finite and transfinite arithmetics, Euclidean and non-Euclidean geometries, the language of time and the language of space, of mind and of brain; these show themselves discontinuous on just this principle. What may be meaningful in the one case may be unintelligible in the other. Thus what may express the state of a fast particle in classical physics may, in Dirac's physics, make no assertion at all. This ought to prove the two languages logically discontinuous. The correspondence principle apparently instructs us otherwise: quantum theory embraces classical laws as a limiting case. Jordan's arguments fail because microphysics "contains" macrophysics.

But how can intelligible assertions become unintelligible as quantum numbers get smaller; how can symbol clusters *become* meaningful just because quantum numbers get larger? The idea of a formula S ranging within a language from "meaningless" to "meaningful" is inconceivable. Either S makes an assertion throughout the language in which it figures, or else the latter is more than one language. It's a matter of syntax. *Either the noncommutativity of positiion and momentum operators holds (i.e., the s of classical physics makes no assertion in quantum physics), or the correspondence principle holds (i.e., the S of classical physics is a limiting case of quantum physics). But not both.* Or else we misconstrue one (or both) of the principles.

So the alternatives are: (1) quantum physics cannot embrace classical physics, or (2) quantum physics is not permanently restricted as the Copenhagen interpretation suggests, or (3) classical physics itself should be regarded as incapable of precise state determination, just as quantum physics.

Dismiss 3. We may grant with Boltzmann that it is more faithful to observation. But it is a self-denying ordinance of little valuε. A classical mechanics *sans* punctiform masses, rigid levers, and ideal gases would be too difficult to justify its purity. Alternative 2 we have considered.

I suggest there is no *logical* connection between classical and quantum physics. Consider: the punctiform mass, a kinematical idea, is the springboard of classical theory. The wave pulse, a dynamical idea, is the fountainhead of quantum theory. Languages springing from such different stock will differ throughout their structure. Notwithstanding the correspondence principle, the languages of classical and quantum mechanics diverge.

How then do hydrogen atoms with large quantum numbers behave as they do? Well, this example may be misunderstood. Such different conceptual structures cannot mesh in this way. Their logical gears are not of the same type. Propositions get their force from the total language system in which they figure. That a formula gives a classical frequency for the transition $\triangle N = 1$ in the case of the hydrogen atom's electron proves at most that there are *formal analogies between certain reaches of quantum theory and certain reaches of classical theory*. That this is only an analogy is obscured by the fact that identical symbols, "$4\pi^2 me^4/h^3 n^3$," are used in both languages. This is no more a logical identity than is the use of "$+$" and "$-$" for both valence theory and number theory. Permit an analogy.

Men are made of cells. Men have brains, personalities, financial worries; but it might be no assertion at all to say such things of cells, especially if cell-talk were constructed *ab initio* as logically different from man-talk. The two idioms could then never merge. "It has schizophrenia and an overdrawn account" would express nothing in cell-language. Even though a complex conspiracy of cells could be spoken of in ways analogous to how we speak of a man, this would not conflate the two languages, not even when both idioms characterize the same object, e.g., me. If someone speaks of me as a man but another speaks of me as a collection of cells, although the *denotatum* of both discourses be identical, the two speakers diverge conceptually. They are not speaking the same language; the logic of their speech differs. These differences are logical, and independent of the facts that such utterances may be made truly in similar contexts, and may even be expressed in the same symbols. The continuity suggested by incautious statements of the correspondence principle may be illusory.

So perhaps the correspondence principle does not make classical physics a limiting case of quantum physics, even though the two formalisms are analogous at points. What the principle does show is that when quantum numbers are high the hydrogen atom can be regarded either as a small macrophysical body set in a classical space-time, or as a large "quantum body" exemplifying to but a vanishing degree the dynamics of elementary particles. In the first case S will constitute an assertion. In the second case it will not. Against this Dr. Feyerabend offers an unconvincing argument. "We may," he says, "admit that macroscopic systems can be described in terms of wave functions if we assume at the same time that a macroscopic observer has never enough information at his disposal in order to set up such a wave function." Feyerabend makes it sound as if *"never having enough information to set up a macroscopic wave function"* is like *"never having enough information to verify assertions about the moon's far side."* But there is a difference in principle here which parallels just that between quantum and classical languages. We never *could* have enough information of the sort Feyerabend remarks. And it is in the logic of this "never could" that the Copenhagen interpretation lives.

We may treat the hydrogen atom as we please, we may interchange Poisson brackets for quantum brackets when we wish, depending on our problem. But it need not follow that there is a logical staircase running from 10^{-13} cm. to 10^{-13} light years. There may be one logical break; that is why we can make assertions about the exact state of Mars, but not about the elementary particle nearest Mars' classical center of gravity. As an indication of how quantum *mathematics* can be managed, the correspondence principle is clear. But when treated as by Professor Mehlberg, it might mislead. Hence I cannot agree that the anticorrespondence argument fails. It fails only if one takes the correspondence principle overliterally. But we can continue to allow chemists and engineers to treat their data realistically. This is just how the quantum physicist regards his laboratory apparatus, even while insisting on a Copenhagen interpretation for the foundations of the theory. Just as the uncertainty principle holds no consequences for ballistics, so quantum theory as a whole need have no conceptual consequences for classical mechanics. Certainly no physicist is *obliged* to generalize quantum physics as Mehlberg and Weyl do.

v

Finally, distinguish *Philosophical Problems of Quantum Mechanics* from *Problems of Philosophers Concerning Quantum Mechanics*. It is a sociological fact that working quantum physicists do not bother with problems concerning, e.g., the interpretation of the Ψ function, not to mention matters concerning "realistic" or "nonrealistic" interpretations of quantum theory as a whole. This is not because the working physicist is intellectually incapable of having philosophical problems; he has plenty. One cannot be exposed to discussions in quantum field theory and meson theory without feeling their logical, analytical character. This is not imported into physics from other academic contexts. Does an otherwise successful algorithm containing inconsistencies (as does renormalization) require immediate examination—or does danger loom only when predictions fail? Historically this is a significant problem: remember the aether! Another is the question of interpreting "negative probabilities." Heisenberg argues that their existence in a renormalized calculation indicates a flaw in the very approach to quantum theory set out in the Dirac notation. Others appraise the matter differently.

Consider also Gell-Mann's taxonomical attack on meson theory. Much of the Dirac theory is unsatisfactory in this region. So Gell-Mann has proceeded like a natural historian—drawing up "phenomenological" charts of particle properties and allowing generalizations to stand forth from the data, if they can. Despite Toulmin's campaign, this "John Stuart Mill"-type approach does exist in physics and can be important.[11] Many such difficulties are the daily fare of quantum physics. How little attention philosophers pay them! This is no reason for philosophers to cease talking about what they wish. But no one should suppose that because most quantum physicists are unperturbed by the kind of question brought to prominence by Bohm, that therefore they are unreflective, computer-ridden predicting machines. What the physicist is likely to find difficult in many philosophical papers concerning the foundations of quan-

[11] S. E. Toulmin, *The Philosophy of Science* (London: University Library, Hutchinson, 1953).

tum theory, is a facile use of terms like "realism," "objectivism," and "subjectivism." One might suppose that philosophers had settled what a discussion of realism, objectivism, and subjectivism was a discussion about. Which reminds me of the question with which an Oxford undergraduate once staggered his tutor: "What is the external world *external to?*" When I see the full sense, or nonsense, in that question, I may see also how quantum theory is going to help, or be helped by, the cracking of old philosophical chestnuts.

SELECTED BIBLIOGRAPHY

This bibliography makes no pretense of being complete, and is intended chiefly as a guide to further study. Moreover, we have for the most part tried not to duplicate items that are cited in other readily available bibliographies. The most useful bibliography is perhaps to be found in Feigl, H., and Brodbeck, M. (eds.), *Readings in the Philosophy of Science* (N.Y., Appleton-Century-Crofts, 1953). See also the bibliographies in Wiener, P. (ed.), *Readings in the Philosophy of Science* (N.Y., Scribners, 1953). For older material, consult Cohen, Morris, *Reason and Nature* (Glencoe, Ill., The Free Press, 1949). A complete bibliography of Logical Positivism is in Ayer, A. J. (ed.), *Logical Positivism* (Glencoe, Ill., The Free Press, 1959). The bibliographies to Sections III and VIII in Edwards, Paul, and Pap, Arthur (eds.), *A Modern Introduction to Philosophy* (Glencoe, Ill., The Free Press, 1958) are particularly useful in connection with Part One of this book.

PART ONE
SCIENCE, LANGUAGE, AND EXPERIENCE

MEANING

Anscombe, G. E. M., *An Introduction to Wittgenstein's Tractatus* (London, Hutchinson University Library, 1959), 25–41, 79–86, 150–60.

Bergman, Gustav, *Philosophy of Science* (Madison, University of Wisconsin Press, 1957), 48–74.

Braithwaite, R. B., *Scientific Explanation* (Cambridge University Press, 1955), Ch. I, esp. 1–9, and Ch. III, esp. 79–82.

Brookes, B. C., "The Difficulties of Interpreting Science," *The Listener*, Oct. 2, 1959, 519–21.

Carnap, R. "The Methodological Characterization of Theoretical Concepts," in Feigl, H., and Scriven, M. (eds.), *Minnesota Studies in the Philosophy of Science* (Minneapolis, University of Minnesota Press, 1956), Vol. I, 38–76.

D'Abro, A., "Phenomenological Theories," in *The Rise of the New Physics* (N.Y., Dover, 1951), Ch. XI.

Hanson, N. R., *Patterns of Discovery* (Cambridge University Press, 1959), Ch. I.

Hirst, R. J., *The Problems of Perception* (N.Y., Macmillan, 1959), esp. Ch. V.

Hutten, Ernest, *The Logic of Modern Physics* (N.Y., Macmillan, 1956), 50–72.

Kneale, W., "What Can We See?", in Körner, S. (ed.), *Observation and Interpretation* (N.Y., Academic Press, 1957), 151–9.

Koyré, A., "Plato and Galileo," reprinted in Wiener, P., and Nolan, A. (eds.), *Roots of Scientific Thought* (N.Y., Basic Books, 1957).

Margenau, Henry, *The Nature of Physical Reality* (N.Y., McGraw-Hill, 1950), 54–74.

Nagel, Ernest, *Logic without Metaphysics* (Glencoe, Ill., The Free Press, 1958), 103–42, 143–52, 341–52.

Pap, Arthur, "Disposition Concepts and Extensional Logic," in Feigl, H., Scriven, M., and Alexander, G. (eds.), *Minnesota Studies in the Philosophy of Science* (Minneapolis, University of Minnesota Press, 1958), Vol. II.

Popper, K., *The Logic of Scientific Discovery* (N.Y., Basic Books, 1959) Chs. I, IV, V.

Quine, W. V. O., "Two Dogmas of Empiricism," *From a Logical Point of View* (Cambridge, Harvard University Press, 1956), also in *Philosophical Review*, 60, 1951.

Ryle, Gilbert, *Dilemmas* (Cambridge University Press, 1956), Chs. V–VII.

Scriven, M., "Definitions, Explanations, and Theories," in *Minnesota Studies in the Philosophy of Science*, Vol. II.

MEASUREMENT

Churchman, C. W., "A Materialist Theory of Measurement," Sellars, R. W., McGill, V. J., and Farber, M. (eds.), *Philosophy for the Future* (N.Y., Macmillan, 1949).

Churchman, C. W. (ed.), *Measurement, Definition, and Theories* (N.Y., J. Wiley, 1959), see especially Churchman, C. W., "Why Measure?"; Menger, K., "Mensuration and Other Mathematical Connections of Observable Material"; Pap, A., "Are Physical Magnitudes Operationally Definable?"; Stevens, S. S., "Measurement, Empirical Meaningfulness, and Three Valued Logic."

De Broglie, L., *Physics and Microphysics* (N.Y., Pantheon, 1955), 78–87.

Evans, Melbourne, "Aristotle, Newton, and the Theory of Continuous Magnitudes," reprinted in Wiener, P., and Nolan, A. (eds.), *Roots of Scientific Thought* (N.Y., Basic Books, 1957).

Pfanzel, J., *Die axiomatisch Grundlagen einer allgemeinen Theorie des Messens* (Würzburg, Physica Verlag, 1959).

Scott, D., and Suppes, P., "Foundational Aspects of Measurement," *Journal of Symbolic Logic*, Vol. 23, No. 2 (1958), 113–28.

Suppes, P., "A Set of Independent Axioms for Extensive Quantities," *Portugaliae Mathematica*, X, Fasc. 4 (1951), 163–72.

Weyl, H., *Philosophy of Mathematics and Natural Science* (Princeton University Press, 1949), 139–65.

PART TWO
LAWS AND THEORIES

LAWS AND EXPLANATION

Alexander, H. G., "General Statements as Rules of Inference," Feigl, H., Scriven, M., Maxwell, G. (eds.), *Minnesota Studies in the Philosophy of Science*, Vol. II, 309–22.

Bergman, G., *Philosophy of Science* (Madison, University of Wisconsin Press, 1957), 84–91, and see review of this by Morgenbesser, S., *Journal of Philosophy*, 55 (1958), 169–76.

Braithwaite, R. B., *Scientific Explanation* (Cambridge University Press, 1957), Chs. II, IV, IX–XI. Cf. review of *Scientific Explanation* by Ernest Nagel, "A Budget of Problems in the Philosophy of Science," *The Philosophical Review* (1957), 205–26.

D'Abro, A., *The Rise of the New Physics* (N.Y., Dover, 1951) Chs. V, XIV–XV.

Frank, Philipp, *Philosophy of Science* (N.Y., Prentice-Hall, 1957), 260–77.

Householder, A. S., *Principles of Numerical Analysis* (N.Y., McGraw-Hill, 1953), Ch. I.

Popper, K., *The Logic of Scientific Discovery* (N.Y., Basic Books, 1959) Chs. III, VII, X.

Reichenbach, Hans, *Nomological Statements and Admissible Operations* (Amsterdam, North-Holland Pub. Co., 1954); and review of same by C. G. Hempel in *Journal of Symbolic Logic*, Vol. 20, No. 1 (1956), 50–4.

Suppes, P., *Introduction to Logic* (N.Y., Van Nostrand, 1957), 246–91.

Turner, Joseph, "Maxwell on the Logic of Dynamical Explanation," *Philosophy of Science*, Vol. 23, No. 1 (1956), 26–47.

On explanation see also papers by Tumners, J. H., Paris, C., Destouches-Février, P., Destouches, J.-L., in *XI International Congress of Philosophy* (Brussels, 1953), Vol. VI, 61–90.

THEORIES

Bergman, G., *Philosophy of Science* (Madison, University of Wisconsin Press, 1957), 131–62.

Birkhoff, G. D., "A Mathematical Critique of Some Physical Theories" and "The Mathematical Nature of Physical Theories," in Birkhoff, G. D., *Collected Papers*, Vol. II, 747–63, 890–929.

Bondi, H., *Cosmology* (Cambridge University Press, 1952), 3–19.

Craig, Wm., "Replacement of Auxiliary Expressions," *Philosophical Review* (1956), 138–55.

Hempel, C. G., "The Theoreticians' Dilemma," in Feigl, H., Scriven, M., and Maxwell, G. (eds.), *Minnesota Studies in the Philosophy of Science*, Vol. II, 37–98.

Körner, S., *Observation and Interpretation* (N.Y., Academic Press, 1957.); see esp. Fierz, M., "Does a Physical Theory Comprehend an 'Objective, Real, Single Process'?"; Körner, S., "On Philosophical Arguments in Physics"; and Polanyi, M., "Beauty, Elegance, and Reality in Science."

Popper, K., "Philosophy of Science—A Personal Report," in Mace, C. (ed.), *British Philosophy in Mid-Century* (N.Y., Macmillan, 1957), 155–97.

Toulmin, S., *The Philosophy of Science* (London, Hutchinson University Library, 1953), Ch. IV; and see review of same by Ernest Nagel in *Mind*, 63 (1954), 403–12.

Von Mises, R., "The Status of Physical Theories," in *Positivism* (N.Y., George Brazeller, 195), 136–50.

Van Vleek, J. H., *The Theory of Electric and Magnetic Susceptibility* (Oxford University Press, 1952), 1–2, esp. note, p. 1. Concerning axiomatic analysis, consult bibliographical references appended to Cohen, R. S., "Hertz's Philosophy of Science: An Introductory Essay" in Hertz, H., *The Principles of Mechanics Presented in a New Form* (N.Y., Dover, 1956). See also Church, A., *Introduction to Mathematical Logic* (Princeton University Press, 1956), Vol. I, 47–58, 317–32.

Curry, H. B., "On Definition in Formal Systems," in *Logique et analyse*, August, 1958.

Kemeny, J., and Oppenheim, P., "On Reduction," *Philosophical Studies*, VII, (1956), 6–19.

McKinsey, J. C., and Suppes, P., "Philosophy and the Axiomatic Foundations of Physics," International Congress of Philosophy (1953), Vol. VI (*Philosophie et Methodologie des Sciences de la Nature*), 49–54. See also Braithwaite, R. B., "Axiomatizing of a Scientific Theory by Axioms in the Form of Identifications"; Simon, H. A., "Definable Terms and Primitive Axioms"; and Destouches-Février, P., "The Logical Structure of Physical Theories," in Henken, L., Suppes, P., and Tarski, A. (eds.), *The Axiomatic Method* (Amsterdam, North-Holland Pub. Co., 1959). On Reduction and its problems, see Adams, E. W., "The Foundations of Rigid Body Mechanics and the Derivation of its Laws from those of Particle Mechanics," in Henken, L., Suppes, P., and Tarski, A. (eds.), *The Axiomatic Method*.

McNaughton, R., "Axiomatic Systems, Conceptual Schemes, and the Consistency of Mathematical Theories," in *Philosophy of Science* (1954), 44–54.

Martin, R., *Truth and Denotation: A Study in Semantical Theory* (London, Routledge Kegan Paul, 1958), 1–31.

Meehl, P., and Sellars, W., "The Concept of Emergence," in *Minnesota Studies in the Philosophy of Science*, Vol. II, 239–52.

PART THREE
SPACE, TIME, AND CAUSALITY

NEWTONIAN MECHANICS

Broad, C. D., "Leibniz's Last Controversy with the Newtonians," reprinted in *Ethics and the History of Philosophy* (London, Routledge Kegan Paul, 1952), 168–91.

Cherry, T. M., *Newton's Principia 1687 and 1937* (Melbourne, University of Melbourne Press, 1937).

Jammer, Max, *Concepts of Force* (Cambridge, Harvard University Press, 1957), Chs. 10–12.

Jammer, Max, *Concepts of Space* (Cambridge, Harvard University Press, 1954), Ch. IV.

Toulmin, S., "Criticism in the History of Science: Newton on Absolute Space, Time, and Motion," in *Philosophical Review*, 68 (1959), 1–29, 203–27.

Toulmin, S., *Philosophy of Science* (London, Hutchinson University Library, 1953), 86–90, 99–100, 145–55.

Whittaker, E., *From Euclid to Eddington* (N.Y., Dover, 1958), esp. Pts. I and II.

Wiener, N., "Newtonian and Bergsonian Time," *Cybernetics* (N.Y., Wiley, 1948), 40–56.

For works on Classical Mechanics, and especially axiomatic treatments of it, consult the bibliography appended to Cohen, R. S., "Hertz's Philosophy of Science: An Introductory Essay," in Hertz, H., *The Principles of Mechanics Presented in a New Form* (N.Y., Dover, 1956).

GEOMETRY AND RELATIVITY

Grünbaum, A., "Conventionalism in Geometry," in Henken, L., Suppes, P., and Tarski, A., (eds.), *The Axiomatic Method* (Amsterdam, North-Holland Pub. Co., 1959), 204–22 (includes bibliography).

Mercier, A., and Kervaire, M. (eds.), *Fünfzig Jahre relativitäts Theorie. Helvetia Physica Acta Supplementarum* IV (Basel, Birkhauser Verlag, 1956), see esp. papers by Von Dantzig ("On the Relationship between Physics and Geometry and the Concept of Space-Time"); Born ("Physics and Relativity"); and Pirani ("On the Definition of Metrical System in General Relativity").

Meserve, B., *The Evolution of Geometry and the Fundamental*

Concepts of Geometry (Cambridge, Addison-Wesley, 1957), 219–67.

Nagel, Ernest, "The Formation of Modern Conceptions of Logic in the Development of Geometry," *Osiris,* Vol. VIII (1939), 142–222.

Peierls, R. E., *The Laws of Nature* (N.Y., Scribners, 1956), Ch. 6.

Rainich, G., *Mathematics of Relativity* (N.Y., Wiley, 1950), 1–23, 64–6.

Robertson, H. P., "Relativity and the Foundations of Mechanics," in Ridenour, L. (ed.), *Modern Physics for the Engineer* (N.Y., McGraw-Hill, 1954), 11–42.

Synge, J. L., *Relativity: The Special Theory* (Amsterdam, North-Holland Pub. Co., 1956), 22–34.

Weinberg, C. B., "Rigidity, Force, and Physical Geometry," *Philosophy of Science,* Vol. VIII (1941).

Weyl, H., *Philosophy of Mathematics and Natural Science* (Princeton University Press, 1949), *passim*. See also the bibliographical references in Grünbaum's paper in this volume.

Whittaker, E., *History of the Theories of Aether and Electricity* (N.Y., Philosophical Library, 1954), 30–7.

QUANTUM MECHANICS AND THE CONCEPT OF CAUSE

Ashby, W. R., *Design for a Brain* (N.Y., Wiley, 1952), 13–28, 203–15.

Bunge, M., *Causality: The Place of the Causal Principle in Modern Science* (Cambridge, Harvard University Press, 1959), 74–86, 307–30.

Bunge, M., *Metascientific Queries* (Springfield, Ill., Chas. Thomas, 1958), Chs. 8–9.

Carnap, R., *Introduction to Symbolic Logic and Its Applications* (N.Y., Dover, 1958), 211–12.

Destouches, J. L., "*Physique moderne et philosophie,*" in Klibanski, R. (ed.), *Philosophy in the Mid-Century* (Florence, 1958), Vol. I, 265–91.

Heisenberg, W., "The Development of the Interpretation of Quantum Theory 1912–29," in Pauli, W. (ed.), *Niels Bohr and the Development of Physics* (London, Pergammon Press, 1955).

Körner, S. (ed.), *Observation and Interpretation* (N.Y., Academic Press, 1957); see papers by Bohm ("A Proposed Explanation of Quantum Theory in terms of Hidden Variables at a Sub-Quantum-Mechanical Level"); Rosenfeld ("Misunderstandings about the Foundation of Quantum Theory"); Feyerabend ("On the Quantum-Theory of Measurement"); Süssman ("An Analysis of Measurement"); Bopp ("The Principles of the Statistical Equations of Motion in Quantum Theory"); and Groenewald ("Objective and Subjective Aspects of Statistics in Quantum Description").

Landau, L., and Lifshitz, E., *Quantum Mechanics* (Cambridge, Harvard University Press, 1958), 1–21.

Ludwig, G., *Die Grundlagen der Quanten-Mechanik* (Berlin, Springer Verlag, 1954), Ch. VI.

McKnight, J. L., "The Quantum Theoretical Concept of Measurement," in Churchman, C. W. (ed.), *Measurement, Definition, and Theories* (N.Y., Wiley, 1959), 182–203.

Reichenbach, H., *The Philosophical Foundations of Quantum Mechanics* (University of California Press, 1944); and see esp. reviews of this work by Hempel, C. G., in *Journal of Symbolic Logic*, Vol. 10 (1945), 97–100, and Nagel, E., in *Journal of Philosophy* 42 (1945), 437–44. See also "Symposium on Quantum Mechanics" in *Philosophy of Science* (1950); and the references in Hanson's paper, included in this volume.

Waismann, F., "The Decline and Fall of Causality," in Crombie, A. (ed.), *Turning Points in Physics* (Amsterdam, North-Holland Pub. Co., 1959), 84–154.

ARTHUR DANTO

Arthur Danto was born in Ann Arbor, Michigan, in 1924.
Educated at Wayne State University and at Columbia
University, where he took his Ph.D., he also attended
the Université de Paris on a Fullbright Fellowship. He is
now Associate Professor in the Department of Philosophy
at Columbia University.

SIDNEY MORGENBESSER

Sidney Morgenbesser was born in New York City in 1921.
He attended City College of New York and the Jewish
Theological Seminary of America and received his Ph.D.
from Columbia University. Mr. Morgenbesser has taught
at Swarthmore College and the New School for Social
Research; and is now Associate Professor in the Department
of Philosophy at Columbia University.